To Dali

Thank you for keeping me alive!

All Bones Are White

Carlo Perez Allen

My diet is healthy because of you.

Enjoy,

Carlo

FLUKY FICTION

Newport, ME

All Bones Are White

Print Edition ISBN: 978-1-7378944-0-7

Published by Fluky Fiction

Dedicated to Willie and Rigo

Introduction

Berkeley stands across the Golden Gate Bridge on the east shore of the San Francisco Bay. It is cold and foggy compared to Mexico. Our Mexican family moved into a hillside home overlooking the bay and the whole expanse of the Golden Gate Bridge in 1964. My Mexican mother and white stepfather had found their dream home with a million-dollar view.

I entered Berkeley High School at the height of the civil rights movement. The assassination of President John F. Kennedy, ten months earlier, still loomed over America.

Berkeley had the distinction of implementing a progressive integration program, known as the Ramsey Act. It voluntarily put Black and White students together on the Berkeley High School — West Campus.

Although it was an exciting time to be in Berkeley for Black and White students, I couldn't feel a part of it. Willie Mays, Muhammad Ali, Harry Belafonte, and Ray Charles were all I knew about Black Americans. I was an outsider. I stuck out like a sore thumb with my not White nor Black skin dressed in a preppy outfit. The whole environment seemed surreal. Berkeley was on the national radar for voluntarily integrating Black and White Americans in schools. It was a symbol of justice, and civil rights, in a BLACK and WHITE world. I was brown. I kept to myself. I was invisible. I had to remember I was in school to get an education.

Mr. Populus was my first Black teacher. He wore brown suits that matched his shaved head. He'd lost three fingers somehow and proudly displayed the remaining portion of his right hand. I stood alone at the edge of the food court during lunch watching the courtyard dynamics. Two groups split right down the middle: Black students assembled on one side, White students on the other. I didn't sit. I didn't belong. I ate, standing up, wondering what group I would be sitting with had I grown up in Berkeley. Either side would have been beautiful. Students on both sides seemed so happy while I felt out of place—again. Why did we ever leave Mexico? I wasn't interested in making friends. I was pissed.

Mr. Populus walked up to me and asked why I wasn't engaging with anyone. I told him I was new to the school. "You're a pretty cool cat. You'll fit right in, Charles," he said. I had not heard the term cool cat. Scaredy-cat? I took offense. My grandfather was a bullfighter. A picture of him—suspended in air, ballet-like pose, toes together, above a charging bull, sticking banderillas in the shoulder muscles— hung prominently in my *abuela's* home.

"I am not scared," I muttered.

"Make friends while you can. Look around right now. A lot of people are curious about you. Look at people checking you out." He pointed his stubby hand to one side, and some White students looked over. He gestured to the other side, and a few Black students looked up.

"I don't belong," I said.

"That's not a good feeling. I have some advice for you, Charles," he said. "Somehow, this whole experience, this experiment, here is going to go into our history books. Black and White students are integrating vol-un-tar-i-ly while the rest of the country is fighting it. He held up his hand. "I was going to write a book, but as you can see, it would be rather difficult." I looked carefully and saw burn marks on his hand that receded up his sleeve. "Now you, on the other hand, seem very capable of writing a book with a unique perspective. And I'm going to give you the title: All Bones Are White."

"All Bones are White," I repeated. The realization that this integration experiment was intended for all of us to look beyond skin color. I felt better. I had my first Black friend in Mr. Populus.

"Yes, only a cool cat like you can write it," he said and walked away. I watched him stroll through the Black and White student body.

Prologue

1982

I stood in my sanctuary reading my favorite childhood book, *Ferdinand the Bull*, to my kindergarten students. It was the first day back in school from Easter vacation. Morning story time would bring us gently back together after a ten-day separation. I wore one of my dad's blue suits, an off-the-rack size forty long, which gave me comfort. He would be proud of me if he could see me teaching underprivileged children of all races. They were happy, and I was grateful to share their innocence and joy. I needed it. I was secure in the knowledge that I was making a difference in a poor neighborhood and leading a meaningful life.

The haunting scream of iron wheels thundering along the nearby railroad tracks interrupted my reading. My thoughts turned to my father. I had asked him at an early age about my purpose in life. He quoted Albert Einstein, mentioning that he was the smartest man in the world, "Only a life lived for others is worth living." He didn't expand the thought. His actions and convictions in the years to come would explain.

Thin shadows from the steel bars on the window fell across my students' faces. It reminded me that many of their parents were in prison, and why I found purpose in teaching these children.

A red ceramic apple on my wooden desk caught my attention. I picked it up. "A is for?"

"Apple!" a chorus of eager voices shouted. We were back on task.

I placed the apple back on the desk next to a framed black-and-white photo of my grandfather piercing an attacking bull in Mexico City Plaza. The picture helped me gather my strength. I read the final pages of *Ferdinand the Bull* and gazed at the happy faces that reminded me of my first year of school in New York. I took a deep breath, exhaled, and thought about the long train ride to kindergarten some twenty-five years before.

1954

I was five years old when I boarded the train in Mexico City that would take my family to the United States. It was morning, and the clouds were full of images like the ones painted on the church walls — winged angels, babies, and saints. Finding pictures in the sky was a pastime that started right after my aunt, Tia Rosita, read *Ferdinand the Bull* to me for the first time. After reading the book, we walked outside, and I pointed out a bull in the clouds that looked like Ferdinand. I named him *Toro,* and after that, always looked for him in the sky.

My mother, Camerina, had married her American boss, William "Bill" Allen, after a yearlong romance. They planned a new life in New York with her three children. Bill would adopt us, and we all would become United States citizens. I was the youngest of three at five years old. Eugenia was twelve and a model student with delicate features and polished manners. Cesar was an explorer without boundaries. He learned the way of the streets of Mexico City and carried a knife for protection at an early age. Without supervision, Cesar became rebellious at home and at school. Camerina placed him in reform school, which he would describe as a snake pit. His stories of the place rivaled the cruelty in Charles Dickens' *Oliver Twist*, and he credited the experience for toughening him up.

Mother met Bill at her job with General Electric Mexico, where she was a secretary in the engineering department. Bill had taken a position there after leaving graduate school at the University of California, Berkeley, where he had been studying philosophy. He abandoned the Ph.D. program after the UC Regents forced the signing of an anti-communist loyalty oath on all faculty members, including teacher assistants. He became a victim of the House Committee on Un-American Activities. Thirty-four-year-old Bill saw the committee itself as anti-American. He refused to sign the University Loyalty Oath along with many disillusioned intellectuals on the principle of academic freedom. He made a quixotic decision to leave for Mexico.

Exciting times awaited Bill in Mexico City, where colorful fiestas, music, and dance appealed to him. Wherever he walked in Mexico, he stood out with his tall frame, baby blue eyes, and movie star looks. Bill had developed an idealistic perspective on wealth distribution, founded on his readings of Karl Marx's and Friedrich Engels' communist theories. It was also a romantic time in Latin culture and art. He headed for Mexico City, where a legion of Marxist Socialists had gathered around Diego Rivera and Frida Kahlo's safe haven. They had helped Leon Trotsky and his wife, Natalia, gain political asylum in Mexico and invited the couple into their home — The Blue House. Every time I heard the story of Bill's journey, I imagined him taking shots of tequila with Frida, Diego, and Trotsky, their faces brimming with delight.

Now we were leaving Mexico to become Americans. Our loving relatives were at the train station bidding us a farewell through tears and laughter, speaking with soft voices echoing Zapotec Indian roots.

It was heartbreaking to leave my aunt, Tia Rosita. She had cared for me since birth. I called her Mami until Camerina brought home her knight-in-shining-armor, Bill. It was the way of the single mother in Mexico at the time. The family cared for the children while the mother went into the workforce where, with good luck and good looks, she might snag a good man. Camerina reveled in the splendor of her own desires, which attracted men. Her intimidatingly good looks kept insecure men away and enticed powerful ones.

She relished telling the story of the day Bill entered the General

Electric plant wearing a beautiful wool suit and tie. He was the spitting image of the big-screen heartthrob James Stewart. Women swooned over Bill's slender six-foot frame and good looks. Camerina fixed her eyes on him and pronounced, "He's mine, girls."

Her face lit up as she recited the story of how she had won Bill's heart. "I wanted to impress the handsome *gringo*," she'd say with girlish enthusiasm. Emphasizing the word *gringo* implied she'd chosen not just a handsome man, but an American, which raised the challenge. "I had access to his personnel records, where I found a copy of his passport. His birthday was coming up. Perfect! Fiesta time and birthday cake, a big fiesta and a big cake." She never failed to stop at this point in her story and wait for someone to ask what she did next. She'd continue as though sharing a secret. "I approached the food service manager with the idea of making a cake for the 'special occasion.' The manager agreed with the condition that the cake was served to everyone. I'd never made a cake, but my older sister, Margarita, had decorated wedding cakes at a bakery before it went out of business. Plus, she had a friend with a mariachi band who owed her a favor. We managed to work the industrial-size pots, pans, and a barrel-sized mixer. Margarita squeezed the icing on all eight baking sheets with the artistic flair of a French pastry decorator. We bought colorful decorations for the cafeteria and snuck in a few bottles of tequila. We hung a red, white, and blue garland with a United States flag across a wall and a red, white, and green one with a Mexican flag on the opposite wall. Margarita's mariachi band arrived and waited for Bill to enter the cafeteria. Bill stepped into a mariachi band, serenading him with 'Las Mananitas.' I draped a serape over his shoulders while a bass player placed a bottle of tequila in Bill's hand and a huge sombrero on his head." She would finish her story, adding, "The cake was terrible, but the *fiesta* was the highlight of the summer."

"Highlight" is an understatement because, within months, Bill Allen proposed to Camerina in his *gringo* accent. "*Came, te quiero mucho. Yo te amo y quiero casarnos."* He tried his best, with unorthodox conjugations, but the romantic marriage proposal was not lost in translation. Mother knew marriage was offered.

"Pero, Billcito, I have three children." She'd learned that phrase in English to be clear in the event their relationship would lead to a proposal.

"Ah, pues, me saque la Loteria!" Bill simply responded he'd hit the lottery. He was not to be deterred from his desire to marry my mother.

It was a tall order to have Camerina agree to leave her beloved Mexico. The Perez family roots were deeply ingrained in Mexico City. Mother's entire life had been spent there where her father had raised a family of eleven children through a revolution and a depression. He was a successful building contractor and bullfighter. Now she was taking her three children away to start a new life with her husband, Bill, who would become my father. We were leaving for a place called New York. All we knew about our future was what our soon-to-be White father had told us in gringo-accented Spanish. He had such a pleasant demeanor about him; he could have been telling us we were going to Hell, and we would have welcomed the news.

We didn't speak a word of English, so he became the window to our new country. He said New York was a beautiful place that we would enjoy, and the city was known as The Big Apple—The Big *Manzana.* I took it literally and imagined city streets lined with apple trees where people could reach up and have a snack whenever they wanted. Mexico City streets had a lot of poor people needing food. The idea of apple and mango trees along the sidewalks seemed simple to my young mind. It would take care of the starving people, and Mexico could be as magical as The Big Apple.

Through nervous laughter and extended hugs, we readied ourselves for the journey. Dark clouds seemed to take away all colors, leaving everything in black and gray. Tia Rosita, like all her sisters, stood five feet two inches, slim, and modestly dressed in a long-sleeved sweater. I gripped her arm tighter than ever. She was my aunt but cared for and loved me like a mother. She slowly let go of me, looked into my eyes, and gave me a reassuring two-eyed blink. It was a simple gesture that had settled my racing heart through scary moments and bedtime fears.

Bill had gone ahead three months earlier to prepare a home for our arrival. It was winter, and we were going to a place we only knew from the pictures we had seen of the town where Bill had been born and raised. We were on our way to Buffalo, New York.

The tearful goodbyes were cut short by a long and loud train whistle. One by one, we walked up the wooden ramp to the train door, waving goodbye in our new clothes that had been purchased to look like Americans'. Cesar and I wore matching outfits—navy blue Robin Hood-themed sweaters, slacks, and shiny, black-laced shoes. Eugenia wore a plaid skirt and collared shirt, while Mother looked perfect in a stylish brown outfit with gloves and matching purse. I lingered in the doorway, clouds swirling overhead, clusters forming in all shapes. I willed the image of my brave *Toro* snorting smoke out of thick nostrils. *Toros* held a unique place in my mother's family because her father was a bullfighter. Cesar and I cherished the pictures of our grandfather alone in a bullring facing a charging bull. It was pure machismo—fearless and courageous. His blood ran through our veins. I would grow up to be just as brave. *Or would I be leaving that part of me in Mexico?* I wondered. A lot had changed in the year Bill had entered our lives. *Que sera, sera.*

Mexico City is located high in the mountains at an altitude of nearly eight thousand feet. It was founded on a lake by the Aztecs in the early fourteenth century and became Tenochtitlán. The pre-Columbian history of the Americas is taught early in school and is celebrated throughout the culture. Descending the hills involves twists and turns that rock the train back and forth. I held on tight and stared out the window, wondering whether I'd ever see Mexico again as our train rumbled away. Riding down the mountains through green foliage and trees at times felt like I was going through a green tunnel with lights flashing between the leaves. I was happy to see the famed snow-capped Popocatepetl twin volcanoes in the distance. *Yes*, I thought. *Snow in Mexico*. I remembered Dad's first mention of taking the family to New York.

"New York has a beautiful white playground in the winter," Bill had said one Sunday while we rode on a gondola through Xochimilco park. Mother was in heaven, watching her two sons and daughter enjoy the memorable experience — especially riding through the colorful floating gardens with the handsome *gringo*. It set her apart. The mariachis and vendors selling scrumptious tacos and fruits winked and smiled their approval. The day had started with a tour of Frida Kahlo's Blue House Museum, where Bill made Mother blush several times with comments about her beauty. He continued, "It's called snow. You can play in it, build snowmen, snowballs, use your imagination to do what you want." Mother's love for Bill was never more evident than in that moment on the gondola. "It's freezing cold and can be scary, but you'll get used to it." Mother had to love this man an awful lot to give up the beauty that surrounded us for a freezing white playground.

Now, on the train headed for ice-cold New York City, knowing Mexico had snow eased my fears. Popocatepetl was fading in the distance, but lava rocks still peppered the ground all around. After a while, the train reached the flat terrain, and the mountains of Mexico City were behind us.

Our train did not have a dining car. Instead, passengers bought food and drinks at the many stops the train made. A few vendors roamed the cars selling sandwiches, tamales, drinks, mangos on a stick, cigarettes, and chewing gum.

I was leaving Mexico to be an American like my new father. That's what Mother wanted for me. That's what Bill wanted for me. I liked the idea of being like the man that made Mother so happy. I cuddled up to her with thoughts of what I was leaving behind.

I was going to miss Sunday dinners at *Abuela's* house for sure. It was the highlight of the week for twenty or more family members. *Abuela* was always stationed in the kitchen when we arrived. I would run into the kitchen to kiss her, but more often than not, she'd be peeling onions with tears rolling down her cheeks and would stop me from entering. I'd stand and watch for a tear to roll onto her apron before joining the family. The scent of *mole* or *bacalao* dishes were the favorites and filled the house until nightfall. One of the highlights of Sundays at *Abuela's* was watching my uncle, Tio Rafael, entertain the family for hours at the dinner table. He had a slight build with average height and wore beautiful suits with thin ties, pressed white shirts, and a handkerchief. His pencil-thin mustache, smiling eyes, and sense of humor kept everyone laughing for hours. He told stories of follies he'd witnessed or been a part of in his endless pursuit of wealth. I wondered what Sundays in New York would be like without my *familia*.

I asked my mother why we were moving to a place she had never been. Looking out the window, she softly responded, "*Que sera, sera.*"

Eugenia looked up from her book. "Because Bill wants us to have the best education possible, and it is in the United States where he studied." She went back to her book.

Making our way down the mountains to the lush green landscape of Central Mexico was a gentle ride. An occasional farmer tilling soil with mules, horses, or oxen dotted the scenery. The farmers wore white cotton peon shirts with wide-brimmed straw hats, just like the *Siqueiros* paintings that symbolize the struggles of the oppressed Mexican peons.

It reminded me of the stories my grandmother told me about the hardships of the Mexican Revolution and the Great Depression. She had pictures of a two-story central courtyard compound my grandfather, Rafael Perez, had built and furnished with exquisite French décor. But there were stories of hardships and loss. In the end, every story centered on the difficulties of hanging on to the family wealth through the depression and Grandfather's early death. The compound was still in the family, with three of my grandfather's sisters occupying separate residences all looking into the courtyard. The sisters made life unbearable for our grandmother, and she moved into a different location. The story changed over time, but it was no secret the sisters looked down on Rafael's widow. She was from Oaxaca and had been raised in a Catholic orphanage.

Oaxacan women are sturdy and smart. My grandmother was no exception. She told us how she embroidered silk shawls at a cathedral entrance where the handsome Rafael would walk past and make eye contact. He purchased a wrap for his mother one day and returned several days in a row to buy one for each of his sisters. By the end of the month, he asked for her hand in marriage. They married, and she moved into the family complex. She bore eleven children and was the matriarch of the Perez clan. It is a matriarchal society in which women run businesses and civic government while the men do the work—like burros, they joke. Oaxaca is in the southern region of Mexico, where gentle voices are the norm in the peaceful lifestyle of the mountainous terrain.

Oaxaca is also the birthplace of Mexico's President Benito Juarez, the short, dark, four-foot-six-inch Zapotec Indian orphan boy. Even for a young child of five, I knew he was a giant in Mexican history. His name and image were all over the city landscape, and Benito Juarez's face was imprinted on our currency. A massive statue of him stood right in the center of the city. I would learn that he was the George Washington of Mexico. I somehow knew I'd seen the last of my history's hero. My new home would teach me about American heroes instead.

What did the Big Apple have in store for us? Bill had painted New York City to be a lot like Mexico City with tall buildings and busy streets. He said there were beautiful lakes in the countryside nearby. It would be a place to make new friends and attend school. I imagined myself playing with little boys and girls running across rolling hills, climbing trees to eat apples in the summer, and playing in the snow in the winter. It would be different than the concrete playgrounds I knew.

The rhythmic sound of the massive wheels rolling across the steel tracks lulled me to sleep all the way through Zacatecas and into Monterey, the last stop in Mexico. I woke up at dusk to the sounds of people gathering their paperwork and belongings. I was curled up next to my mother as we slowed to a stop. The day-long ride to the border was over.

The train ground to a halt in El Paso, Texas. It was tiny and flat compared to Mexico City. I looked for skyscrapers and apple trees, but none were in sight. Buildings were flat, and traffic was slow. I felt out of place. We had a long wait. Eventually, we were led to the U.S. Customs office. I held my mother's hand and felt safe. We walked toward the uniformed men who greeted us with the same gentle kindness that reminded me of Bill. He had said everyone was friendly in America. He was right, and we were only at the border. My mother's grip eased a bit as the men smiled. Eugenia and Cesar still held hands. They watched everything with suspicion.

Mother was an articulate speaker, a proud woman with a sense of dignity about her. But now, dwarfed by the tall Americans in uniform, she seemed to lose her confidence. None of us spoke English. She became unsure, and her usually bright eyes looked pained to me. Eugenia stepped forward with an English/Spanish dictionary, but before she could put a phrase together, a hog-faced woman stepped up in uniform and translated the necessary instructions with a harsh tone that none of us were accustomed to. The woman developed a snout, and her vast body filled the corners of the room in my imagination as she continued with her loud voice.

Mother handed our papers to the woman who snapped them away from Mother's hand, prompting one of her patented expressions of being insulted. Cesar looked on unable to defend our mother, as he would have done in Mexico. Eugenia glared on helplessly as well. I gripped my mother tighter. I wanted to go back to Mexico City. I started to cry, but Cesar pulled me toward him and told me not to cry in front of Americans because they did not like crybabies in the United States. He warned me that if I got caught crying, I'd be sent back to Mexico alone. I believed him and vowed I'd never cry in the United States. Cesar saw my face fighting tears and whispered, "The woman's got upside-down jalapeno-*nalgas*." It distracted me enough to laugh a little and register the hog-faced customs lady. She laughed with me or at me, I didn't know, but I watched her big red face jiggle like I'd never seen skin bounce before.

A customs official finished the paperwork and led us to a room where a nurse was waiting with what looked like foot-long hypodermic needles in front of her. It was immunization time. I gripped my mother's gloved hand. She whispered an assurance that the needles staring at me would not be stabbing me. We had had inoculation shots a month before, and my arm still stung from the memory of it. I fixated on the shiny steel syringes on the cart. Mother asked the nurse what the shots were for, but she did not answer. Instead, she focused on the paperwork and lined up four syringes. Then she motioned for one of us to step up. I recoiled as I heard my mother's soft pleas of protest. She tried to point out something on the passports and gestured an imaginary syringe with her fingers. Still, the lady overpowered Mother with a bark-like order to step up.

The look on my mother's face scared me. She was powerless. Cesar squirmed away to the door, and I followed, trying not to show my burning eyes. My sister opened the door and called for a customs official, but a loud train whistle blasted from the roaring locomotive engine and drowned out Eugenia's pleas for help. The sounds of suitcases on steel rollers crashed through. Eugenia closed the door and rushed to Mother.

They consulted on strategy, and my sister stepped up to the table for her shot. My mother was shaken, stripped of her power—her position—and unable to protect us. We were defenseless, and the Mexican paperwork was worthless. I edged my way to her side and held her. She said the shot wouldn't hurt, but I knew it would. I was more afraid of being caught crying and getting sent back to Mexico City alone than the long needle waiting for me.

Eugenia took the shot without a sound. My mother went next, rolling up her sleeve and not flinching at all. Cesar stepped up and looked at me with a smile as the needle punctured his arm. I was too scared to cry and pretended to laugh as the needle entered my scrawny shoulder. I had to be as macho as my older brother, and that was extremely important for a five-year-old Mexican boy stepping into his new country.

The nurse put down her weapon and handed me a piece of candy that looked cleaner than the candy I was used to. It was delicious. I heard Mother speak some words of comfort, but the train whistle blasted again, signaling us to hurry. Mother slipped on her gloves in front of the lady, regaining her dignity, and without looking back, she picked up the paperwork and led us through the door. We walked toward the train, feeling violated. It was our turn to board the train heading north.

The porter led us to a sleeper car, which seemed odd because on Mexican trains everyone traveled sitting up. We settled in and waited for vendors to pass by with some sandwiches or food of some sort since we were all hungry. The train rolled out of El Paso toward our destiny under a star-studded night sky that seemed bluer and cleaner than the Mexican sky I'd lived under all my life.

It never occurred to any of us to leave the sleeper car because we were comfortably huddled, and that was what we needed more than anything. We were all on the same bed, enjoying each other's warmth. After a while, Cesar jumped up, startling everyone. He had instinctively sensed a candy vendor making her way through the aisle. Mother handed Cesar a dollar. He waved the bill through the curtain, signaling the lady to stop. He opened the curtain and saw the woman's goods—cigarettes, candy, peanuts, and chewing gum. There were no *tortas* and no sandwiches. We tasted our first American candy bar—a Milky Way.

Exhausted from the border experience, deep in our thoughts, we all fell asleep. My thoughts were about swimming in the lakes that Bill had described so clearly from his childhood memories and accompanying black and white photos. I fell asleep in my mother's arms but woke up longing for my Tia Rosita. I couldn't fall back asleep, for fear of being caught crying, so I buried my face in my mother's coat until I dozed off.

The smell of bacon woke me. Cesar was awake and down the aisle near the water cooler at the end of the sleeper car. I ran toward him just as a porter carrying a ticket tray stepped out. I tried to stop but was too excited and bumped my head into the man's plate, sending it up in the air and the paper hole-punch across the floor. A bump quickly swelled above my eye, and I went numb. I was too embarrassed and scared to react. I froze while the porter sized me up and down. With his prickly scowl, he looked angry and meaner than anyone I had ever seen. I thought he had the authority to turn the train around and send the whole family back to Mexico.

The porter looked straight at me as I tried to push the knot in my forehead back down. I lowered my face and spotted the steel hole-punch. He saw me looking at it. I saw him looking at me. He hesitated. I didn't. I picked it up and handed it to the man apologizing the best I knew how, *"Perdon, perdon."*

It didn't work. He was pissed.

Cesar leaped forward and handed over some tickets he'd picked up, but that didn't change the man's scowl. He motioned for us to leave and grunted something scary. It was the meanest sound I'd ever heard. My heart pounded like it was going to leap out of my chest. I feared the man in uniform. Cesar stepped between the porter and me. Then, in one swift motion, he took a new stance, pointed his toes outward and mimicked the man with a voice that sounded like Donald Duck, before walking straight ahead like a penguin.

We rushed back to our compartment. I jumped into my mother's arms expecting the porter's arm to reach inside and throw me off the train. Mother felt my fear and saw the bump on my head. "Did anyone hit you?" I said no, but I told her about the man's rough voice and knocking over his tray. "Good!" she whispered with a sly smile. She stepped out holding our cards and handed them to the porter. He took our tickets and vented with an annoyed expression. It didn't matter that we didn't know what he said. Annoyed doesn't need a translation. We all apologized one more time, but that only solicited a wagging finger at Cesar and me. Mother wagged her finger right back, telling the man not to scold us. Cesar added his opinion with his middle finger and stared defiantly. It only made the man dismiss us with a spiteful mumble. Eugenia started writing some notes. Mother stared ahead for a moment before closing her eyes.

I was responsible for the misery I had brought to our trip. The man would not have yelled at us if I hadn't bumped into him. I promised I'd never leave the bed again. The bacon smells still filled the compartment, but we would not venture out to find it after the commotion I'd caused.

It was still morning when we reached Oklahoma, and we had not yet eaten a meal. Cesar left and returned with four paper cups full of water. We expected a vendor to come by with breakfast offerings, but it didn't happen. No one knew what to do, and we were afraid of causing any more problems. Mother said the train would stop soon enough, and we would get plenty of supplies then. We waited and waited, but the train didn't stop before a candy vendor came by again. We loaded up on chocolate and peanuts that we ate while smelling the different foods from the dining car.

After a while, Cesar and I pretended to eat what we smelled.

Bacon in the morning. He made an imaginary taco with a candy bar. He gently, delicately, placed it in his pretend tortilla before carefully adding imaginary lettuce, beans, hot salsa, and finally rolling it up into the perfect taco. I followed his moves, and we both ate gracefully to my mother's laughter and approval. We debated the lunch meal. I said it was hot dogs. Cesar said hamburgers. Neither of us had ever tasted a hot dog or burger, but we had learned about those two being picnic favorites. Again, we tried to pantomime eating the food but couldn't stop laughing at the ridiculous looking phallic symbol. Mother put an end to it after Cesar took it too far. Dinner smell was a mixture of something with garlic and tomato. It didn't matter. We all ate peanuts and chocolate and were too sick of the combination to imagine anything else.

It was a long and quiet ride the rest of the way. The only sounds that came from us were our stomachs rumbling, each with its own personality: Cesar's roared like a lion, Eugenia's purred like a cat, Mother's swished like a squirt gun rattling a tin can, mine squealed like a mouse. I caught my mother's smiling eyes, acknowledging each unique sound. We both reacted, in our own exaggerated way, after each grumble. Mother's expressions were different every time and solely for me. She was my private entertainment and I hers. She could express her happiness a hundred ways with her eyes and smile.

New York:
GRAND CENTRAL TERMINAL

We arrived in New York's Grand Central Terminal tired and hungry. We stepped off the train and walked to an open area looking for Bill. He would have been easy to find in Mexico with his tall frame and white skin but not in New York City. We couldn't find him, and he wasn't calling out our names. We must have had confusion on our faces because a uniformed man asked if we needed help. Mother tried to explain our destination by saying, *"Cataratas, cataratas,"* and gesturing a waterfall the best she could. Eugenia was busy with the dictionary, and Cesar kept saying, *"Agua, agua."* It didn't help. I spotted a postcard of Niagara Falls on a vendor's rack across the floor. I ran toward the card yelling, *"Catarata, catarata!"* as loud as I could. The man saw the card I pointed to and told us we wanted to go to Buffalo. He said we needed another train and looked toward the ticket window. I felt I'd made up for a little of the trouble I'd caused.

We bought the tickets for the trip and learned we had another five hours to reach Bill. Mother secured a table in the dining car using her charm and placing three hungry children in front of her. We couldn't read the menu, so Mother ordered the featured meal pictured on the menu's cover. Two plates of T-bone steaks with vegetables and an oblong aluminum foil wrapped object arrived. It seemed out of place, this shiny ball on the dinner plate, looking as though it were ready to fly off into space. We didn't have a clue what to do with it, but we were so hungry it didn't matter. Mother poked a knife into it as we covered our faces. The potato didn't explode, but butter oozed out. Mother took one bite, assuring us that it was food. Eugenia skipped the potato and went for the vegetables. Cesar picked off the onions, poured sugar all over the cream, stirred it, and ate the whole thing. I stared at the steak, wishing I could pick it up and bite into it. Mother cut a few pieces and offered me a fork. No one said it, but we all wished for tortillas.

We arrived in Buffalo to unimaginably cold weather. We had no hats, or scarves, or thermals. Mother wore gloves, but they were simply a fashion statement. We strolled the station, studying our new surroundings. People walked cautiously, bundled up with thick *Lucha-libre* masks, thick coats, hats, and gloves. Cesar found a brown paper bag on a bench and made a mask. He kept us entertained using different voices and making scary sounds until a passerby scoffed at the mask. Mother took it off.

We walked past a large mirror, and I noticed we looked out of place. We were the only Mexicans in sight. Everything blurred, and people moved in slow motion. The loud hissing of the steam engines stopped, and the drone of the crowd faded. We were in a different reality. Then, one image cut through the blurry crowd quickly. We all turned around to see Bill's smiling face. His friendly image grew closer and he kissed Mother, whispering something that made her smile. Our hero came to our rescue. There was a collective sigh of relief.

Bill picked me up and held me above everyone else. I instantly felt safe with him in the United States, and I laughed hysterically. Suspended in his arms, I drifted to the memory of the first time Bill picked me up like this. It was in an open field across the street from our new apartment in Mexico. I had been prohibited from playing in the area ever since I came across the body of a dead soldier that smelled like cigarettes and alcohol. Mother and I had waited for Bill on the balcony overlooking the field. Eugenia stood behind me, trying to tame my cowlick while Cesar snuck peanuts from the bowl on the coffee table. It was the first day we would all eat together in the new apartment Bill had rented and given Mother the keys to. It was a second-story apartment with lots of books and an unusual lampshade he had made from a custom ordered tortilla. This real tortilla draped over a lampshade. It was Bill's sense of humor and ingenuity all in one. Mother glowed with excitement when she spotted Bill across the field. We all waved. I ran out the door, down the stairs, and across the area to greet the man I would call Dad for the rest of my life. I ran so hard I lost a shoe as I reached him. His sparkling blue eyes matched the sky above. And now there I was suspended just like before in the USA.

"Welcome to New York, Charlie," he spoke in English, unlike in Mexico, where he had spoken in Spanish. His soft voice was music to my ears. I giggled and squirmed in the air, saying, *"Que? Que?"*

"You have to learn English, and it starts now. From now on, your name is Charlie." Bill explained something I wouldn't understand for a long time. "Charles Perez Allen," he beamed. Charlie? I didn't understand what Charlie meant nor why Oscar wasn't going to be my name any longer. "New country, new name." Bill smiled. "You want to melt right in. A new name will make it easier for you." Okay, I got it. No crying, no Oscar.

Melt right in. It would be a phrase I'd learn about later as Bill would explain the importance of assimilation. I saw the pride in his smiling face. I felt protected from everything, including that mean man on the train. Losing my name was a small price to pay for the comfort of being loved by this man who wanted to be my father. He put me down and hugged and kissed Eugenia and Cesar before we walked to pick up our luggage. "Eugenia, you are now Mary," Bill said. "Can you say, Mary?"

"Mary," Eugenia repeated.

"And you, Cesar, are now Donald. Can you say Donald?"

"Donald Duck," said Don.

"I am Dad," said Bill. "I am your father now, and you will call me Dad. Do you understand?" The three of us nodded. "Good. We are a family, and we each have a role, a responsibility. It's like a rowboat, everyone helps make it work. We all have a job. Your mother will take care of our home. My job is to provide for all our needs." He paused, looked at Mother lovingly, and continued. "And your job is to assimilate, become Americans." Mother smiled and kissed Bill on the lips.

That was the end of Oscar Perez, Cesar Perez, and Eugenia Perez. From that day on, we were Charles Perez Allen, Donald Perez Allen, and Eugenia Perez Allen.

We drove through quiet, snow-banked streets in slow traffic. Everything was different, so white, so calm. Snow-capped cars moved along, spilling clumps of powder with clapping windshield wipers. An occasional bundled up body would appear and cautiously cross a street. Through one opening in the snowbanks, I spotted a group of men huddled around a steel barrel burning a fire. "Let's learn this song," Bill said and started singing. "Row, row, row your boat gently down the stream. Merrily, merrily, merrily, life is but a dream." He had such a genuine smile and desire while he sang that we learned that song right away. We were a family rowing our boat together into New York.

Mother sat next to Bill gleefully as we made our way to the home where Bill had spent his childhood in Buffalo, New York. His family roots, of several generations, were there. Now we were going to meet his mother and aunt in the very home he had grown up in. We arrived late at night to a house that was kept like a museum. His mother, Florence, and his aunt, Gertrude, were as gracious as Bill. They took us in with gentle gestures and friendly smiles. Bill proudly held Mother's hand as he introduced us with our new names.

Florence and Gertrude were so gracious they each repeated our new names lovingly.

Cesar, or Don, eyed a plate of cookies on a coffee table in the living room. Two large logs burned in the fireplace under a stately mantle. Gertrude saw Don savoring the cookies and invited us to sit and enjoy them along with the warmth. A thick, black picture album lay on the table. We leafed through hundreds of pictures of Bill's childhood: fishing in the lakes, swimming, boy scouts, school sports, graduating from high school, boarding a train with a college letterman's sweater, studying in a library; on the baseball team, rowing team, cheerleading, gymnastics; U.S. Naval officer, flying with his pilot's jacket, cooking over an open fire with a crashed plane in the background. This was a very different photo album than the photos I remembered seeing of my *abuelo* bullfighting, in church gatherings, and at weddings.

One picture showed Bill standing on the deck of an aircraft carrier, dressed in a ceremonial officer uniform, receiving a medal with his arm in a sling. Sandwiched between the pages were his grammar school and high school report cards. Gertrude picked it up and read, "Straight As, never absent." She was proud of Bill, but he was embarrassed. Don stared suspiciously at the grades. *"Tenemos que ser perfectos o nos mandan a Mexico,"* he whispered. We have to be perfect, or they'll send us back to Mexico, he'd whispered. His humor left me.

Bill's Boy Scout picture drew Don's attention. "Yes, that's the Boy Scouts of America you're looking at," he said, taking out the photo and handing it to Don and me. "One day, you two boys will be Boy Scouts just like this." My job had started.

There were a lot of black and white photos of him sailing, picnicking, driving in long convertibles with suits and ties. They looked like movie stars. There were several pictures of young Bill with a well-dressed man throughout the photo albums. I asked if that man was his father. Bill answered that he'd lost his father at a young age, and the man in the pictures was his uncle, Florence's brother. Bill pointed out a picture of the uncle standing at the U.C. Berkeley's Sather Gate entrance. "And here he is at Berkeley."

Syracuse

A few days later, we moved into a Syracuse suburb, Baldwinsville, where Bill had taken a job with Westinghouse in research and design. He wanted his family to be near a university. The two-story Victorian-style house was enormous. Bill suggested we all explore and get familiar with our first family home. Mother and Bill walked to the kitchen through the dining room while my brother, sister, and I stood at the staircase. We didn't move. The whole place was too dark. Bill turned on the radio and ran through a few stations, all in English, before stopping on a swing station. Benny Goodman's music was inviting and somehow made the house seem less scary. Don and I ran upstairs to explore our new home.

The next day I started kindergarten at my new school. I didn't speak a word of English and couldn't pronounce my new name. A nice lady in the office led me to my class. It was a whole new world. The windows faced a sparkling playground with a vast snow-covered field and trees in the distance. A bright, ceramic, red apple stood on the teacher's desk. My new dad said New York was the big apple, and there was proof. The children were mostly blond, blue-eyed Polish Americans. Everyone turned to look at me. I stood in the doorway, looking for a friendly face. I thought I was in heaven with these angel-like children. All they needed were wings and halos, and it would be a picture straight out of a church. The teacher, Mrs. Brown, also blond and friendly, wore cat-eye green glasses that matched her shoes and belt. She took my hand and led me to the front of the class. It felt like we were walking on clouds with these little angels looking up at me. One by one, they sprouted wings, and halos floated over their blond locks while harps appeared. I was unquestionably in heaven.

"Okay, boys and girls, let's all sit Indian style on the rug," Mrs. Brown said. She sat on a chair, and all the children scooted closer with their legs crossed. Then, much to my surprise, she sat me on her lap and introduced me as the new boy from Mexico. "Can anyone tell Mrs. Brown where Mexico is?" she asked. No one raised a hand. The curious eyes studied me carefully. "This is Charles, and he's from Mexico. Right?"

I sensed a question and repeated the only word I recognized, "Mexico."

"Welcome to Van Buren Elementary School," she smiled and went on, "your new school. Can you say school?"

"Escool." I couldn't initiate the "s" sound without the soft *"e."*

Mrs. Brown pointed up and said north, then down and said south. "Mexico is in the South. Right below the United States." I got the impression south wasn't as good as north in everyone's opinion. Then she asked me my name. "What's your name?" I practiced the name Charles in my head but instinctively answered, "Oscar."

I repeated Oscar, and a boy repeated it louder while another boy started chanting, "Oscar Meyer Wiener, Oscar Meyer Wiener."

Then another boy joined in, "Oh I wish I were an Oscar Meyer Wiener!" Everyone laughed and jeered in a way I didn't understand.

The teacher stopped the noise and corrected me. "Well," glancing at the paperwork, "your name is Charles. Now repeat after me. My name is Charles."

I wanted to repeat it exactly as she had said it, but instead, I said, *"Mi nombre es Char-less."* It only brought more laughter. Mrs. Brown asked me to repeat it again, but I panicked. The children were laughing at me.

I slid off her lap and fell to the floor next to her green shoes, trying to hide my embarrassment. I wanted to bury my red face in the rug. I gripped the teacher's shoes. I wanted to cry but was afraid of being sent back to Mexico, so I tightened every muscle in my face. Mrs. Brown lifted me back on her lap, and the class settled down. But before I knew it, I wet my pants. Mrs. Brown stood up, setting me down on the rug. That brought more laughter.

The children in front moved away, laughing and screaming. The teacher motioned for everyone to form a circle with a predetermined hand signal as she retreated to the back of the room. Everyone stood up and formed the circle. I stayed slumped on the floor sitting Indian style with my head down, fighting off the tears. Just then, a big boy with a loud voice blurted out, "He looks like Tonto." Then another boy started dancing, putting two fingers over his head and singing, "Oo-oo-oo-oo-oo-oo." He was mimicking an Indian war dance, and a few other kids joined in chanting, "Tonto, Tonto, Tonto!"

Tonto in Spanish means dumb. Tonto to them was the Lone Ranger's sidekick. These blond, blue-eyed children who were supposed to be my new friends were laughing at me and calling me dumb. One by one, their wings fell away like crumbled glass, and the halos dissolved into thin air. This wasn't heaven. My throat started burning and choking me, cutting off my breath.

Mrs. Brown turned off the lights, and everyone froze in place. She reached for me and took me to the corner where she handed me a small carton of milk and a graham cracker. I couldn't drink the milk or eat the cracker. I was hyperventilating. Bill Allen had been wrong about everyone being friendly. I was in a room full of people that did not want me in their class. I wanted my life in Mexico with a name I could pronounce, Tia Rosita who loved me and cared for me, the food I recognized, and children that liked me.

The teacher wrote something on a paper and handed it to a blond girl with soft blue eyes just like Bill's. She wore a white ribbon-laced bobby skirt and a matching shirt that looked like a television ad. She walked straight to me, looked into my eyes, and smiled. That smile was trust and understanding. She reached for my arm. Her white fingers on my brown arm said it all. I was different. She squeezed my arm. It was a warm and comforting feeling that reminded me of Tia Rosita's touch. "I'm Linda," she whispered. "Can you say, Linda?" That was easy since *linda* means *pretty* in Spanish. I tried to repeat her name, but my throat burned. I couldn't talk. She took my hand and led me through the door and to the nurse's office.

I went home that day with a knot in my throat and didn't say a word that night. In everyone's excitement about our new life, dinnertime was focused on learning English. Mother established the routine of waiting for Bill to take his first bite before picking up our silverware. Don and I watched Dad with such anticipation we could almost taste the food. But that night, I didn't touch my food. My concerned mother tried to feed me, but I wouldn't open my mouth.

Bill loved classical music during dinner. We listened to Beethoven, Bach, Mozart, Chopin, and Tchaikovsky in the dining room on the windup phonograph Bill had rescued from his mother's house. Tchaikovsky's "Nutcracker Suite" was the favorite, but it sounded much better on the stereo console in the living room. I guessed the old windup reminded Bill of his father. I studied Bill's mannerisms: the way he used a knife and fork with such precision and placed the silverware on his plate, the way he handled a napkin and sipped his drink, everything. Assimilation meant doing as Americans do, and Dad was going to be my role model, my ticket to becoming an American. My silence caught Bill's attention, and he asked me a question, but I couldn't hear him. I saw his lips move and blue eyes focus on me, but I couldn't answer. I thought maybe there was a connection all blue-eyed people had that would betray me and expose my shame. I ran away to the foyer and buried my face in his gabardine coat that reminded me of my Tia Rosita. I ran upstairs with it and jumped in bed.

"Hi-yo Silver!" The Lone Ranger saluted astride a silver-studded saddle on his majestic white horse, Silver, before riding off down the mountain to the tune of the "William Tell Overture." His companion, Tonto, followed riding bareback on his brown and white horse. Tonto reminded me of Aztec warriors so proudly displayed all over Mexico. Together they rode through the rocky hills fighting crime. Tonto called out, "Kemosabe!" He pointed to a ridge. The Lone Ranger stopped, looked at me. I became Tonto. I had his powers until a train rumbled through—I woke up from the dream.

A few days passed, and I'd lost my appetite. I still had a lump in my throat and couldn't talk. I stood naked in front of a doctor while he checked my throat, nose, ears, chest, and testicles. Then he motioned for me to lie on the table. I did. I didn't know what he said or what he did, but he had a long conversation with Bill about me. They walked together toward me and lifted the gown, looking at my penis. They looked concerned, pensive. Were they worried about my having peed in the classroom? I hadn't peed in my pants ever for any reason that I could remember. Is it that big of a deal to have one accident in this country? Bill's face registered deep thought. In Mexico, he was always pleasant and light, but now he had an almost stern look. "Now what?"

I wished we'd stayed in Mexico.

Circumcision.

A railroad train whistle woke me from a deep sleep. I was in a hospital bed with a privacy curtain and a window overlooking a snow-covered field carved by a steamy train track. Beyond the ground lay a forest with a gray sky. The mint-green walls reminded me of Mrs. Brown's classroom. A monitor beeped steadily at my bedside, and there was an intravenous tube attached to my arm. I was thirstier than ever, and I had to pee. My penis throbbed and itched. I reached down to scratch but felt a lumpy glob attached to my organ! My hand recoiled and flew up, my hips pushed back, my legs kicked in every direction, sending the covers off. I looked down and saw a golf ball sized ball of gauze suffocating my penis. I calmed down enough to inspect this calamity. What in the world had I done to deserve this? Could all this be the punishment for peeing on the carpet in Mrs. Brown's classroom? I couldn't remember what the doctor and Bill had told me about needing an operation, but I was sure it wasn't about having my penis cut off.

I pulled back the curtain and spotted an open door where I could see a toilet through a mirror. I had to risk making my way to that room for fear of peeing in bed. I unplugged the tube in my arm and carefully swung my leg off the bed, fearing I'd rip off whatever I had left of a penis. Having succeeded on the first leg, I carefully maneuvered the second leg off the bed. I inched my way to the room, turned the light on, and closed the door. I took my usual stance over the toilet bowl and tried to point the dangling gauze ball in the right direction. I relaxed and let the urine flow, but it exploded like a garden hose in all directions except the toilet. I tried to stop but couldn't. The tide was too strong; pee squirted everywhere, leaving urine dappling across the walls, mirror, and floor. I wished we had never left Mexico, where I was sure peeing on a carpet wouldn't be punishable by a penis slicing.

The door swung open, and a friendly face smiled at me. A concerned nurse with a soothing voice stepped in, saw my embarrassment, and took me by the arm. "Oh, sweetie, don't be embarrassed," she said. "Let's clean this up." She took my gown off and ran the water from the sink with one hand, grabbing a washcloth with the other. She cleaned me up and took me back to bed, where she pulled up a porcelain urine collector with a wide spout. It didn't need an explanation.

The nurse turned on the television. Charlie Chaplin's silent movie *The Gold Rush* was playing. It had music, but Charlie didn't talk. He didn't need to. His expressions and body language said it all. I was captivated by the similarities between Charlie and my hero, Cantinflas. Cantinflas was Mexico's biggest movie star. His pranks and expressions were universal. I thought there was a connection between the three of us now that I was Charlie. He held a cigarette, toying and playing with it, using it to tell his story, until he finally inhaled with deep satisfaction. I picked up the straw in my food tray and practiced Charlie Chaplin's gestures. Eventually, I fell asleep, imagining myself playing with the two great movie stars.

Bill, whom I now addressed as Dad, walked in with a box of chocolates and Mother at his side. She placed flowers on my nightstand and soothed my breathing, gently rubbing my chest. Her two-eyed blink didn't make me feel any better. Eugenia and Don followed, each holding a card. I could see Don was anxious about the unopened box of chocolates, so I offered it to him. Eugenia handed me a card. It was a handmade get-well card with beautiful lettering and a drawing of a red apple tree. It was addressed to Charlie, which was the first time I saw a family member use my new name in writing. Don handed me his card, also with the name Charlie. It was a drawing of a ferocious bull with massive horns and a little cowboy riding on its back. The sombrero had a "C" in front. I couldn't smile because I was wondering if my penis would grow back. I gazed out the window, wishing I'd never peed on my teacher's lap.

The railroad tracks outside were sending vapor into the cold air. Don made a comment about how hot the tracks must be. "They're a good place to keep warm on a cold day in New York," Dad started. "Growing up in this climate, one learns the best ways to stay warm. In Buffalo, sometimes we'd walk the tracks for the warmth and warm our hands on that steel." I wondered what would have happened to him if he had peed on a carpet. Would he have had his penis sliced off? He continued, "We walked to school, and we'd wait for the trains to heat the tracks. Sometimes it would be so cold and windy we'd lay down right on the tracks just to warm up before running to school." I remembered the Navy picture we'd seen of him with the crashed airplane. He was standing over a campfire with snow in the background. I wondered how my bullfighter grandfather would have handled crashing an aircraft. How would he have felt having his penis cut off?

The doctor walked in. Don and Eugenia left the room. He closed the curtain and pulled my sheets down. Mother turned away, giving me some privacy. The doctor gently removed the gauze and whistled an approving note. Dad smiled, providing a supportive wink. I was relieved to learn I still had a penis. The doctor re-gauzed the remaining penis, saying the new gauze would fall off in a day or two. "This is the American way, Charlie," Dad said. "You're circumcised now, just like all your friends." Don didn't have a circumcision, for some reason.

That night, Eugenia practiced perfect posture techniques by balancing a book on her head and walking around the dinner table. "Uno, dos, tres," we counted as she circled us. I couldn't help feeling this was part of the assimilation process since Eugenia had studied ballet and had good posture. "Seis, siete, ocho." One time around the table. "Nueve, dies, once!" She made it around the table one and a half times.

"Uno, dos, tres." It was Don's turn. He couldn't stop laughing and dropped the book.

"Charlie?" Dad asked. "Okay, I'll fill in for you." He put the book on his head and carefully started his way around the table.

"Uno, dos, tres," we counted. "Dies!" Dad made it around once. Don tried again and again and never made it around.

"Dame ese libro," Mother asked for the book, placed it on her head, maneuvering it just so, checking its stability, all the while still sitting. She pushed back her chair and stood.

"*Uno, dos, tres*," we counted. Mother gave me a wink and proceeded to not only walk around the table but picked up five dinner plates along the way before heading to the kitchen. We stopped counting. She returned without the plates, book in hand, "*Mexicanas cargan hasta sus ninos con la cabeza.*" Mexican women can carry even their children with their heads.

The next day I didn't want to go to school; I couldn't face my classmates. Bill insisted I attend, saying something about going to school, rain or snow, builds character. That may be true, but where's the part about going to school with half a penis?

I walked into Mrs. Brown's classroom like a bow-legged cowboy. The gauze hadn't fallen off, and I felt a tug with each step as my legs sent the bandage from side to side. I sensed everyone staring at me and wondered whether anyone knew what I was carrying underneath my pants. Embarrassed, I looked straight out the window at the bright playground. A man was placing a tetherball on a steel pole. I sat down carefully and crossed my legs Indian style.

Mrs. Brown read a story, pronouncing every syllable perfectly, and looked over at me every time she looked up. I felt she wanted me to understand. One boy always stood out because he was bigger and louder than everyone else. His name was Gene, and he was the same boy who blurted out the name Tonto that had prompted the Indian dance on my first day of school.

We broke into two groups after the story. I felt vulnerable and walked with my hands in a protective stance for fear of having someone knock the gauze off my penis. Boys played with big wooden blocks and paper on one side of the room while girls had dolls and tables with butcher paper. I sat watching the boys. Gene immediately took the biggest blocks and started piling them. Another boy tried to get a big block, but Gene claimed ownership. One by one, the boys retreated without resistance. Gene was the center of attention and had all the toys he wanted. Across the room, the girls played nicely and with more laughter.

After a while, Mrs. Brown approached me and reached out for my hand. I stood and ambled along, one arm still in protective mode, to the music corner. She handed me the steel triangle. I remembered it being the signal for cleaning up. She gave it to me and said, "Bell, can you say bell." I was still in mute mode. I twirled the striker around all three sides softly. She signaled for me to play it again. I felt the power of that simple act and held the triangle tightly. Mrs. Brown noticed my delight. She smiled and said, "Do you want to do that again, Charles?" I twirled the striker again and handed the instrument back to Mrs. Brown, who seemed pleased. Everyone rushed to the area where we had placed our coats and jackets.

We rapidly bundled up in our winter wear and formed two lines, one for boys, the other for girls. We walked outdoors to the asphalt playground in front of our classroom. The bright snow-covered field and trees beyond were picture-perfect but still felt foreign to me. The girls went to the jump rope and hopscotch area. The boys went to the tetherball and foursquare area. I couldn't participate in anything, so I stood next to Mrs. Brown and watched. The girls played gently compared to the boys. The blond ponytails bobbing up and down in the jump rope area reminded me of the horses in the Mexican rodeo, *chariadas*. I watched the clouds forming pictures of faces and animals that lived in my imagination. Elephants and dinosaurs roamed the skies peacefully above just as they had in Mexico's glorious clouds.

"Get out of here!" screamed Gene holding the foursquare ball. He was yelling at a defenseless boy, half his size. I wanted to help the small boy, but I couldn't speak English.

That night I dreamt I was in my classroom naked with the golf ball gauze on my penis. I was in the center rug with the whole class circled around me. The children's faces were exaggerated as they laughed at me, moving in and out of view while I turned and twisted in horror. Somehow the children's faces morphed into snakes with their poisonous tongues wagging at me. I screamed myself awake, waking everyone in the house. Don rushed over and held me, telling

31

me I was safe. I tried to keep my tears back, but it was useless. "I want to go back to Mexico!" I screamed. The door flung open.

"Calm down, Charlie," Dad said, standing in the doorway.

"*No te asustes mijo,*" Mother tried to soothe my tight body. "*Mexico ya no es.*"

"You are an American now, Charlie," Dad spoke like a soldier, his silhouette blocking the doorway.

The next morning my golf ball gauze fell off during my morning shower. I walked to school without the cowboy gait. I felt free, loose, and one step closer toward being an American. I took a deep breath and looked around at this new place in my world. Ford and Chevrolet station wagons seemed to be in every driveway. The sound of traffic was very different from Mexico's; there were no buses, no honking, no smoke billowing out the back, and it wasn't dangerous. Mexico traffic was a constant flow of two-ton machines jockeying for positions with the right of way over pedestrians. I started running and jumping over and over in the excitement of being healthy again.

Children navigated the slushy sidewalks on both sides of the street. A two-story corner house stood out from the rest with a huge yard, big oak tree, a white picket fence, and new dark Cadillac in the driveway. To my surprise, Linda walked out, pushing one arm in her coat sleeve, just as I passed by. She wore a green dress that reminded me of the dress Mrs. Brown wore the day we met. "Good morning, Charlie," she said, closing the gate and then skipping a step to match my pace.

We walked in sync without talking, paying more attention to our steps. I slowed down, and she slowed down. She'd speed up, and I'd speed up. We continued that way for two blocks until we turned the corner and saw the school. We looked at each other, and without saying a word, we both took off racing as fast as our legs would take us. Before long, a boy screamed "race" and ran alongside us, then another. I didn't know what race meant but quickly caught on as more kids yelled "race" before running along with us. I could hear everyone breathing and giggling in English while my grunts spewed out in Spanish. Soon ten children were racing toward the school. I was in the lead, my heart pounding like the Mexican train going through the mountains.

I saw Gene walking ahead. He heard us, turned, and joined the race. He was probably twenty feet ahead. I set my mind to pass him. Pumping my arms and legs faster and faster, I was soon sprinting alongside him. I wanted to win this race so much and felt so free without the golf ball holding me back. I pushed through the pain in my chest and legs. I reached the front gate first. I turned around and saw Gene rushing toward me. I moved out of his way, and he slammed into the gate. He suddenly didn't look so tough. Linda reached me and laughed with a big smile. Her cheeks turned as red as the apple on Mrs. Brown's desk. It made me laugh. It was the first full belly laugh I had in my new country. "You won!" screamed Linda. I felt like a new person having beat the bully of the class in a race. Life without the gauze inhibiting my every move was going to be a lot more fun.

At the start of the class, everyone sat Indian style while Mrs. Brown brought out a lap harp and strummed rhythmically through the alphabet song. "A-B-C-D-E-F-G-H-I-J-K-L-M-N- O-P-Q-R-S-T-U-V-W-X-Y and Z. Now I know my ABCs, next time won't you sing with me?" She looked right at me, waiting for me to sing along. I subvocalized as best I could. She played it again, and I took an inventory of the letters. A was for apple; B for ball, boys, and bicycle; C for car; D for dog. E was still for *es-scool*, and people would laugh at me if I said it, so I didn't.

Fingerpainting was the next activity of the day and a way to learn our colors. There were four easels set up near the sink with three primary colors in paint dispensers.

Mrs. Brown called me up with my new name, Charlie. She put an apron on me and pointed at the blue paint. "Can you say bluuuuuue?" I didn't answer. "Can you say greeeeeeen?" She looked at the green while I said *verde* to myself. "Can you say red?" She pointed at the red paint. She wore a white shirt with a red skirt, matching scarf and shoes. I pointed to her red dress. "Yes! Yes! Yes!" she shrilled. I fell back, surprised. I'd painted an angel with a halo.

A girl came over, then a boy. I was not sure what would happen with all the attention I was getting. The last time I had everyone's attention, they all turned on me and ridiculed me. Would they break out into an Indian war dance? Would they call me dumb as they did before with Tonto? I wasn't about to stick around and find out.

I slid into the coatroom, where we hung our winter clothes and buried my face in my jacket. I heard girls giggling and boys laughing. Could they be laughing at my painting? I peeked around the wall and saw Linda pointing at the "angels". Mrs. Brown saw me and smiled. I pulled my head back. Laughter. I peeked out again, but this time I moved my eyebrows up and down like Charlie Chaplin and quickly pulled my head back. More laughter, friendly laughter, came in unison every time I peeked out.

"Charlie, come out here," Mrs. Brown called out. "Class, no more laughing." She ordered the class to the rug. I could hear the rustle of everyone rushing to the carpet. Everyone except Mrs. Brown, who reached into the closet and offered her hand. I took her hand and followed her out of the coatroom.

"Charlie," she started. "What color did you learn today?" I didn't answer. She looked at me again and asked again, "What color is my skirt, Charlie?" I could feel my face getting hot. Now, moving toward the center of the room, Mrs. Brown turned to face her students, "Class, what color is my skirt?"

"Red!" everyone shouted. With the teacher's back to me, I involuntarily, or accidentally on purpose, moved my eyebrows up and down like Charlie Chaplin. Everyone laughed. I moved my eyebrows up and down again, and again I got a laugh. "Children, we don't laugh like that in class," Mrs. Brown said and turned to me. "Now Charlie, do you want to tell us what color this is?" She pointed at her skirt.

I didn't move. I stared silently ahead, aware that all eyes were on me. Gene chortled, and everyone followed. Mrs. Brown's red dress swirled up and around as she addressed the class. I moved my eyebrows rapidly three times. The class roared with laughter. The same kids that had laughed at me for being different were now laughing in approval. I had an audience. The fallen angels were under my control.

I took full advantage of it. Every time Mrs. Brown turned her back to me, I'd make a face. I added a nose-twitch, then a single eyebrow lift and an alternating eyebrow move, and finally a left-side lip raise to a right-side lip twitch. I had the class in belly-aching laughter, and Gene was rolling on the floor by the end of my Charlie Chaplin-Cantinflas routine.

"Enough, boys and girls. You are being rude, and we cannot have this sort of behavior." Mrs. Brown must have turned around a million times by the time she put an end to the art lesson.

I walked home alongside Linda and Gene, in silence. When we got to Linda's house, we simply waved goodbye. Gene and I continued on, making figure eights as we walked along the curb. He'd go up, I'd go down and around. I'd go up, and he'd go down and around. We giggled down the block. I looked at a house. "House," Gene said, pointing at the house. I didn't respond. He pointed to the sidewalk and screamed, "Sidewalk!" I picked up the pace, and he cried louder. I ran faster. He chased after me screaming words, "Ball, cat, dog, table, chair, hot dog," until we reached my block. We both laughed, catching our breath at the curb. His blue eyes matched Bill Allen's. He could have been Dad's son, I thought. He continued on, "Tree, car, street," and ran away, screaming the words all the way to his home half a block away.

Don and Eugenia were reading their report cards with Mother. She was pleased. *"Muy bien,"* she said. "Bill will be happy." They were doing their "job," and I wasn't doing mine. I needed to learn English: tree, car, street. Gene was helping.

The Mickey Mouse Club became a fixture in our home from the very first episode we saw. It taught us words with songs, and all the club members were perfect Americans. It came on at five P.M. right before dinnertime. We had to finish our homework beforehand, or we couldn't turn on the television. Annette Funicello changed Don's life forever. He discovered girls. I learned that M-I-C-K-E-Y M-O-U-S-E spelled Mickey Mouse along with millions of other children around the country. I sang the song in my head day and night:

Come along and sing a song

And join the jamboree

M-I-C-K-E-Y M-O-U-S-E

MICKEY MOUSE!

MICKEY MOUSE!

Once in a while, Dad would come home early enough to watch some of the show with us. I think he enjoyed watching the three of us so involved in an English-speaking show. "These children are all wonderful. Assimilation into this country couldn't be easier for you with role models like these. Here they are right in our living room," he said gleefully. We had a job to do.

The show included a lot of kids, but Annette Funicello was the only one that mattered to my brother. He drew her face, wrote her name, and composed poems to her. It was a part of him I'd never known. He kept a private scrapbook under his bed that he only shared with me. I didn't have much interest in it, but since he swore me to secrecy about it, I listened to the entries he made. It took on a clandestine tone. He whispered as he read his poem, and I huddled close. "Roses are red, Violets are blue, But not as cute as you." Funny as it was, it was music to our ears. It was his significant attempt at expressing himself in English.

One morning at recess, I got in line where Gene was pounding the tetherball around the pole, playing against a small freckle-faced boy who didn't seem to know the purpose of the game.

Gene easily won game after game when I reached the front of the line. Gene held the ball like a trophy as I stepped in to face him. He smacked the ball in a downward motion and sent it high. Tetherball was a simple playground game in Mexico, so I was ready when the ball came to me. I smacked it back, and Gene leaped forward, hitting the ball before it went up. The ball spun back over my head and made a full rotation around the pole. Gene was one rotation up. I pounded the ball with two hands, sending it spinning over his reach. We were even.

We volleyed back and forth, exchanging power punches that attracted everyone's attention. The kids playing four square stopped and came over to watch the match. Gene was pissed and edgy as though he and I were in a fight, not a game. Cheers started coming for both of us with each strike of the ball. I anticipated his volley and sent the ball spinning back just as quickly as he had smacked it, and it spun over his reach. When the ball came back around, I propelled it even higher with my palm, and it whirled around again. The cheers were now all for me. The ball spun tightly around the pole. I had won.

It was the first time Gene had lost a game, and he didn't like it. Another boy who had been waiting in line for his turn stepped forward. Gene pushed the boy away and challenged me to another game. He reached for the ball, but I grabbed it and held my ground. I motioned for him to go to the end of the line. He stood staring, puzzled, confused. A gasp came from the group. Gene looked lost, alone. I felt his anguish. I looked above his head and saw a bull in the clouds. I thought about the picture of my grandfather killing a beast. If he could stand up to a bull, I wasn't about to back down from Gene. He sensed it, stepped closer, screamed, "TONTO!" and leaped for the ball. I moved it, and he stumbled forward. Everyone laughed. He jumped up and reached for the ball again. I moved it again. Everyone laughed again. We repeated the moves until Gene and I were laughing along with everyone. Gene and I were suddenly a comedy team. *Ole,* I thought.

Walking home that day was different. I had a following of boys that had watched me stand up to Gene. They jockeyed for positions closest to me and talked excitedly, jumping and skipping along as I led my parade up and down the curb and around trees. Linda rushed over to my side, and I stopped the circuitous trek. By the time we reached her house, all the kids had gone their own way, all except Gene.

She opened the white gate to her yard just as her father drove into the driveway. Linda kept the gate open until her father stepped out of the Cadillac and walked over to us. He wore the uniform of the neighborhood: starched white shirt and cufflinks, wool pleated pants, shiny brown leather shoes, and a silk tie with a clasp. I thought he must work with Bill. "Hi, sweetie," he said with a deep and friendly voice, "who are your friends?"

"I'm Gene," Gene said. I didn't react.

"You must be the new boy, Charlie," the father said, looking at me while patting Linda on the head.

"He doesn't talk," said Gene. He touched the white gate and yelled, "Gate!" Then he ran off down the street naming and pointing, "Car, house, tree."

"He's from Mexico," said Linda. "This is Charlie. He's learning new words."

"Well, lucky us," said the father. "We have a lot to learn about our south-of-the-border neighbor." His large frame came closer, casting a shadow over me. He squatted down in front of me like the New York Yankees catcher Yogi Berra and stuck his hand out for me. "Welcome, partner," he said. I placed my hand in his and felt a strong and friendly grip. He had deep-set eyes and upturned lips, which looked a lot warmer up close. I sensed he wanted to be a friend. "You look like you could be a shortstop." He waited for my response for a moment then stood up. He put one hand on Linda's shoulder and his other hand on mine. He led us to the porch, where he sat down on the second step and pulled out a pack of cigarettes from his shirt pocket. "Maybe a pitcher," he continued and lit up an unfiltered cigarette. Linda and I moved away from the smoke. "Gomez, best darn left-hander I ever saw. He was a Mexican fellow just like you." He pointed his cigarette at me with a smile of excitement. I knew he was saying I was Mexican, and Gomez was a Yankees player. I liked hearing the Spanish word *Gomez* from this man. I was trying to make sense of it when Linda, sensing my confusion, tapped me on the shoulder.

"Let's go inside," she took my hand and opened the front door. Her mother appeared from the kitchen with a tray full of cookies and two glasses of milk. A beige silk scarf knotted around Linda's mother's neck matched perfectly with the belt and patterned dress she wore. The house looked a lot like ours but felt unlived in for some reason.

"Charlie," Linda's mother welcomed us. "You two look like you're ready for a treat." We followed her into the den. Autographed baseballs, hats, gloves, banners, and pictures of Yankees players filled the room. On a side table, next to an encased baseball, stood a red, ceramic apple just like the one on Mrs. Brown's desk. Dad was right about New York being big on apples. Linda bit into a cookie while I stared at the picture of the New York Yankees.

"My dad loves the Yankees," she said.

"Oliver grew up in the Bronx," said Linda's mother in a soft voice. I immediately liked the Bronx because of the "x" that reminded me of Mexico. "Why aren't you eating the cookies, Charlie?" She nodded toward the table. I bit into a cookie. Linda's father walked in with his coat draped over his arm. He loosened his tie and kissed Linda's mother on the cheek. He said something about Yankee Stadium and picked up a bottle of whiskey from a table with tumbler glasses, liquor bottles, and coasters. Linda's mother rushed into the kitchen and returned with a few ice cubes. He poured himself a glass of whiskey and quickly downed it.

A family picture of Linda and an older boy hung prominently on a wall behind him. Linda's mother put her head down and took a deep breath as Oliver poured himself a second drink. Linda's mother looked heavier in all the pictures than she did sitting in the room. Oliver continued talking about baseball when I noticed a framed photo of another baseball team. It was Oliver standing next to a young group of boys, including the same boy in the family picture. It had to be Linda's brother. Oliver saw that I was staring at the picture, quickly downed his second drink, and left the room. Linda's mother rushed after him.

Linda and I finished the cookies and milk. "My brother," she said. "He's dead." I didn't have to know a lot of English to understand her feelings. Her body language said it all. Her shoulders dropped, she let out a sigh, and her eyes welled up. I had the words I wanted to say in my head, but they wouldn't come out. *I'm sorry, I'm sorry, I'm sorry*, echoed in my head, but I think Linda heard my thoughts.

I headed home feeling a little closer to becoming an American, knowing somebody with the name Gomez was a New York Yankee. I practiced the words baseball and Yankees when I was startled by: "Boo!" Gene jumped out from behind a parked sedan with a huge smile. I wondered whether he was mad about the tetherball game, but his eyes revealed his humility. I walked to the curb and started up and down as Gene circled. We didn't miss a beat and started our figure eights. By the time we reached my house, we were laughing again. "Bye, Tonto!" he screamed, then hollered more vocabulary words for me as he ran off.

"Light, tire, fence," I repeated his words.

Dad dedicated dinnertime to learning English. We practiced our names by addressing each other with our new titles. "Charlie, please pass the bread," "Don, please pass the butter," "Mother, please pass the salt," and so on. I still wasn't talking. I never asked anybody to pass anything, but I repeated everything I heard in my head. We were on the fast track to becoming as American as apple pie.

The next morning on my way to school, I vocalized a phrase. I looked around nervously making sure no one could hear. "Good morning. My name is Charlie." It sounded good in my head. Then I started out loud, "Good mor—"

"Tonto!" screamed Gene running up behind me. He tapped me on the right shoulder and ran past my left side.

"Kemosabe!" I replied unconsciously. Kee-mow-sa-bee flew out of my mouth with a hard e, a long o, and another hard e. I surprised myself. Gene laughed and went to the curb to start our figure-eight routine. Up and down we trotted, and circled, and laughed all the way to school.

On the way home, after school, we repeated the up and down trail but added a "Tonto!" in unison when Gene was up and "Kemosabe!" when I was up. One by one, more children joined in behind us. And by the time we reached Linda's house, we had a band of little Indians chanting "oo-oo-oo-oo-oo-oo-oo" and dancing around in a war dance. We stopped in front of Linda's gate.

"Linda!" her mother called from the porch. "Soup's cold." Linda ran right past her mother.

"Say goodbye to your friend," said the mother. But it was too late; Linda was in the house. "You'll have to excuse Linda's manners. Goodbye, Charlie." She turned and closed the door. It felt good hearing Linda's mom call me Charlie. I galloped away, pretending I was on horseback. I was Charlie, and I was learning to be an American.

Dark clouds moved in, and suddenly I felt sad. I wanted my Tia Rosita with me. I wished I could tell her about my new life over a fresh plate of her homemade tamales. Emptiness came over me, and I stopped galloping my pretend horse. I came upon three loud boys rushing in my direction. I'd never seen this group. They didn't appear friendly by the look on their faces and anger in their voices. Two had yellow hair, the third had red hair with dots all over his face.

I instinctively covered my penis and veered left to let them by, but they moved the same way. I turned right. They did the same. I stopped. They reached me and stopped. Bam! A blow to my side knocked me down. I crumbled, not knowing what hit me. One boy, the freckle-faced boy, stood over me, taunting me with a menacing laugh. I started back up, but a fist knocked me down. I rolled over and heard, "Tonto!"

It was Gene. He smashed the boy that stood over me with one shoulder so hard, so suddenly, the other two boys ran away. I sprang up and stood next to Gene. "Kemosabe," I said. Gene dove on the boy, leaving him face down, legs kicking, and whimpering. Gene sat on him and farted. I couldn't believe what had just happened. All the while, he had an Almond Joy bar in one fist. He took a bite. "Chocolate," he said, enjoying the taste. He seemed more interested in teaching me a new word than the sobbing boy underneath him.

The boy under Gene cried out like a baby. Gene stood up. The boy ran off. "Troublemakers," Gene said. "They're always in trouble." Then, he pulled out a second candy bar, held it up as though offering it to me. I didn't take it. He dangled it closer to me. I reached for it. He pulled the chocolate back just as I had teased him with the tetherball. "Chocolate," he goaded. I hesitated. "Say chocolate," he demanded.

"Cho-co-la-te," I sang to myself, remembering the Mexican nursery rhyme that extolled the Aztec discovery of chocolate. *"Chocolate, chocolate, vate, vate, chocolate."* Gene giggled. "Chocolate," I whispered. He handed me the candy bar. We walked on without saying a word, savoring the chocolate until we reached my house.

"Bye, Tonto," Gene said, again without looking back and walked away.

"*Adios,* Kemosabe," I said, and walked inside. I finished the chocolate bar and put the wrapper in my shirt pocket.

That night Dad led his English lesson. We all had notepads. I took out the chocolate wrapper and wrote my first word: chocolate.

The next day Dad brought home a surprise bag and placed it in the dining area. After dinner, before the English lesson, he pulled out a sturdy crimson red and tan cardboard box with the words "Almond Joy"! The box alone was beautiful, and mother would use it for keepsakes for years to come. He offered individually wrapped candy to Eugenia. "Ladies first," he said.

"Thank you," she said.

"Charlie, would you like a chocolate?" He offered me one.

"Thank you for the chocolate," I said. Then I added, "Daddy." He was proud. We were a part of the life he wanted for us, and we were falling into the melting pot on schedule.

Thanksgiving

One November day, Mrs. Brown wore black square shoes, black stockings, a white linen dress with bubble sleeves, an apron, and a white cap. She had a play for the class to act out the Thanksgiving feast. "Indians were friendly people who helped the Pilgrims cook," Mrs. Brown said, looking straight at me. She pointed to a drawing of Indians and Pilgrims eating in the woods. Turkeys and corn were indigenous to Mexico. The only thing missing was tortillas.

She needed ten little Indians. I was not surprised when she selected me to be the chief. She called for volunteers to be part of my tribe that would welcome the Pilgrims to Plymouth Rock. Gene jumped up while everyone else raised their hands. Mrs. Brown asked me to pick people I wanted for my tribe, but I was too shy to do so. Gene volunteered or pushed his way into my tribe and chose three more boys and five girls, including Linda. The rest of the class was to be the Pilgrims. We colored and cut out paper turkeys, corn, bread, green vegetables, deer, and fish. Everything made of paper seemed empty until we made Indian headbands with real feathers while Pilgrims made black buckle hats. Throughout the two days it took to make all the dinner stuff, Mrs. Brown sketched a log cabin and a teepee on canvas paper. Indians helped paint the teepee while Pilgrims painted the log cabin. The whole room was decorated with a Thanksgiving Pilgrim feast theme. Dry corn with husks in a basket was something I'd seen many times before in Mexican markets, so I really felt connected to this scene. Acorns and tree branches lay across tables on all sides of the room.

After two days of being chief and helping decorate the whole room, I was ready for the big day. Mrs. Brown wore her Pilgrim costume all three days and handed out Pilgrim bonnets and buckle hats to the invited parent volunteers. They put together a complete Thanksgiving dinner that looked just like the pictures, including a giant turkey. We all sat Indian style on the rug and waited for the food. Mrs. Brown and her helpers passed out plates of turkey and fixings that smelled delicious.

"Boys and girls," called Mrs. Brown, holding up two fingers in one hand and a dry ear of corn in the other, "Listen to Mrs. Brown." Dressed in a Pilgrim costume, she sat next to an easel displaying a detailed picture of the first Indian Pilgrim dinner, including deer, cows, mules, corn, turkeys, pots, and pans. "This is how the Indians and Pilgrims celebrated and gave thanks for the food God provided through nature. All that we see here is from the land we shared with the Indians. Indians taught Pilgrims about the food around them like this corn, and vegetables, and turkey."

She held out the ear of corn. "This is corn. What do we put on corn? Raise your hand." Nearly everyone raised a hand. She looked around proudly, displaying her students' manners, knowing Gene wouldn't jump up with his mother in the room. Gene sat Indian style, biting his tongue right next to me. "Can anyone tell me?"

"Butter!" came a chorus of hungry voices.

"Yes, that is correct. We put butter on corn." She reached for a piece of cornbread and held it up. "This is cornbread. And everyone knows it comes from . . ."

"Corn!" Everyone knew the answer.

"Yes! We make cornbread from corn." Mrs. Brown was on a roll. "And what do we put on cornbread?"

"Butter!" another whole-class answer. I whispered the right answer. I was on a roll.

"Now, raise your hand if you can tell us where butter comes from."

My hand shot up just like Gene, minus the urgent gyrations. I was ready to tell the world I knew the answer in English. I was on my way to becoming an American. I knew I could nail this answer just as surely as my grandfather had hammered a bull with a sword. Mrs. Brown looked surprised to see my hand up. "Charlie, can you tell the class where we get our butter?" She picked up her wooden pointer and placed it right on the COW just as I belted out:

"Butterflies!" I pronounced each syllable carefully, imagining butterflies flying out of my mouth.

Laughter, deliberate mocking laughter, just like the crows' laughter in *Dumbo*, rang in my ears. Everyone, including the parents, looked straight at me. I choked up. My esophagus burned, and I was in a daze. I could have died.

The next day our family celebrated Indians teaching Pilgrims how to eat. It was Thanksgiving Day. But first, the house underwent a makeover. Eugenia had prepared the whole house the night before with beautiful napkins, tablecloths, dishes, and decorations everywhere. She placed holly, pinecones, and berries around the fireplace. Don and I helped with small chores. We were excited and nervous about meeting Dad's friends. They were friends from work along with a fellow Navy officer from the war. We felt confident that we would not embarrass Dad in any way as we'd practiced our best manners every dinner. Classical music played in the living room since morning while the smell of buttery turkey, cornbread, apple pie, and cider wafted from the kitchen.

At one moment, Eugenia and Dad almost collided in the doorway as a waltz melody played. They jockeyed left then right to pass, but the music got to them, and they danced together into the living room as though they'd practiced. Eugenia had studied ballet and taken dance lessons in Mexico, so the waltz was smooth. Dad was light on his feet and, in my eyes, moved just like Fred Astaire.

Dad checked his watch, announced the guests would be here soon, and went upstairs. Eugenia went to the kitchen, Don and I followed, Mother stood basting a golden-brown turkey. *"Guajolote,"* said Don resentfully. *"Is puro Mexicano."* He said turkeys were from Mexico.

"Pues este lo mataron aqui, vino congelado, entonces es Americano." Mother said this turkey was killed and frozen, so he was an American turkey. Then, having a hard time with the baster, she winced. *"Mas necio tambien."* She added the turkey was more stubborn, too. A frozen turkey was new to us.

"Indians gave the Pilgrims turkeys here just like we gave Cortez turkeys in Mexico," Don said.

"One hundred years before the Pilgrims came." Eugenia knew everything.

"Pues no se los dimos congelados." Mother said we didn't give it to them frozen. She was still frustrated with the process.

Eventually, Mother came to terms with the way of the frozen turkey. It was time to get ready for the big event. "Pleased to meet you," Eugenia practiced.

"My name is Donald Duck," joked Don.

I wanted to say, "Hello, my name is Charles Allen." But the words just wouldn't pass my throat.

Everyone dressed up. Dad wore a perfect suit, and Mother radiated in a blue and white wool dress. Don and I wore suit jackets without ties, and Eugenia wore a light blue dress. Don stuck a handkerchief in his jacket pocket. Macy's Thanksgiving Parade played on the television while everyone built up appetites with the savory cooking in the kitchen. Eugenia was fascinated with the floats and commented on each one in perfect English, much to Dad's delight.

Dad's friends arrived bearing gifts, mostly liquor and cookies. I could feel the admiration Dad received from his friends as we were introduced. Gentle, kind, caring people, just like Dad. Bob, Dad's Navy friend, stood slightly taller than Dad but appeared a lot bigger with his angular face and broad shoulders. There was a comradery about them that I wanted. They belonged together, and it started in the Navy. I saw Don in a Navy uniform and I would be a sailor.

Don and Eugenia showed their perfect manners when they were introduced, "Hello, a pleasure to meet you." I still couldn't push out a word, but my arm went up in a salute, and that seemed fine as Bob saluted back. The two couples that came, one older, one younger, were the whitest group of people I'd ever seen. They looked too much alike: tall, slender, pale, and blond. And their blue eyes stared like headlights and teeth smiled like the front grill of a new car. One of the women was pregnant. I chuckled at the thought of seeing them walking together in Mexico. Mother acknowledged their appearance to me with a twitch of the lips and wry smiles.

It was a special day with polite laughter, lots of food, and perfect manners. We had passed the Thanksgiving Day Americanization test. Afterward, we captured the night with a family picture in front of the fireplace. We huddled around Dad's chair under his prized picture frame given to him by his artist father on his fifth birthday. It was a drawing of a three-mast schooner out at sea. The family picture would turn out to be our family's Christmas card.

After Thanksgiving weekend, I didn't want to go to school. I couldn't get out of bed. I was numb and short of breath. I couldn't face the children who had laughed at me. I went limp, unable to put my clothes on. Dad came into the room and took my temperature. He was adamant about not missing school without a fever. I'm not sure what my mother said to him, but I stayed home from school that day alone with her.

She brought me chamomile tea and sat with me, waiting for the tea to cool. We didn't say a word. I didn't want to be alone. I wanted her to stay, so I pretended the tea was too hot to drink. After a dozen or so tries, she wrapped her hands around the white cup. "Ay, Charlie," she said. "*Ya esta frio.*" She was on to me. The tea was cold. It was the first time she called me Charlie, and she pronounced the starting syllable, just as I had the first day of kindergarten. We were together. "*Que te paso en la escuela?*" She asked what happened to me in school.

"*Todo el mundo se rie de mi,*" I said. Everyone laughs at me.

"*Sabes por porque?*" She asked if I knew why. I shook my head, no. "*Por ignorantes,*" she answered like the punchline to a joke — because they're ignorant. I laughed with her. "*Y los ignorantes no te van a quitar tu educacion. Ya, manana vas a la escuela y aprendes todo lo que te ensenan. Punto.*" She said the ignorant kids weren't going to take away my education. I got the message. She checked my forehead for a fever with her palm, gave a two-eyed blink, and kissed me with a grin. She left the room and turned on Benny Goodman Big Band music on the hi-fi stereo console in the living room.

I gulped the cold tea and snuck out to the living room, where I found Mother dancing to Benny Goodman's infectious beat. She swayed her hips and fluttered around her new home free as a bird. She twirled her way in and out of the furniture, gesturing to her image in the mirror every time she passed it. It wasn't long before she found me watching. She didn't miss a beat. She spun across the room to me, took my teacup, placed it on a credenza, and pulled me onto her dance floor. We danced around her ballroom until the album made a whirring sound. I gave her a double-eyebrow wiggle and tried not to smile, but her smile was contagious. We both burst out in laughter, knowing I wasn't ill. I was getting away with something that only she would know. She opened the stereo console and replaced Benny Goodman's Big Band with Pedro Infante's Mariachi Band.

Mother's hips swayed with the first beat. Soon she was moving to the beat, singing the words we both understood. I curled up in Dad's chair and watched Mother roam around the living room dusting and tidying up. "*Cielito Lindo*," a Mexican classic, played, and I thought about my bull in the clouds. I grew melancholy for Mexico. Mother noticed my retreat into sadness. She went into the kitchen and came out with an Almond Joy chocolate bar. She placed the chocolate on the table next to me. She walked toward the stereo when Pedro Infante's patriotic song started, "Mexico." I listened to the first two verses, longing for my sweet Mexico. By the third verse, "*México lindo y querido si muero lejos de ti que digan que estoy dormido y que me traigan aquí*," the song got to me. It said, "Beautiful Mexico, if I die away from you, let them say I'm asleep and take me back to Mexico." I wished I were dead, so they'd take me back to Mexico, where I was free to be me. Free to be me. I started shaking. Mother crossed the room and slid into the chair, wrapping me in her arms. "*Mami, cuando podemos regresar a Mexico?*" With tears rolling down my face, I asked when we could go back to Mexico.

She sighed, "*Que sera, sera.*" I knew she wasn't free to be herself.

I wasn't allowed to watch *The Mickey Mouse Club* that day as that was the rule: too sick to go to school, too ill to watch television. I slept in my comfortable flannel sheets, wondering how Tia Rosita was feeling without me. Mother brought dinner for me in bed and forced me to eat my vegetables. She told me to come out and say goodnight before falling asleep. Don and Eugenia came into the room to say goodnight and wish me well. I asked Don how *The Mickey Mouse Club* episode was that day. He announced Annette Funicello's *chi-chis* were getting bigger, and he was going to marry her.

I waited a bit, brushed my teeth, and went downstairs to say goodnight. Mother was curled up with my dad in the same chair where we had cried earlier. She draped her arms around his neck with her head resting on his shoulder. His bronze statue of Don Quixote shone under the soft lamplight next to them. She was in the safety of her knight in shining armor.

I avoided Linda the next morning on the walk to school because I was still embarrassed about the butterfly comment. But at snack time, when I helped pass out the milk, I had to look at her when I reached her desk. "Baseball," she said. "My dad says the Yankees are going to win the World Series." That was a salve for my embarrassment. I didn't know what she meant by the World Series, but I knew that anything to do with the Yankees was important toward being an American.

"Baseball," I whispered. She smiled. "*Linda,*" I pronounced in Spanish. She didn't know it meant pretty. I repeated "Linda" in English.

That afternoon walking home from school, I was flanked by Linda on one side and Gene on the other. I felt safe and started repeating all the words they came up with along the way. I was free to be myself with these two friends. Stop was es-stop, and sidewalk was es-sidewalk with or without the "es." Gene and Linda were okay with it. We reached Linda's gate giggling together. I realized I was trying to laugh with English intonation. Did I sound like Dad, I wondered? Linda's mother opened the front door.

"Linda, I'm going to the store," she said. "I've put some cookies on the table for you and your friends. I'll be back soon." She left in a hurry. We walked inside the house and resumed our collective giggle. Gene grabbed two cookies and said goodbye before running out.

"Do you want to see my secret room?" Linda whispered with fingers to her lips. She led me up the stairs to the second floor and then up another narrow staircase to the attic. I had explored the scary old attic in our house with my brother and didn't like the idea of entering another one. Linda's attic was clean, filled with books, toys, a dollhouse, two chairs and table, and a bed. A record player stood on the small table. A naked light bulb hung from the ceiling over the bed with a string switch. A window provided enough light to see everything until Linda closed the curtain. I stood waiting for her to turn on the light.

I heard a box spring whine when she stepped on the bed and pulled the light string. The secret room felt cozy and private, away from the world. Linda turned on a record player and placed a record on. Elvis Presley's "That's All Right, Mama" popped on. I didn't know how to react. The music entered Linda's body. She turned and swung and danced, unlike anything I'd ever seen. I wanted to run away, but I trusted her. She was doing what she wanted, and she wanted me there. I watched Linda's pink poodle skirt bounce back and forth as she twisted and turned, laughing. I thought the poodle would bark at any moment, so I whispered, "Shh." Instead of slowing her down, she picked up the pace. I had no idea what I was looking at or why she seemed so happy.

I jumped up and followed her lead. We giggled, twisted, twirled, and hopped around the table. She approved. I was one step closer to becoming the American Dad wanted me to be. We were together in her secret place, safe and sound. Suddenly she stopped and turned to face me. She wanted me to lead. I turned and tripped over a giant pair of brown leather shoes at the corner of the bed.

An engine growled to a halt at the driveway, then roared ahead, tires crunching rocks up the path. Linda and I ran downstairs. Her mother flew through the kitchen door just as we reached the bottom stair. "Your father will be home soon," she said nervously and placed the new whiskey in Oliver's baseball room. "Charlie, do you play baseball?"

"He doesn't talk, Mother," Linda said.

"Baseball," I said. "I like baseball. I like Yankees." I surprised myself.

I left and headed home when my brother came up behind me. He carried Dad's baseball glove and wore a cap. It started to snow.

"Charlie," he whispered, "Annette loves me. Run!" He took off running.

We walked on until I recognized the three boys that had pushed me heading our way. I wasn't scared with my big brother next to me. I was about to tell Don what had happened when he blurted out, "Annette Funicello's *chi-chis* are coming on TV!" We started running. The three boys must have thought I was rushing toward them because they turned around and ran away screaming. We made it home in time to watch *The Mickey Mouse Club*.

The sound of Dad's car in the driveway alerted us that he was home. I ran out to greet him just as a police car pulled up to our house. A lazy looking policeman stepped out. I recognized two of the three boys that had tried to fight with me sitting in the back seat. A gruff looking man sat in the front. Dad had just parked the station wagon and was getting out as I ran to kiss him. He smiled briefly at me and walked to the policeman. The gruff man stepped out of the police car in a work shirt and scuffed work boots. He marched to join the conversation. Don appeared at the front door with a curious look.

"That's him," shouted one of the boys in the back of the police car, pointing toward Don.

"What's this about, officer?" asked my Dad.

"These boys say that boy in the doorway chased and threatened them with a baseball bat," the policeman reported.

"If that's your son," said the parent, "you better control him. He looks dangerous." I felt uncomfortable realizing Don and I were the only brown people there. I felt Dad grip my shoulder.

"Now just a minute," Dad demanded. "We can get to the bottom of this right now. Donald, please step over here." Don hurried over. Dad took his hand and mine. "Donald, this officer claims there was an incident with you and a baseball bat."

"I don't have a bat," answered Don confidently. His nostrils flared like a bull. He stared at the policeman and the boy's father before pinning his sight on the boys. Don spoke English well enough to defend himself. "Did somebody say I had a bat?" he asked the police officer. "A baseball bat? I—"

"Are you denying it?" the gruff man challenged.

"I am saying I did not take a baseball bat to school—"

"See, officer, lie pure and simple. No one said anything about school."

"Dad, I didn't lie," Don pleaded. More concerned with the accusation of telling a lie than having a bat.

"No one is saying you lied, son," Dad assured.

The gruff man smirked and rolled his eyes. The police car in front of the house caused a stir, and soon a few neighbors were outside. Gene showed up, walking past the boys in the car. He looked in the window and said something to them. They slumped.

"I could press charges if I felt it necessary," said the gruff father. "Then again, I am an Army man myself, and I understand fighting, sometimes war, is the only way to settle a dispute. Then again, bringing a baseball bat to a children's dispute is a serious violation. How about you? Where did you serve?"

"I don't find this conversation constructive or in good taste. Your question is unnecessary, and quite frankly, irrelevant. My son said he didn't do any such thing, and I'd like you to get back in the car and get on your way." Dad spoke with such authority, the man shrunk. I imagined Dad passing a matador's cape over a charging bull's horns, swiveling, and walking away without looking back. "Officer, I'd appreciate you moving your vehicle ASAP."

"Of course, unless you want to continue this investigation," the officer said to Mister Gruff.

"Pop!" yelled the freckle-faced boy from the police car. "I said hat, not bat."

Everyone turned to look at the boy who quickly dropped out of sight behind the seat.

"Now, if you'll excuse us. We have dinner waiting. Unless you have anything else, Officer," Dad said and led Don and me toward the house. Again, I imagined Dad passing his matador's cape and walking away.

"*Ole*," I said.

Later that evening, I rushed downstairs to kiss Mother and Dad goodnight. They were in their usual position, curled up on Dad's favorite chair. He was reading Hemingway's latest book, *The Old Man and the Sea*. Dad seemed unusually pensive when I interrupted. He looked up, startled. "Goodnight, Daddy," I said and kissed him before kissing Mother.

"Cuba," he said without an explanation.

Tortillas

We all missed tortillas. One day Dad surprised us with sacks of cornflower, black beans, and dried chilies he had ordered from Texas. He had picked them up at the railway station and brought them home. We were now the only family on the block who would eat tortillas and beans. Everyone rushed out to help bring in the heavy load of Mexican staples. He popped open the trunk, and we all peered in. The dry chilies and brown burlap sacks looked like candy to us. It seemed out of place and contrary to our goal of assimilating into the American Melting Pot. Still, at that moment, it felt glorious. Mother kissed Dad while Eugenia, Don, and I jockeyed for a position to hug Dad. There were more surprises in the cab of the car. Dad handed Mother two Mambo albums and a new Harry Belafonte album — *Calypso*.

The Mexican staples were cause for celebration. Dad cracked the seal of the new album and played it on the hi-fi console. Mother started moving to the music. I joined her, and then Dad jumped in. Or it may have been the other way around, but the three of us danced together.

The next night, Mother and Dad put up a system unlike any other in the history of tortilla making set to Harry Belafonte's *Calypso* album. It was a family assembly line that involved shower hats and rubber gloves. To say Mother was a germophobe would be an understatement. She made everyone, except Dad, wear rubber gloves and shower hats. We all had a job. First, Mother mixed the tortilla dough, *masa*, in an enormous bowl to just the right consistency. This delicate procedure required patient kneading skills. She swayed to the music, expertly keeping her hands busy, watching us with a *Mona Lisa*-like smile. Next, Eugenia pieced together golf ball sized lumps of dough of precise measurement, all the while swinging her hips. She placed the *masa* balls on wax paper at one end of the kitchen table for me to do my job.

I had the task of patting the balls into small disc-shaped circles and placing them on a wax paper area in front of Don. He would flatten them out with a kitchen roller to fit in the five-inch diameter makeshift container—a one-pound Maxwell House coffee tin. Mother would then place them on large skillets and stand over them, flipping the tortillas with her bare hands. Dad would, in the end, set the cooked tortillas in a tin. He got the biggest thrill when Harry Belafonte's "Banana Boat Song" came on, and we all swung our hips together and belted out the "Day-O" in unison. Harry Belafonte instantly became an honorary Mexican. Dad had created a castle for his new family, and we all loved being in his kingdom, where we could still be free to feel ourselves. Assimilation around the clock wasn't easy, and we all cherished those moments of tapping into our Mexican roots. By the end of the night, we had enough tins full of tortillas to last a month. We spent hours laughing, singing, dancing, and imagining what kind of tacos we would make with our first tortillas in The Big *Manzana*.

Soon it was the Christmas season, and the whole neighborhood lit up like Mexico City, but instead of the Three Kings and the Nativity scene everywhere, there were Santa Claus, elves, reindeer, Christmas trees, and snowmen up and down the block. One Saturday, we drove out to the countryside and came back with a Christmas tree and a bag of chestnuts. Dad put up lights around the house. Don and I watched, cheered, and helped in any way we could. Dad climbed all the way up to the top of the roof's edge. I felt I'd climbed up with him and it was the most exciting feeling ever. We roasted chestnuts in the fireplace and decorated the enormous Christmas tree while trying to learn Christmas carols.

All of a sudden, like magic, Doris Day sang *"Que Sera, Sera."* The lyrics hit us all smack in the heart. We all stopped and looked at one another, acknowledging the Spanish lyrics. I thought Doris Day had made this song just for my sister. I envisioned her asking Mother what she might become and having Mother respond eloquently, *"Que sera, sera."* Rich, pretty, not knowing the future were mysteries of the past because we were now safely entrenched in the Melting Pot. Eugenia, the new American Eugenia, would grow up, fall in love, and live the American Dream.

The impact this song had on all of us was overwhelming. We, the four of us, lit up like Christmas tree lights in unison, as though Doris Day and the whole United States of America had welcomed us. We could be a part of our new country and still have a little Mexican in us. The notion, or idea, of The Melting Pot hadn't entirely made sense until now with those three little words *"Que sera, sera"* that included our roots. Dad placed Doris Day's album cover on the table. She looked just like Linda, a blond, blue-eyed, wholesome American girl. We played the song over and over all weekend, making it our patriotic anthem.

The following Monday, I walked to school with the lyrics of *"Que Sera, Sera"* ringing in my head and feeling warm through the snow-packed sidewalk. I imagined, almost heard, Doris Day singing the Mexican words inside each home I walked past. I was in heaven. I reached Linda's house and saw her waiting on the front porch. She ran to the gate, looking every bit like Doris Day. Gene screamed for us to wait up as we left Linda's house. We turned around and saw Gene wailing and wobbling through the sludgy sidewalk toward us. Linda laughed, and we waited for Gene to catch up. Linda and Gene were excited about the presents they were going to ask Santa Claus for and asked what I wanted. I was too excited about Doris Day's song to think of an answer. Gene realized I wasn't paying attention to them. He screamed, "Peanut butter!" and ran away, taunting me to catch up with him. I didn't have to. He slipped, falling backward, arms flailing, and landed on the snow-covered sidewalk. All I could do was contain my laughter.

When Mrs. Brown asked the first question of the day, "Can anyone tell me what day of the week it is today?" my hand shot up. I desperately wanted to be like everyone else, and speaking English was going to be my ticket. If Doris Day could sing in Spanish, I could speak English. I answered her question and started asking my own questions after that successful venture. Mrs. Brown seemed pleased with me and encouraged my verbal skills by asking me questions directly. "Charlie, can you tell us what color Little Red Riding Hood's coat is?" Simple questions were met with simple answers that soon assuaged my fear of talking. It helped that I had Mrs. Brown, Linda, Gene, Charlie Chaplin, and Doris Day on my side. My classroom was now my sanctuary, where I could feel a part of something rather than apart from everything.

Linda's dad was waiting for her when Gene and I walked her home. He had a baseball glove in one hand, a bat in the other. A half-full glass of whiskey stood on the porch step next to a pack of cigarettes. Linda rushed through the gate and up the stairs, barely acknowledging Oliver. His eyes were red like Little Red Riding Hood's coat. "Red," I said. Gene agreed, slapped my arm, and took off running. I followed Gene on the slippery sidewalk until we were clear out of sight.

"Drunk," said Gene. "He's drunk." And with that, he whinnied like a horse, slapped his butt, and rode off yelling, "Hi-yo Silver! Away!" We walked to Gene's home, just past mine. We walked through his front door and straight to the kitchen, where his mother stood over an ironing board, creasing men's pants, inhaling a filtered cigarette. She wore a light blue dress under a starched checkered apron. A line of perfectly ironed shirts hung on a bar across the doorway behind her. She told me to call her Jane and to help myself to the snacks on the table. A loaf of white bread, cheese, bologna, mayonnaise, peanut butter, and jelly were placed neatly on the table. This was a new kind of being an American I did not expect. She didn't look up from her ironing and only raised her head to inhale the cigarette. "Gene says you're from Mexico?" she asked, not waiting for an answer. "How long have you been here?" "What part of Mexico are you from?" "Have you gotten used to the weather here?" "What brought you to New York?" I could see where Gene got his gift for talking. His mother was a non-stop question machine. Gene handed me two slices of bread before starting his own sandwich. "Kimosabe," I said.

"Peanut butter," he loaded up a knife with peanut butter and made the fastest PBJ sandwich ever. "Can you say peanut butter?" he said in a challenging tone. I lost the challenge.

Jane stopped her ironing, came over, and poured two glasses of milk for us. She stared at me with dilated pupils and asked if my parents played bridge. I couldn't imagine them playing on a bridge, so I said no. "Too bad," she said and went back to her task. I waited for Gene's reaction to the taste of the sandwich, and it seemed fine. Gene stopped chewing, looked at me, mouth agape, dropped his lunch, and ran to the front door. He threw it open as though something was willing him. We saw Linda running away in tears. We rushed out to catch her, but her dad drove up next to her in his big sedan. The car door opened, and Linda slid into the front seat, surrendering to her father.

Gene's mother rushed to the door and saw the car drive away. We stood in silence for a moment, then a cuckoo clock sprang into action cuckoo-ing four times. Gene jumped around and headed back to the sandwiches. "Ten days and how many hours, Mom, till Christmas?" he asked. She didn't answer. She flipped the light switch on the front door wall and lit up the Christmas lights that looked just like the ones on our house.

"Mom, Linda's dad is drunk."

Linda's secret room smelled different the next day when she invited me up there. I couldn't figure out the new smell until I saw an ashtray full of cigarette butts and an empty tumbler glass on the table. Linda didn't seem to mind the scent and continued with what she had planned for us. She wanted to play school, and I was her student. She opened an alphabet book and drilled me with her best imitation of Mrs. Brown. "Okay, repeat after me. A is for apple," she said, pointing at the book. I repeated. "Can you say a word that starts with A?"

"Apple." I didn't feel like playing. I couldn't stop thinking about her running off Gene's porch.

"B is for?"

"Ball."

"C is for?"

"Cat." I was done. I saw her worry. Just as I'd seen the day before. She put on some Christmas music. I picked up a cigarette from the ashtray, straightened it out, extending it as Charlie Chaplin had done in a movie. I twirled the cigarette around and around until she broke into a smile. I continued dancing with the cigarette butt in my mouth. I saw her growing interest in my moves and added my eyebrow twitches and lip curls. She let go of whatever was bothering her and raced around the room. I slid my shoes into her dad's shoes and performed my own Charlie Chaplin penguin walk. We giggled and gyrated around the room, going faster than the Christmas songs. Watching her dance and laugh with me, pretending to be Charlie

Chaplin, was magic. We laughed uncontrollably until we couldn't stand.

Linda fell on the bed, and I sat right next to her, both of us in belly-aching laughter. The cigarette fell out of my mouth and on the floor. I got up to put the smoke back in the ashtray, still stumbling from laughter. As I turned around, Linda threw her underpants at me. I threw them back at her as she raised her skirt. Was this another test of how much I wanted to be an American? Whatever it takes, I thought. I pulled my pants down, trying to keep up with her new game. She jumped up and threw her shirt over her head and romped around the room. With my pants at my ankles, I hopped like a bunny. Linda turned around and stared at my penis. Her eyes opened wide, and she pointed. I looked down and saw my penis pointing straight up like a rocket ship. I didn't feel like peeing, but there it was, my pilfered penis crying out for attention; it jumped up and down to my laughter. And with that, I took control of my little rocket and made it jump up fully synchronized with my eyebrows. If Charlie Chaplin could only see me now, I thought. I raised my eyebrows, alternating left and right. I twitched my upper lip up, again alternating sides, and made my penis jump to the rhythm of "Santa Claus is Coming to Town." It was more than either of us could take. We stopped, fixed our clothes, and walked downstairs just in time to see Oliver drive in. I rushed to the front door, hoping he didn't see me. Linda walked me to the front door and said she'd never tell anyone she saw my baseball bat. I didn't care because I felt Charlie Chaplin and Cantinflas would have been proud of their number one fan, making a sad girl laugh.

After dinner that night, Dad placed two boxes on our dining room table. One box of Christmas cards. The other of our first family portrait, taken on Thanksgiving. We all gathered around to look at the proud and happy family. MERRY CHRISTMAS from THE ALLEN FAMILY it said. We assembled the cards and pictures with the same precision we'd used on the tortilla making line. We all wrote our names and good wishes on the cards. Doris Day kept us company as we bobbed our heads and sang along with *"Que Sera, Sera"*. Dad wanted Don, Eugenia, and me to make our own individual cards for his mother and aunt. Eugenia drew beautiful flowers and a Christmas tree on the outside. She wrote lovely greetings with perfect penmanship on the inside. Don did the same with a masculine touch of a boy and girl ice skating on a frozen lake. I knew it was Annette Funicello and him because he snuck in carefully drawn breasts. I drew stick figures and a lean Christmas tree on the outside. On the inside, I wrote: Dear Ant, Merry Christmas and Happy New Year.

I showed Dad my work expecting a smile of approval, but instead, he frowned and rejected the whole card. "Oh, Charlie," he said sadly. He took the card and pointed out the word ANT. "Your aunt is not an insect." He handed me another piece of paper. I spelled what I heard. There are no silent letters in Spanish. I took extra care on the second card. I used a ruler to make straight lines of a house and a Christmas tree. I made sure I colored inside the lines and wrote the letters straight. When I finished, I looked up and saw that Dad and I were the only ones still awake. He sat in front of his Don Quixote statue signing cards. I handed him the card, praying he'd be happier with me. "Much better," he said.

Doris Day's lyrics rang in my head. "Dad, what will I be when I grow up?" I asked. He stopped writing, looked up, and pondered a thought. "Hm, good question, son," he started. "Why don't you take a seat here." I rushed to his chair. He reached for a book and quoted Albert Einstein, "Only a life lived in the service to others is worth living." I stared blankly. "That means doing for others, helping the less fortunate," he said. I waited to try to make sense of what he meant. "Giving one's heart to others. Like teachers." I thought of Mrs. Brown's gentle face. He didn't have to give other examples.

Saturday morning, Dad surprised the family with a trip to New York City. We had a 6:00 A.M. train to catch, so we got up before dawn and drove to the railway station in the dark. Boarding a train with Dad felt calm compared to our last trip. We now had a secure sense of belonging. Secretly, I fantasized the mean porter would walk down the aisle just long enough to knock his tray over.

Don and I wore matching green winter coats, and we all had gloves and hats. Snow muffled the sounds of everything around except the train's roaring steam whistle. The iron wheels whined into motion. I curled up between Don and Eugenia, closed my eyes, and listened to the steel wheels moaning and meld into a baritone drone that lulled me to sleep.

Mexico City streets were just as fast and just as crowded as New York City. Still, the tall buildings and traffic intimidated me when we stepped out of the train station. I gripped Mother's gloved hand the moment we stepped outside. It seemed as though the whole world was present, and everyone was desperately rushing somewhere. Men and women carried colorful shopping bags; sales ladies smiled like movie stars; everyone wore gloves, hats, long coats, short coats, boots, and scarves. And we fit right in. Street vendors seemed bored compared to Mexico's street hawkers. We walked to Macy's, where Christmas carolers sang right in front of the circular sliding door entrance. A crowd hovered around to listen and keep each other warm, it seemed. We stopped and listened to one song. Dad handed Eugenia a coin to drop in a Salvation Army bucket before we walked through the doors. Magically, Tchaikovsky's "Nutcracker Suite" shot through the din. I knew, I just knew, Dad had planned this welcome. He must have called ahead and talked to Santa or whoever was in charge because that music was just for us. We all acknowledged the music, quietly hiding our delight with tight, knowing smiles. Mother reassured my suspicion that Dad had arranged the music with her two-eyes wink. I thought about Tia Rosita and wondered how she'd feel inside this magic store.

We continued through the crowded store where I spotted a section featuring The Lone Ranger regalia, including Tonto gear and lunchbox. I tugged Mother's hand as we walked by. She smiled and watched me stare at the Lone Ranger as we went up the escalator to Santaland where the music changed. A chorus of Santa's beautiful elves sang Christmas carols. A mountain of gift-wrapped boxes displayed a train set near Santa. Dad picked up a box. We waited and watched with excitement until we reached the front of the line. Boys and girls sat on Santa's lap and talked to him while a photographer and parents took pictures. The children all looked happy sitting on Santa's lap and listening to his ho-ho-hos. The chorus sang "Santa Claus Is Coming to Town." I tuned into the words:

You better not cry

Don was right about not crying. I shouldn't have cried in this country. Would Santa make an exception?

You better not pout

I wasn't allowed to pout, so that didn't matter. Only one more person stood in front of us. The blond girl in front of us rushed to Santa's lap. She handed Santa a paper and jumped off.

Don pushed me ahead just as the little girl jumped off Santa's lap. Santa pulled me up on his lap. "Ho-ho-ho, young fellow," Santa said. "Have you been naughty or nice?"

Santa knew everything. He knew what I'd done in the secret room. He knows if you've been bad or good, so he knew I was bad.

"Have you been a good boy?" Santa asked. A light flashed in my face, sending my heart and mind to another stratosphere. My breathing shortened, heart raced. Don's warning about crying swirled through my head, my longing for Tia Rosita, and my *Toro* all but telling me I'd been a bad boy, paralyzed me. The thought of Santa telling Dad that I'd been bad after he went through all the trouble of

65

playing "Nutcracker Suite" for us in this magical store terrified me. I didn't want to disappoint him.

Had I been a good boy? Why was Santa asking me if he already knew? My throat tightened. I couldn't breathe, couldn't talk, and I couldn't lie to Santa. Dad readied his camera and pointed it directly at me. There would be a record of my telling a lie to Santa. I saw an opening—a gap toward the escalator. I jumped off Santa's lap and ran to the rolling stairs, leaped over a heavy red cordon rope, took a deep breath, and hurled myself onto the down escalator.

I was out on the streets faster than a mouse. I had no idea where I was going, but I had to get out of Santa's store. I blasted through the packed sidewalk, confused. Snow started to fall. I ran until everyone stopped for a red light. I looked up and saw my *Toro* snorting with a smile. Why was he smiling? I ignored it. I was a disappointment in the family. I was sure Santa had told Dad that I'd smoked a cigarette. I was doomed. It didn't matter now if I cried. The worst that could happen was going to happen. I'd be thrown over the border and have to find my Tia Rosita. She might not even want me after learning I'd smoked a cigarette, even if it didn't have any smoke.

I took a few aimless steps and ended up staring at what I perceived to be a deformed sugar-laced *churro*. It was a pretzel. Tears, sweat, and melting snowflakes rolled down my cheeks while I stood alone in front of the pretzel and chestnut stand. I didn't move. I was afraid to walk. I stared at the funny looking *churro*. "You lost, son?" a burly red-faced policeman asked in a friendly tone. I didn't answer. I tried to bury my face in my jacket, not wanting the man to see my tears. "Where are your parents?" I still didn't answer. The policeman reached in his pocket and paid for a pretzel. He knelt down in front of me and handed me the paper-wrapped pretzel.

"Thank you," I managed. I used my good manners, hoping Santa and Dad would find out I was being a good boy and forgive me.

"Take a bite, young fellow," he said after carefully wiping my tears with a napkin. I thought maybe life was supposed to go this way, and I would end up being this man's son in a new house in another part of the world. I couldn't take a bite of the pretzel. I thought that if I took a bite, I would become this friendly policeman's son. I couldn't betray William Allen. More tears flowed down my face, and I started shivering. "Okay, little one," he said. "Let's see if we can find your parents." And with that, he picked me up and, in one swift motion, stood me on top of a mailbox, holding my hand until I found my balance. He was tall and muscular and stood above the crowd, but I was now above him. I could see a little snow on top of his blue hat and big shoulders. *Ole*, I thought.

"Watch your ears," the policeman announced before he blew a whistle in a pattern I'd recognize later as SOS—three short, three long, three short. He repeated the call once more.

"Charlie! Charlie! Charlie!" I heard soft, Spanish-accented voices calling out my name amid the holiday noise. Dad, Mother, Eugenia, and Don rushed toward me, yelling my name. The policeman lowered me with a secure grip back to the sidewalk. I leaped up into Dad's open arms. He held me tight, letting me know I was still his son. Over Dad's shoulder, I saw the policeman's face watching me. Our eyes met, and he nodded in a way that calmed my heart. Dad shook the policeman's hand and thanked him. They exchanged words about the Navy and service before he walked away. Don looked at my pretzel. I offered it to him. He took one bite, didn't like the taste, and handed it back. I bit into the pretzel, expecting a sweet taste, like *churros,* and realized why Don handed it back. No one asked why I disappeared, and I didn't mention Santa again. I promised myself I'd never pick up a cigarette again. "Ole," I said, glad I had not been sent back to Mexico.

Don and Eugenia held my hand for the rest of the stay in New York City. After a meal, we boarded the train for the ride home. Dad carried a suitcase-size shopping bag, and Mother held a couple of smaller containers. I fell asleep to the same rhythmic drone of iron wheels rolling along the railroad tracks. *Que sera, sera.*

The next day Linda knocked on the front door covered in big waterproof clothes and a Yankees cap over her winter hood. She wanted to build a snowman. I grabbed my snow gear and rushed out the door, excited to play in the snow. Linda picked up a branch and ran it across every white picket fence we passed. The clatter reminded me of Gene, who liked to make loud triumphant noises, but coming from Linda, the sound felt sad. "Do you believe in Santa?" she asked.

"I met him at Macy's," I answered unconvincingly, aware I was now speaking English.

"I don't, either," she said and scraped the stick louder on the fence. We turned the corner and reached a park. It was quiet from the fresh snow. We raced to make as many tracks as we could. She circled me, and then I circled her, our boots crunching through the snow, giggling the whole while. It felt good to hear her laugh in the quiet blanket of snow. A soft mist of snowflakes fell over us. Linda stuck her tongue and started counting the flakes she caught. I did the same. "A million," she said and stopped. "Snowman!" She reached in the snow.

Together we formed a snowball and rolled it around, getting bigger and bigger until we had the bottom of our snowman. We continued making the chest and, finally, the head, leaving clear zigzag lines across the park. We had our very own snowman. But it needed a face. "Eyes," I said. "He needs eyes." Linda was one step ahead. She pulled a pinecone out of her pocket, pulled off two wedges, and handed them to me. I gave our snowman eyes. Linda placed a few more wedges on the front for buttons and handed me her Yankees cap. I put it on top. It was beautiful. We admired our creation, panting like hungry dogs, snowflakes falling faster around us.

"What do you want to call him?" Linda asked. I didn't answer.

"Mickey," she answered her own question.

"Mickey Mouse? No," I said.

"No," she said, "Mickey Mantle." She pulled a carrot out of her pocket and stuck it right in the snowman's crotch. We laughed so hard I nearly fell over. Linda held me up until a snowball flew in from behind us and hit Mickey's face. Then another snowball flew in, and another. The last one knocked the hat off. I grabbed the Yankees cap and took Linda's hand. We ran away without looking back. We turned the corner and heard three young voices closing in on us. Then the voices turned to laughter. Then the carrot flew over our heads. We ran right past my house and finally stopped at Linda's house. We were safe, but a stream of smoke was billowing out from the side of the house, and the sound of Oliver's V8 engine idling came through loud and clear. "That's Dad sleeping in his car," she said.

The front door opened, and Linda's mother rushed out, looking tired and worn out. "Linda," she said, "you need to get inside." She didn't look at me as she said, "Charlie, you need to go home now." Then she sneezed in her handkerchief and walked back inside. Linda watched the door close and suddenly had a worried expression. I knew she was thinking about her dad in the car. We slowly made our way to the driveway and to the vehicle. The windows were steamed up so we couldn't see inside. Linda walked ahead and knocked on the window. No response.

I edged forward, looked in the driver's side window, and recognized cigarette smoke floating inside. I knocked on the window as hard as I could, until Oliver's comatose head appeared, swiveling slowly without direction and gently stopping on the steering wheel. Linda's mother opened the side door of the house. "Linda, I told you to get inside," she whimpered. The car horn blasted, and the door flew open, letting out a cloud of smoke. A boy's baseball glove fell out. Oliver's head had hit the horn. The odor of alcohol and cigarettes slapped my senses all the way back to the memory of finding the dead soldier crossing a field in Mexico. Linda yelled for her mother and ran into her house. I ran away as fast as I could.

I reached our porch holding Linda's Yankees cap. Don opened the door, saw the horror on my face, and pulled me inside. He asked what was wrong, had anything happened, but I couldn't answer. I dropped the hat. Don picked it up and hung it on the hat rack, where it would remind me of Oliver and the dead soldier.

Christmas morning, Santa left the Lionel train set Dad had bought at Macy's under the tree. Santa also brought me a Lone Ranger lunchbox. Don had a way of exploring and testing things that only made sense to him. He liked having me as his guinea pig. I didn't have a choice. I always went along with anything he wanted to do. The train circled in what Don thought was a monotonous motion. He wedged a pen underneath the tracks on one side, then a pencil on the opposite side. The train had a new dimension. Don wanted more. He placed one more wedge underneath the tracks and asked me to use my finger on the opposite side. I knew electricity was dangerous, but I couldn't admit fear to my brother.

I slid my finger under the track, hoping my hand would not tremble. I built up my courage by making the train a bull and my finger my grandfather. How would Dad have responded to a train thundering along toward him? Was he as fearless as a matador? I guessed he would be. The train bucked together and over the rises. I watched it, dreading my decision. The train got closer. Finally, it sped over my finger without hurting. "Ha," I said defiantly at the train. Then Don told me to put my whole hand underneath. I had to prove I wasn't afraid, so I did. I was a fearless matador. The train raced around again like a bull. I was in a face-off with the beast. I faced the thundering bull boldly, head up, but when it reached my hand, the train derailed and flew into the Christmas tree. Don laughed, the lights blew out, the tracks separated on my side. Dad and Mother rushed in.

Don keeled over, trying to hide his laughter but ended up on his back, legs kicking like an upside-down beetle. His laughter became contagious. One by one, everyone rushed in, and we all ended up laughing with him, if not at him. We escaped disaster.

Don and I put on our snow gear and walked outside. I took the Yankees cap, and we headed toward Linda's house. Steam radiated from Don like a hot engine as we trudged through the snow-packed sidewalk. We reached Linda's home and found the car was gone. I stepped on the porch to look inside and saw uneaten breakfasts on the table and no Christmas tree.

"Tonto!" Gene startled me from afar. Don looked relieved to see it was a friend. Gene climbed the steps holding a present in one hand and wearing a beautiful New York Yankees cap. "Merry Christmas, *amigo*," he said, holding out a gift for me. *Amigo*? Yes, we were *amigos*! I was happy, surprised, and embarrassed all at once. I'd never imagined a gift from Gene. He offered the present and pulled it away just as I reached for it. "Christmas present," he said. "Say Christmas present."

"Thank you, *amigo*, for the Christmas present," I said, taking the gift. I was getting comfortable with some words.

"Thank my mom. It was her idea." He looked in the window and drew back. "Creepy," Gene said and ran away as though he'd seen a ghost. I dropped Linda's cap on the porch and ran after him. Don followed until we stopped at the corner.

"Why are we running?" asked Don. Suddenly we were speaking English like Americans. It was as though Santa Claus had brought us a secret gift, a new skin, a new sensation. My brother's voice sounded more dominant in English. As though, under the open sky, it reached all the way to Mexico. It had a musical quality to me. Maybe he'd been inspired by Annette Funicello and wished he could be on the

Mickey Mouse Show.

"Open your present," said Gene. I ripped open the wrapping paper and saw a gleaming New York Yankees hat. I slipped it on my head and felt taller, stronger, faster, and more American.

"*Ole!*" I screamed while my feet started jumping in place. I rolled up a snowball and hit Gene with it. "Merry Christmas," I said and ran away. I heard Gene's approving laughter as I thrashed through the snow. I must have yelled Merry Christmas a million times along the way. A few neighbors looked out. Some smiled. Some laughed. Some looked angry. I didn't care. After all, I was wearing a New York Yankees cap, and I was speaking English. I walked into the house, showing off my new identity, my belonging. Dad smiled and called me slugger. Mother asked where I got the cap. I told her Gene had given it to me as a Christmas present. She gasped and retreated into the house.

Embroidery and needlework were a family trait in the Perez line of women. Mother embroidered every handkerchief and shirt Dad owned with his initials—WA in Old English lettering. That night she organized her sewing materials, placing them in the Almond Joy chocolate boxes. Mother sat with Dad embroidering a set of handkerchiefs while he read the newspaper. Dad's classical music played softly on the hi-fi. Mother stayed busy threading the needle in and out of the embroidery hoops. She appeared regal sitting next to Dad with his book. She was happy with her knight in shining armor. The next day mother showed me the embroidering she had finished. It was a set of embroidered handkerchiefs with the letter G for my *amigo* Gene.

Speak Up

The first week back at school, I was ready to go with all my might. I knew every letter in the English alphabet and could come up with a word for each and every one, more than one name. A was for apple, astronaut, April, and August. B was for baseball, boys, beans, bathroom, bed, and a lot more. I had the whole chart in my head and no fear in my throat, except for the X. The X in Mexico was my favorite letter because it was alive everywhere, from money and billboards to monuments and books, but it did not appear as much in English. The picture of a xylophone was the only word with the X, and the single word that scared me because Mrs. Brown never said it, and I didn't use any words that started with an X. No matter, I was prepared with X-ray and ready to prove I belonged in Mrs. Brown's class. I volunteered for everything. Taking a page from Gene's book, my hand went up with every question Mrs. Brown asked. I'd raise my hand and ask questions before Mrs. Brown had a chance to call on me. "What is a hoop?" "What is a curve?" "What is yarn?" "Why does the word *bat* mean one thing in baseball and another when it's a black bird in a cave?" I couldn't ask enough questions about the meaning of words. Mrs. Brown didn't seem to mind my incessant questions. I think it may have had something to do with calming Gene's spirited practice, or maybe because my voice wasn't as loud as his. I got a thrill walking home with Gene, both of us in our Yankees caps, and bombarding him with questions.

"What is that?" I'd ask, pointing at a house.

"A house," Gene would respond.

"No not that." I would then point at a particular part of the house, like the window.

"Window."

"No, not that." I moved closer to Gene and nudged him to follow my finger. "That."

"Roof."

"No, not that," I'd go on pointing at different things, "that."

"Bush."

"No, not that." My hand was faster than his mouth. "No, that." The sooner I asked, the faster he'd walk. Finally, he'd run away, and I'd chase him pointing at everything yelling, "And that, and that, and that!"

A few days later, Linda, Gene, and I walked home from school in silence, careful not to slip on the icy sidewalk. I was happy to be with my two friends and not feel like an outsider. Before long, a fire engine thundered by so loud, Gene tripped when he turned to look. He took Linda with him, and she took me with her. We sat still and watched the red fire engine roll down the street until it stopped in front of Linda's house. Together we squirmed up to our feet and raced to the scene where two firemen were rushing up the driveway. Linda froze. She didn't rush to Oliver's car. A new garden hose was now attached to the exhaust pipe and curled around into the window. A fireman tore open the car door and grabbed Oliver. His Yankees cap fell off as the fireman reached in and turned off the engine. Gene and I instinctively held Linda and moved slowly toward the front porch. Linda's mom sobbed, slumped on the steps. An ambulance showed up, and we watched Oliver roll away on a gurney into the back of the ambulance. Linda's mom reached for her daughter and led her into the house without making eye contact. Neither turned to watch the ambulance roar off. Linda did not cry. I'd never know why.

The next day Linda wasn't her usual self; neither was I. I couldn't say a word. She only talked when she handed out the milk and crackers. Mrs. Brown must have known something because she spoke with Linda several times in private, each time Linda seemed to fight back the tears. The three of us walked home together again, but no one said a word. Oliver's car was still parked in the driveway when we reached Linda's house. She rushed up to the porch and slammed the door without saying a word.

"You're it," said Gene, and he punched me on the shoulder and ran away. I ran after him and found myself in front of his house before I knew why we ran.

"I'm what?" I asked.

"You're it," said Gene, "that's all." His mother opened the door and invited me in. I thanked her for the Christmas gift and smiled.

"What are you, Charlie?" Gene's mother asked.

"He's it, since Linda's house." He tapped me again lightly with a fist.

"You are not to go inside that house," Gene's mother said.

"I don't want to go in that house," Gene answered. "It gives me the creeps."

"Good," she said. "Keep it that way. Oliver needs to go to church and find his way again. He's just never been the same without his boy." Gene punched me in the arm again.

"You're it!" He ran off around the living room and out the side door. I saw his shoulder through the side window, heading toward the front of the house, so I ran to the front door. I opened it and found Linda standing on the porch just staring at the floor. Gene roared up and stopped.

"Creep!" Gene yelled and ran back around the house.

I walked with Linda in silence back to her house. Her mother was on the porch, waiting, and invited me in for cookies and milk. I didn't know what to say, so I walked in and sat down with Linda while her mom mended one of Oliver's socks. Linda didn't move. I was scared. I wanted to go home, but the look on Linda's face reminded me of how I felt on the first day of school and how she made me feel better. It was too quiet. I could hear Linda's mom mending Oliver's socks.

The phone rang, startling me. Linda grabbed my arm. Linda's mom reached for a cigarette pack and picked up the phone. "Hello?" she answered. "Yes, oh, thank goodness." She lit up a cigarette and grabbed an ashtray. She took a deep inhale of her cigarette and continued listening to the apparent good news. Linda and I went to her secret room.

The room smelled of alcohol and cigarettes. Linda played Doris Day's song, *"Que Sera, Sera."* "What happened?" I asked.

"Dad is sick, and it's my fault." She saw me staring at his shoes under the bed. "He's mad at me."

"What's this?" I asked, picking up a silver thimble that reminded me of Mexico's silver crafts.

"I wish I was a boy." She looked straight at me.

"I wish I was a girl," I said, staring back. We locked eyes in a staring contest. We listened to the whole Doris Day song without blinking.

"Do you really?"

"What?"

"Wish you were a girl?" She giggled. I gyrated like Charlie Chaplin getting electrocuted on an open wire. She laughed hysterically until her mom stepped in.

"Dad's coming home tomorrow," Linda's mom said and picked up the ashtray and tumbler. Linda stopped laughing.

Tequila

"What is suicide?" I asked one night at dinnertime.

"Why in the world would you ask?" Dad responded.

"Gene said Linda's dad tried to suicide himself," I said, "and if he does it again, he's not going to Heaven."

Dad's face turned grave, making me wish I hadn't asked the question. I took a bite of my dinner. I'm not sure what classical music was playing, but it may as well have been Johann Sebastian Bach's "Come, Sweet Death" because food got caught in my throat, and I panicked. Dad rushed to me, picked me up, held me upside down, and patted my back. I thought I was getting spanked for asking a wrong question. I burst out crying. A fishbone flew out of my mouth. Don picked it up and gave me a wink. I was not getting sent back to Mexico.

The following week, Dad and Mother invited Linda's and Gene's families to dinner. Dad served tequila margaritas, and mother prepared Mexican food, including our family-made tortillas. Doris Day's *"Que Sera, Sera"* played while Dad made margaritas right on the credenza. He placed a green glass pitcher and goblet set, then stirred a homemade lemon and sugar concoction in the pitcher and added ice cubes. "Anyone care to taste this margarita?" He held out a spoon full.

"Margarita, I've never had one," said Linda's mom.

"Neither have we," said Gene's mom.

"I will," said Oliver, reaching for the sample. "Good, mighty good, Bill."

"Sure?" Dad asked.

"Aw, go ahead, put some more of that Mexican fire in there," Oliver said with a blink. Dad poured more. I was amazed at how well Oliver and Dad got along at that moment. It made me feel good. Dad stirred a bit longer and ran a lemon around each goblet before dipping them in a plate of salt. He poured the margaritas like an expert.

"*Salud.*" Dad held up his drink, and everyone followed. "A toast to peace and happiness—" Dad stopped. The song *"Besame Mucho"* had started. "*Mi amor.*" He offered his hand to Mother as the song took over the room. Mother and Dad had center stage.

"How lucky can one man be?" Dad announced, taking Mother in his arms and kissing her softly on the lips. The song elicited their emotions as they forever exchanged a look of love whenever and wherever it played. And if the tune came on at any of their fiestas, they would be up on their feet and in each other's arms.

Dad impressed everyone with his bilingual skills when he introduced each mariachi album cover in Spanish and English. Mother beamed with pride. Perry Como and Benny Goodman albums stayed at the ready. We all spoke English, practicing our best elocution. Mother didn't say much but smiled a lot and seemed to light up the room, getting everyone to dance. Linda and I joined in the dance at one point while Gene and Don played with the electric train. Gene's mom and dad kept very quiet and seemed content with drinking alcohol and smoking on the couch. Oliver smoked and drank a lot. After a while, he was all legs and elbows dancing and grooving to the high-fidelity rhythms. He even belted out a few "*gritos*" with Dad. That got everyone's attention, and Dad walked away, saying he'd go for his camera in the other room.

Mother was sipping a drink, enjoying the Latin rhythm near the food and smiling when Oliver downed his drink, crossed to Mother, and took her arm. Linda's mother punched out her cigarette with alarm. All of a sudden, Mother was in Oliver's arms laughing but holding on for dear life, it seemed. He was being too aggressive. It was a fast song, but he was groping for a slow dance. Mother squirmed, trying to push away, laughingly, but Oliver was too strong. He looked like a bull next to Mother. Linda sprung to Oliver, grabbing one arm while Linda's mom took the other. Don and Gene stopped and came to the action. I reached for Don. Gene's parents stood motionless. Dad returned and moved into action like a fearless matador. Oliver stood four inches taller and fifty pounds heavier. Dad reached in and took Mother's hand, saying, "Stand down, fella," to Oliver, who snapped to attention. The room grew silent, and we all watched as Oliver lowered his head like a gored and wounded bull.

"*Ole*," I whispered. Mother buried her face in Dad's chest. He had taken the bull by the horns and defended his wife. Bullfighters are macho men because they stay calm in the face of danger. William Allen would have been the most elegant matador ever. But Mother was shaken and would not leave the house without Dad after that night.

Spring

Springtime came quickly. Snow melted, and everything was different. Linda quit talking to me. She avoided me in school and walked home alone. Gene stopped teaching me English, and I quit driving him crazy with questions. I developed a way of asking the meaning of words without asking. I scrunched up my face when I didn't understand, and Mrs. Brown would explain without my having to ask. I remember a boy saying something about some teenagers having gotten in trouble for breaking a window. I didn't know what the word *teenager* meant and scrunched my face. Mrs. Brown picked up on it and quickly explained. I was learning new words every day just by listening to my teacher and friends.

Don joined the Boy Scouts of America and made friends. He invited them over to the house where they played in the backyard. A big, fat tree with long arms was the main attraction for them. They competed, climbing to the top and jumping off. The yard became Don's domain.

One day Annette Funicello appeared on a new television show, *Spin and Marty's*. It featured a treehouse and members of *The Mickey Mouse Club*. Immediately, Don had to build a treehouse. The tree in the backyard was perfect. He needed wood, hammer, nails, and a little help. There was a treasure trove of building materials in the garage left by the previous house owner. I became his helper. Don spent hours drawing the treehouse. Dad's carpenter tools came in handy, and there were plenty of nails around. An old ladder hung from the garage rafter that was perfect for the tree. Don had the knack for seeing where things were possible and making them work. The tree was made for his vision. He set the ladder to climb up and slam nails into the boards that somehow fit perfectly into his dream. He curled his tongue out between his teeth a little to his left just before each swing of the hammer. He stuck his tongue out whenever he was concentrating on any physical task. I wondered whether our grandfather curled his tongue out, like Don, as he faced a bull. I helped him with every board and every nail, and every cup of water he needed all day long.

The next day we set out to finish the house. Don hammered, and I climbed up and down the ladder handing him whatever he asked for. One time, a board slipped out of his hand and back into mine. I caught the board, but a splinter dug deep into my palm. I felt the wood wedged into my skin. I looked up at Don. "Good catch," he said. Then he pulled it up and out of my hand. Blood dripped out. "Don't cry. Don't tell Dad," he said with a snap. "Suck it up!" I pretended it didn't hurt. *Ole*, for me. After hours of clattering, climbing up and down, looking for dropped nails, and holding up sides, we had what looked like a real treehouse complete with a front and back door.

Gene came over just as we finished, climbed up the stairs, and yelled: "Hi-yo Silver!" I was happy watching Gene up in the tree in his Yankees cap. "This is better than *Spin and Marty's*," he said and screamed again. I could see on Don's face he imagined Annette Funicello in our treehouse fort. Eugenia walked out of the house with two pieces of fabric she had rescued from the attic. Don covered the front and back openings with the cloth. We were on our way to being as American as Spin and Marty.

Gene and I were inseparable on the playground and spent a lot of time challenging one another in games and races. I felt one step closer to feeling American wearing the Yankees cap he'd given me, especially when we both had them on. On weekends our competitions continued to other things like eating the fastest or stuffing the most marshmallows in our mouths.

One weekend Gene came with our family for a lake picnic. Gene and I competed to find out-of-state license plates; whoever saw the plate first could punch the other. I could tell Mother didn't like the noise we were making, but I sensed she enjoyed watching and listening to my new American ways. Don and Eugenia were content to stay silent during the entire trip. When we reached the lake, Dad parked the car facing the water. The lake looked like a painting, a mirror image of tall green trees, and the sky reflected on the water like a mirror. No one swam in the lake.

As soon as Dad turned off the engine, Gene punched me on the shoulder and screamed I was "it." He ran away, tearing off his clothes, first his plaid shirt, then skip-hopping while yanking off his sneakers and socks. I followed doing the same until we reached the edge of the lake. Neither of us wanted to feel the shock of jumping in the cold water, so we hesitated.

Then Dad sidled up to us, pale white skin and swimming suit, standing fearless at the edge of the water for a brief moment, and then diving into the lake headfirst. He swam out like Tarzan in a movie. I had to beat Gene. "Tarzan!" I yelled and jumped in after Dad. Gene followed, quickly tagging my foot, and screamed I was "it." We swam and raced around, teeth chattering until we were exhausted and hungry.

Eugenia and Mother set up the food at a clearing near where we had jumped in. They had packed a yellow and black steel tartan picnic basket with deviled eggs and everything to make sandwiches. Don was now a proud Boy Scout and had learned how to make a fire without matches. He built a perfect fire with rock edges and sticks. I was impressed. Dad and Mother laid everything out on a tablecloth and passed out two slices of bread to make our own lunch. Gene and I started a competition for the most creative sandwich possible. I put on peanut butter; Gene followed. He put on jelly; I followed. I put on a slice of cheese; he followed. He put on potato chips; I followed. He put on a deviled egg. I didn't. Gene won. Mother enjoyed watching me have fun in our new country.

"What's your favorite television show?" Eugenia asked Gene, looking up from her thick book that I realized was in English. Assimilation 101 was complete for her.

"*The Mickey Mouse Club.* Annette is my favorite," Gene answered. Don's ears perked up. "I like the song M I C K E Y." He sang until food flew out of his mouth.

"*The Lone Ranger* is better," I said.

"*The Mickey Mouse Club* has cartoons," said Gene.

"*The Lone Ranger* always beats the bad guys."

"Mouseketeers are all good," said Gene. Don rolled away on the grass.

"*The Lone Ranger* has Tonto."

"Mouseketeers are all kids."

"Hi-yo Silver!" I yelled. "We have Silver."

"We have Annette Funicello!" Gene screamed. Don squirmed away, stood up, trying to keep his back toward us and ran toward the water. He must have had an erection that was about to jump out of his tight swimsuit. He leaped in the water with a giant cannonball splash. A blond woman with oversized sunglasses and robe sheltered her two infants and frowned at Don as he passed by. Don must have sensed he was bothering the blond lady because he swam around the bend out of sight.

A few moments later, Don showed up right behind us with a big smirk, as though he'd performed a magic trick. I noticed a few other people on both sides of our spot looking, staring at us. I realized we were the only brown-skinned people in sight. The tables nearby were filled with blondish white families. I looked at Mother and Eugenia sitting together, legs crossed; withdrawn, it appeared. I wanted to hug them. Maybe because the other families were all white, I took their looks as a frown. Frown or not, we were with Dad and Gene, and we were becoming as American as anyone at the lake.

Don picked up a Y-shaped branch and studied it. I knew he saw the potential to make a slingshot. I leaped up, tapped Gene's shoulder, said "slingshot," and looked around for a similar branch. We ran toward some trees and scrounged around like hungry dogs in search of a bone. Don rushed over. The three of us scoured a clearing at the edge of the lake. Gene and I spotted a slingshot branch simultaneously. We both realized that one of us would lose the hunt and leaped for it. Don somehow beat us to it, picked it up, and ran toward the lake.

Gene and I followed, eyes fixed on the branch until it flew in the water right in front of the mean blond lady. Without hesitation, Gene and I leaped in, determined to beat the other to the slingshot branch. We smashed into each other in mid-air, Gene's shoulder knocking me off course and flipping me around. I landed on my back, splashing the blond lady while Don ran off. Underwater I felt a sharp bite on my thigh. I thought there had to be sharks in the water. I pulled away, but the pain rushed up my leg. I couldn't scream. I reached down and felt what I assumed were twisted branches or spiny fish. I ripped away gasping for air, kicking and reaching for land. I splashed up as fast as I could, imagining long-toothed fish chasing me out of the water. I reached the shore, glad to be alive, and saw the blond lady scream in horror. I didn't know what to do: jump back in and get eaten by the fish or run past the hysterical woman.

She grabbed a towel and came to me. I was too scared to move. Gene came up with the branch just as the lady wrapped the towel around my leg. I looked down and saw a bloody mess. Blood gushed down my legs and chest. Just as quick, Dad and Mother were at my side with more towels. For some reason, or maybe because the water was cold, I didn't feel pain. Looking up at Dad, I saw my *Toro* over his shoulder, almost smiling at me. *Ole.*

I wondered how many times my grandfather had been gored worse than me. Dad inspected my legs. He stood up, waded into the lake, and reached down, looking into the water. He found what he was looking for: a roll of barbed wire. "For crying out loud," he said, pulling on the tangled barbed wire. Everyone, even the blond lady, gasped. "What a thoughtless act to dump this here." He finished pulling the cable out and crunched it into a trash can. Don held up two Y shaped branches and handed me one. I knew it was to make a slingshot.

Piñata

Leaves filled the trees again, and springtime flowers popped up everywhere. My first birthday in the United States would be the first without Tia Rosita. I wanted her with me. I wanted to go back to Mexico. I wanted to stay in bed, but Eugenia and Mother planned a party for me. Eugenia spent two days making a piñata that had to be the first in the neighborhood because no one knew what it was. She made a beautiful and delicious boat-shaped cake. Twenty classmates turned out for the party, including Linda, whom I hadn't talked to since the dinner party episode. She stepped in, wearing her pink poodle skirt and handed me a gift. "Happy Birthday," she said without looking at me. It was awkward.

"I wish I was a girl," I muttered, hoping for a smile. She looked up at me and grinned. We walked outside together. Don took charge of raising and lowering the piñata from the treehouse. It was one of Don's favorite piñata rituals. Breaking the piñata included blindfolding and spinning the person around three times before swinging the bat, so Dad took special care in making sure no one got hurt. He placed the garden hose in a semi-circle to mark off the boundary for kids not to cross while someone swung the bat. Eugenia handed me the bat to choose someone to go first. I chose Linda over Gene, who had been screaming he wanted to go first.

Eugenia blindfolded Linda with a scarf and spun her around three times counting in Spanish, *"Uno, dos, y tres."* She taught everyone to count to three and told us to count that way with every swing. Linda swung, *"Uno!"* we all shouted. She swung again, *"Dos!"*

we all cried. We screamed together on her third swing as she missed and fell over. A few more kids took turns before Gene finally broke the piñata. Everyone rushed in and grabbed as much candy as we could. We played games and ate the cake that turned out better than any cake I had ever tasted. I never imagined opening so many gifts and cards for a simple birthday. My favorite, of course, had to be the Tonto outfit Gene gave me. Linda was last to leave. We lingered in the backyard after everyone left. I sensed my *Toro* in the sky and stared at the clouds trying to find him.

"Talk to her," I imagined the voice from the sky that sounded like Tia Rosita.

"What are you staring at?" Linda asked. I didn't know how to tell her about my secret *Toro*, but she shared her secret room with me, so I took a chance. I lay down on the grass and looked up. She joined me. I pointed up and asked her if she could see the bull in the clouds that peeked over the long tree branches. "I don't see a bull," she said. "Where?" She moved closer to follow my finger. "Yes, I see it," she said, getting excited, patting my arm.

"*Toro* talks," I said, then whispered, "*ole.*"

"*Toro*, what's my name?" Linda asked and waited for a response. "What's my favorite color?" Again, no response. "What will I be when I grow up?" "How many babies will I have?" "Is my brother in Heaven?"

"Yes," came a voice. Linda grabbed my hand. I struggled to get up, fumbled to my knees, holding Linda's hand. We ran into the house, slammed the door, and hugged like monkeys staring at the door. Mother came in. Then Eugenia. And finally, Dad stepped in.

"What's the commotion?" Dad asked. I didn't answer. Linda shivered and squeezed me so tightly I could barely breathe. Don appeared at the door, smiling ear to ear.

"Yes," Don snickered and walked right through to the living room.

I walked Linda home making circles around her as we had in the past. She circled around me once just as we reached her house. Oliver's car was not in the driveway. She looked surprised at the empty path. We walked to the front door looking through the window for Linda's mom, but there was no sign of her. Linda opened the door and called out, but no one answered. She didn't walk inside. I saw a bottle of liquor next to a half-eaten sandwich on the table. "No one's home," I murmured.

She took my hand and led me upstairs to her secret room. A whirling, crackling sound came from a record player; it was the needle spinning off the track. An empty glass and bottle of liquor rested next to a full ashtray. Linda opened the window and walked to the record player. She put the needle back on track. One of Dad and Mother's favorite songs came on, Glen Miller's "In the Mood." Before we knew it, we were dancing and screaming louder than ever. With my new voice, I cried out as loud as Linda and jumped as high off the bed as I could. Her poodle skirt swirled around and around, each time rising higher. I spun around with her until the music ended, and we collapsed on the bed. The record player needle screeched its whirling sound, but neither of us stopped our belly-aching laughter. My stomach hurt. Linda screamed and kicked straight up. We laughed hysterically, rolling around until we were wrapped around each other. But gradually, her laughter turned to tears and then sobbing from deep down. I felt helpless. She made me happy after feeling so unwanted, and now she was crying in my arms. I wanted to go home but couldn't leave her. "Why do you call this a secret room?" I asked.

"It's a secret crying room," she said. "Daddy says men don't cry, but he does here. It's our secret."

"Linda!" a sharp voice rang. "Charlie, you're still here. It's late." It was Linda's mom. I hadn't seen her in months. She looked scary. She had yellow skin now and had lost a lot of weight. I jumped up. Linda rolled up and mumbled something about not being hungry. I stared at Linda's mom, barely able to contain my fright. Her cheeks were matching triangles hanging from her eye sockets. It was hot, but she wore a long sleeve sweater and a white blouse buttoned up to where her skeletal neck seemed to dangle out of the collar. I thought she'd turned into a witch with long bony fingers and huge eyes. She noticed my fear because she pulled her hand away as I stared. "Happy birthday, Charlie. Now you better get on home. I'm sure your parents are wondering where you are." I dashed out before she finished the sentence. Oliver didn't look up from his newspaper as I scuttled by the living room.

I ran home feeling special, knowing Oliver's secret. Big men like him weren't supposed to cry. My grandfather faced fierce bulls and killed them without tears. *Ole*, I felt macho. I ran into the house just as Dad and Mother were leaving for a walk. I joined them. "Dad, do you ever cry?" I said and walked between them.

"Well, you have every right to cry. There's certainly plenty to cry about in this world," Dad said, putting a hand on my shoulder. Mother did the same. "But having a family like ours keeps a smile on one's face."

"So people who cry don't have good families?"

A crow cawed overhead, setting off a flurry of rustling on a tree branch. A mad squirrel flipped off the tree and fell facing Mother. Mother thought the sky was falling. I laughed so hard I fell off the curb. Mother lost her senses. She slipped into another world, holding on to Dad. We stopped at a bench and sat with her. Slowly she eased back to her senses. Dad told me to go ahead, he'd take her the rest of the way home. I ran back to the house.

The loud sounds of Don's friends playing in the backyard boomed as I approached the front. I ran around the side and saw Don hammering the two slingshot sticks over the entrance. They were the branches from the lake. The treehouse now had a painted sign on the side, THE APACHES. I was going to be the best Apache in the club. I ran to the steps, excited to join the treehouse club. Don and his three friends were all in the freshly painted house. I started up the stairs.

"Boy Scouts only," warned one of the boys. I stopped, not sure what that meant.

"No one else allowed," said another boy.

"Back down, buster!" yelled the smallest. They were talking to me. I froze in mid-step, clinging on to the ladder.

"Boy Scouts only," said Don. "You're too young to be a Boy Scout." My brother was telling me I couldn't go inside the treehouse. "Don't cry," he warned as he saw tears well up in my eyes. He looked different. His eyes looked mean, and his nose flared out like a wolf's. I didn't understand what had happened to him.

"Look, he's gonna cry," said the first boy, laughing and pointing.

"Apaches don't cry," said another boy.

"Crybaby," teased the smallest boy. "This club is for big boys."

I jumped off the ladder and ran up to my bed. I could hear the boys still laughing through the open window. Don's voice rang through the din loud and clear. Becoming an American Boy Scout had changed him in a way I'd never understand. I closed it and fell asleep, determined not to cry.

I woke up to a quiet house. I wandered down the steps carefully, not wanting to find my brother or his friends. Eugenia was in the dining room, working on a school project. I walked past and into the kitchen. I looked out the window to see Don's treehouse. It seemed empty. The sun was setting, and the sky looked red. I walked out and climbed the ladder. THE APACHES sign stared at me menacingly, letting me know I wasn't welcome. I peeked under the drape to the front entrance. The room was dark and smelled like paint. I slithered inside, watching the light disappear as the curtains closed. I bumped into something that sounded like glass. I pulled back the drape a little and saw a glass lantern I recognized from the garage. A box of matches sat to the right. I opened the box and struck a match. It lit the room. On the walls, I saw BOY SCOUTS APACHES and Don's name along with more signatures before the match went out.

I reached for the matchbox and struck another match but knocked the lantern over, spilling the liquid across the floor. The lit match flipped out of my fingers, sending fire across the entrance. I jumped back as the front drape caught fire. I kicked the lantern and tried to get out, but the heat and flames were too much. I couldn't get out the front. I heard the lantern crash and break outside. Then a scream came from the house next door. I turned, saw the back opening, and slid out dangling between two branches. The screaming next-door neighbor, a middle-aged woman, turned a garden hose on the tree and screamed even louder when she saw me hanging out, feet kicking. I dropped down to safety, the water cascading over the fence and on the treehouse.

Another neighbor, a man, rushed to our hose and sprayed the other side of the tree. In a short time, there were plenty of people watching the treehouse crumble as four hoses sprayed the fire out. Don showed up with his Boy Scouts of America friends and watched the Apache treehouse burn to the ground without saying a word. The red sky turned dark, highlighting the red embers of the fire. Dad and Mother showed up and rushed to Don's side. I ran away as fast as I could.

I waited and waited and waited, expecting someone to come to my room, but no one did. After a while, the voices in the backyard stopped. I tracked the sounds of footsteps in the kitchen and dining room. I heard the dishes clattering in the sink, but still, no one came to get me. I was better off left to die in my bed than face Dad and Don. I started planning my getaway. I could go out the window, as Tonto would have done. The door slung open. Don stepped in. He flipped the light on and said Dad wanted to talk to me. He still looked like a wolf when he walked over to me and patted me on the back. I didn't let him know I was scared. He said he didn't care about the Apaches and handed me the slingshot branch from the lake. I thought he was lying. How could he not care about the Boy Scouts of America Apaches? They had become so important to him, more important than me.

I stood up. Was I going to get sent back to Mexico alone? I promised myself I wouldn't cry. I walked downstairs through a gloomy smell of ash and dirty water. Don and Eugenia sat side by side, staring at Dad. Mother held his hand. Mother, Don, and Eugenia looked scared, as though they'd been told we were being sent back to Mexico because of what I had done. I may as well have stayed in the treehouse while it burned. The pain in the room was all my doing. I was used to smiling at first sight of Dad, but this was not a time for that. He looked grim, full of sorrow, and it was all my doing. He was my Master Yen Sid. I fought the urge to smile, then to cry. Dad's steely blue eyes and downcast lips seemed to blend together into the Sorcerer's hat, and I was the Apprentice.

Time stopped. I fell on the rug. I could have been killed if it hadn't been for Don being smart enough to make the two doors in the treehouse. Dad handed me a pencil and paper. He told me to write an apology letter to the neighbors and to thank them for helping put out the fire. I didn't know how to write, so I drew a house with a big tree and a treehouse on fire. Dad looked mortified. It hurt knowing I caused that reaction, that feeling in him. He tore up my drawing and helped me write a real apology letter.

By the following summer, I was speaking unaccented English. Dad was pleased with his children. We had done our job.

Assimilation lessons had paid off. He taught by example and quickly corrected our tenses so that it became second nature to find the best words for our expanding vocabulary. Don and I would learn to love baseball more than soccer. Eugenia became an outstanding student and was recognized for her academic achievements right away. Dad was pleased to read our report cards. We all passed on to the next grade despite the language barrier that we'd faced.

Mother started having blackouts shortly after the incident with

Oliver. She had a hard time socializing and learning English after developing a fear of leaving the house without Dad. She stayed home alone, door locked, curtains drawn, reading, listening to music, and writing long letters to the *familia*.

Every day I thought about Mrs. Brown and all the words she had taught. One morning, Gene and I walked by the school and found Mrs. Brown placing boxes in her car. She wore a flowery long-sleeved dress with a high collar over a baby bump. She said she was proud of us and told us how happy it was to have been our teacher. She said she was especially pleased to have known someone from Mexico. I thought about how much she had taught me and how careful and kind she had been with me all year. I thanked her for teaching me so many words and promised to do well in school forever and ever. We followed her to the building and into our old classroom. Being inside the school without anyone else there felt special. All the rooms were empty. The chairs were turned up on the desks. All the bulletin boards were bare, and the alphabet letters across the chalkboards had been removed. The lime green walls and gray linoleum floor in the barren hallway reminded me of the hospital. I instinctively raised my hands in a protective position.

Mister Lloyd, the school custodian, was busy mopping the hallway. A New York Yankees hat caught the smoke spewing out of the cigarette that dangled from his sad face. He stopped and walked over to us. "Your students, Mrs. Brown?" he asked. She nodded. "Lucky for them," he said. "Now boys, pick up some of those boxes for your teacher." Gene and I each picked up a box and waited for instructions. We made several trips carrying out the boxes and helped Mrs. Brown until the car was full. It was an important job for Gene and me, and Mister Lloyd made us feel special by handing us each a piece of gum.

We would never have been allowed to chew gum in school, but there we were chewing gum right in the middle of the hallway. We walked past the main office and tried to blow bubbles, but we were laughing too hard to do so. A phone rang, and we raced away on the freshly waxed floor. We headed back to Mrs. Brown's room, picking up speed, but a door edged open, and we bumped into each other, barely dodging the door. Gene screamed, trying to keep his balance and slammed into the wall. I laughed as loud as his scream, and we turned the corner at a hallway and ran toward the parking lot door where Mister Lloyd had just mopped the floor. It was wet. Gene and I both slipped and slid along the floor, bouncing along the wall like a bowling gutter ball. The first one to the door would win, but neither of us made it. We stopped a few feet short of the door, fell back, looking up at the ceiling, and both blew a perfect bubble. Mine popped first, and we stood up, expecting Mister Lloyd to shoo us away, but he didn't come around.

We continued on looking in all the rooms, guessing where we'd be the following year. A red, ceramic apple, exactly like Mrs. Brown's, stood out on a teacher's desk as we walked by. I ventured in to study the apple. Gene followed and went to the chalkboard. He picked up a pointer and made a stern face, trying not to smile. "Boys and girls sit down and be quiet," he said, waving the pointer. "You, Tonto, sit down before I call your mother," he ordered. I sat down, holding the apple. Gene continued telling me, and the imaginary students, how bad we were and how things had to change, or we'd all be in trouble. Then he said, "Okay, now it's your turn. You teach, Tonto!" He handed me the pointer and went to the back of the room.

The red apple reminded me so much of Mrs. Brown, I imagined being her. I stood up, a pointer in hand, swiveled my hips, and addressed my imaginary class. "Good morning, boys and girls," I said in a high voice and pushing back my imaginary long hair. "Young boy back of the room, what's your name?" I asked Gene.

"Why my name is Roy, Roy Rogers."

"Roy," I started and swiveled all the way to him, swinging the pointer high up in the air. "Roy, repeat after me, A is for apple."

"A is for apple," he used a different voice, trying to sound like a cowboy.

"Good, can you use it in a sentence?"

"Sure, teacher. A is for almost. Tonto is almost as fast as me." Gene squinted.

"B is for Ball," I said.

"No, B is for better. I'm a better cowboy than you," he continued.

"C is for Cat," I said.

"C is for you can't catch me," and he ran toward the door, daring me to chase him. But we didn't get far. Mrs. Brown stood at the door, watching with a smile.

"Charlie," she said, "I think someday you'll make a fine teacher." I imagined myself standing in front of a class speaking English and telling stories and helping children just like Mrs. Brown had taught me.

On the way home, we walked past Linda's house and stopped. A FOR SALE sign was staked on the front lawn. "Mom said they'd be moving," Gene said. "They don't go to church anymore."

Gene was right. The last time I saw Linda was the day a moving company packed up the whole household. Gene and I stood watching, waiting for Linda to come out, but we never saw her. The moving men carried all the boxes and furniture into the big van and closed the giant doors. I told Gene I wanted to knock on the door. We started for the front steps, but Linda's mom appeared at the window skinnier, yellow, and sickly. She had turned into the Wizard of Oz's Wicked Witch. Gene and I stopped dead in our tracks and ran away faster than we had ever run before. We were so scared we ran right past my house, both of us screaming our lungs out. We reached Gene's house, skipping the front door, and ran to the side entrance shivering, unable to talk. Gene locked the door, and we both ducked down.

"What's the matter, boys?" said Gene's mom.

"A witch is chasing us," said Gene.

"A real witch," I added.

"There's no such thing as witches. Now you two calm down and tell me what you are up to," she said.

"Linda's mom turned into a witch, a real witch," Gene said.

"Heavens no. That poor woman is ill. That's all. Did you disturb her? Say anything?" We both shook our heads no. "Now, let's not hear any more of this subject. You understand?"

"But she's really —"

"Not another word," she commanded, and we obeyed. A loaf of bread, peanut butter, and jelly appeared in front of us, and we raced to make sandwiches.

Later as I walked home, I heard the familiar roar of Oliver's car heading in my direction. I stopped and waited. Oliver sat behind the wheel in a Yankees cap and sleeves rolled up. Linda's mom sat in the front, wearing a scarf, sunglasses, and a hat. The car moved gently along, almost in slow motion. Linda sat in the back, looking out. Her eyes pinned on me and stayed as she drove along. She didn't smile but sent me a two-eyes blink. It would be the last time I ever saw her.

I ran the whole way home. Don opened the door before I reached it. He pulled me close to him. "Mom's sick," he whispered. It was the start of a dark and mysterious chapter in Mother's life. Her blackouts had intensified.

Tia Rosita came to visit for two weeks. Mother seemed better with Tia Rosita at her side, even out of the house. Dad took all of us to a hockey game at Syracuse University one Saturday. The sights and sounds of an indoor hockey game with men crashing into the boards were so different from soccer, we were frightened stiff. We were the quietest people in attendance. After that, we went to Niagara Falls, a lakeside picnic, a visit inside the United Nations building in New York City, the Statue of Liberty — all without a single episode of Mother's blackouts. Tia Rosita was the salve for Mother's condition. But the blackouts returned soon after that. A series of doctor visits and tests were of no help.

For the next year, we settled in as a fully immersed family, living the American Dream.

Don continued his Americanization in the Boy Scouts, without his Apache fort. He came home with good grades and was doing his job and fulfilling Dad's dream.

Eugenia kept busy learning beyond her grade level and developed a sophisticated view of the world. She read Dad's newspaper and could carry an informed conversation with adults. She even talked about attending Syracuse University.

Gene and I played countless hours of pitch and catch wearing matching Yankees caps at the park. Gene was a good hitter, and I spent more time chasing the ball than anything else. Soccer was a lot easier than baseball, but Assimilation 101 included learning the national sport. I had to chase baseballs if I was going to be an American. Best of all, I could understand the Yankees games on the radio.

We spoke English at dinnertime now and didn't have language classes. Instead, we played games in English. Dad's three children had successfully assimilated into the American middle class. Eugenia's book balancing challenge was still a favorite game for Don and me. One summer night, Don challenged me for the fastest time around the table. "One, two, three . . ." I went first, as everyone counted. I hurried around, holding my laughter until I saw Mother, eyes closed, head nodding. Mother's blackouts cast a dark shadow on the dream.

Within the week Dad announced, "Your mother and I have important news. We are moving to Mexico." They decided Mother needed to be in Mexico. *Que sera, sera.*

Back in Mexico: 1958

After all the work to drop our language and culture, we were right back in Mexico City. It could never be the same for me. I wasn't Oscar anymore. I was Charlie with a *gringo* accent. Dad got his job back. Don, Eugenia, and I were enrolled in private schools.

Mother and Dad immediately saw a team of Mexico's finest doctors in a prestigious medical center. Electroshock treatments were prevalent in medical practices around the world at that time. Mother underwent painful sessions in short order. One rainy afternoon I found her sitting by the dining room window staring blankly at the dark view when a sudden bolt of lightning thundered across and lit up the sky. "Be careful," she cautioned, in Spanish, and moved quickly away from the window, alarmed.

"Scary?" I said. Then I asked, "What did they do to you in the hospital?"

"*Me castigaron,*" she said, they punished her.

Punish? Why would anyone punish my mother? "*Porque?*" I asked why.

"I don't know. I don't know, but it was torture," she said in Spanish, and continued, "I must have done something bad because nobody deserves to go through that." Her brow furrowed together.

"What did they do to you?" I asked. She must have seen the fear on my face as she paused and pulled me close to her.

"Don't worry, Charlie." By now, my name was fixed in English and Spanish as Charlie. "It can't happen to you."

"Sorry."

"I hope," she sighed. I picked up a banana from a fresh fruit bowl near the window. I tried to give Mother a calming two-eyes blink, but my eyes fluttered multiple times. I peeled the banana instead and offered it to her. She took half. "It was like falling in a pit. Like the movie *The Snake Pit*." Mother's favorite movie star was Olivia De Havilland. She portrayed a tortured woman in an insane asylum. I reached for her hand. She gazed out the window, held me, took a deep breath, and swore me to secrecy.

She described the sessions, her treatment. She said the team of nurses and doctors placed a tooth guard in her mouth then strapped her limbs with leather body restraints before zapping her brain with electricity. She contorted and shivered as she described the treatments showing me how painful it must have been. It hurt me to imagine her alone in so much pain. I could see Olivia De Havilland suffering through *The Snake Pit*, Mother next to her. I squirmed. Mother noticed my fear. "*Que sera, sera*," she said.

I didn't fit in Mexico anymore. I'd worked so hard learning English, I had blocked out a lot of the Spanish I once knew. Once again, I was an outsider. I had to learn a new set of rules for getting along in school. I was placed in an all-boys Catholic school. The name Charlie Allen didn't go over well with the Mexican boys, and they immediately ridiculed me. Nuns never smiled and didn't put up with my humor. I sang the alphabet song in English and Spanish, emphasizing the *ch*, *ll*, and *n* as though they were going to choke me. I was angry and confused. I acted out using my face contortion repertoire. Prank falls also got a lot of laughs, but for that, I sat in the corner with a dunce hat facing the wall. Nuns didn't put up with a clown named Charlie in class, and that is what I had tried to become—Charlie Chaplin/Cantinflas.

It didn't take long for boys to start picking on me for knowing

English and asking questions about Spanish words. I was called names and had to watch my back at all times. The only game to play in school was soccer. Every day I lined up along with everyone else to form teams. I was always the last one chosen to be on a side, and when the game started, no one passed me the ball. I missed my life in New York, especially Gene and Linda.

One day I wore my New York Yankees cap to school. It got a lot of attention. A skinny-nosed boy with sharp features sauntered next to me, eyes on my cap, *"Dame tu—"* he mumbled.

"Perdon, que dices? No entiendo," I said I didn't understand. Instead of answering, he spit in my face and called me a hot dog, saying I should go back to New York. I didn't know how to react, so I wiped it off and told a nun, but she didn't seem interested. I told her the boy had no reason to spit on me and asked what she was going to do about it. She asked me where it happened. I told her on the courtyard where we crossed from one class to another. She told me to avoid the boy next time by walking around the mainstream of foot traffic. She suggested I stay on the outskirts along the walls. I should walk around to avoid the kid who just spits in my face? That's it? That's the way of this school? I had a lot to learn.

On the way home that day, I told Don about the spitting kid. He told me not to tell Dad or Mother because if they came to school, and the boys found out, things would be worse for me. I'd be marked a snitch and would never make friends. The next day the skinny-nosed boy was in the middle of the courtyard taunting and pushing another boy. A horde of students closed in on the action and swept me right next to it. The skinny-nosed boy was now slamming his shoe into the defenseless boy's face on the ground, still taunting and now spitting on the fallen boy. A couple of nuns made their way to the center without urgency. They merely helped the fallen boy up and pointed him to the bathroom. Blood and tears were part of the way of the world in my new school.

The crowd scattered, and everyone went on their way as though nothing had happened. I turned and walked away but felt a sharp puncture in my back. It was Skinnynose, running away, laughing with a group of friends. I didn't go to the nuns since they hadn't done anything about the fight. It turned out he stabbed me with a pencil and broke off the lead, leaving it lodged in my back. The boy was popular and always had five or six boys with him. They sought me out every day, menacing me in one way or another. He and his friends would randomly kick and taunt me. After a while, I had lead pencil tips lodged in my knees, back, and thighs that would never leave my skin. I showed the two nuns what was happening. I lifted my pant leg and exposed a bleeding knee, but they didn't care or take action. It was as though they blamed me.

After school, Don and I rode the bus home together. I was silent and sad, not knowing what to do about the kids at school. I looked out the window riding through Paseo de la Reforma and watched the traffic that reminded me so much of New York City. I remembered the policeman that gave me a pretzel and wished I could tell him about the mean boys. A loud, squeaky bus brake just outside of my window startled me out of my thoughts. When I turned my attention back into the bus, I found Don staring at me, studying my face. "What is wrong with you?" Don asked.

I showed him a fresh bruise on my shin, and the pieces of pencil lead stuck in my knee. "Who did that to you?" he wondered. I told him what was going on with the boys and what the nuns had done about it. He said it was time to fight back, warning that it would never stop unless I stood up to the main guy. "You have to fight," he said. I didn't respond. I knew Dad would be disappointed in me if I did fight. His biblical "turn thy cheek" theory was ingrained in my head by then. I looked out just as we came to the statue of *Cuauhtemoc*, the proud Aztec emperor. He defied Cortez's torture and kept the secret of Moctezuma's treasures. The monument stood high above the traffic and reminded every Mexican that we were brave warriors. "You are a warrior like *Cuauhtemoc*," Don said. I remembered the story about Don having chili and lemons squirted in his eyes. I got the message. That was not going to happen to me.

The next day I wore my cowboy boots and New York Yankees cap. The courtyard was calm, and a nun stood stationed dead center. I figured this wasn't going to be the day for any trouble, but just in case, I stayed close to the nun. I thought about Mrs. Brown. I knew Mrs. Brown would never have let the boys do those nasty things to me. She would have done something, but the nuns were only interested in what the priests wanted them to do. And in my case, they didn't want to be bothered, so I stood next to the nuns. A few taunts came my way, "*Maricon*," "Yankee," "hot dog." Calling a boy *maricon* is a low blow; it's a fighting taunt; it's saying you're not a macho; it's a call for flight or fight. The nuns knew it and ignored it. In class, one boy told me to watch out because the group of kids that had been bothering me was looking for a way to hurt me. By this point, I didn't care. Another boy said I'd get hurt in the bathroom. A third boy told me I better watch out before and after school because the group would be waiting outside with a knife.

Don was in the upper-grade school next door, so I didn't worry about getting to and from school as long as he was with me. The following day I found the group of boys standing near the entrance. "That's them," I said, looking straight at the group. I figured they had a knife, so I stayed close to my brother. Don walked deliberately toward the entrance, staring straight at the boys, walked with me to the door, and shouted he'd be waiting for me after school. He let the kids know I wasn't alone.

I stayed quiet, not asking a single question about anything to anyone. After lunch, the courtyard was back to normal with the nun at the side rather than in the middle. Skinnynose saw me and walked in my direction. I changed my course and headed toward the sister, who looked up right as the boy unloaded a mouthful of hot saliva in my face. The nun saw it and called him. She took my hand, telling me not to wipe off the slime that covered my face and dripped on my blue sweater. She walked us into the director's office.

The director's window looked onto a courtyard with a fountain. A lifelike water-squirting gargoyle fed the fountain. The scrawny director with white hair sticking out of his nose and ears sat at the desk in front of the window. The gargoyle over his shoulder stared directly at me. The priest didn't move. "Father, this boy spat on this boy as you can see," she said, pointing to Skinnynose then me, but the priest didn't look up. He mumbled something cryptic about God and asked Skinnynose why he spat on me. The boy said he was sorry. The priest looked up and stared at me, just like the gargoyle. The resemblance was too much; they were twins. I did all I could to hold my laughter, but my cheeks were turning red, and I had to pee. "Do you accept this boy's apology?" the priest asked. I nodded in the affirmative. The priest instructed Skinnynose to lick the spit off my face. I squirmed away as the boy licked my cheek once. "Do it again," the priest said, not satisfied with the quick lick. I had to stand and wait for the boy to lick harder. Period. Nothing else. That was the total punishment for spitting a pound of slimy saliva in my face, but I was glad I didn't have to stare at the gargoyle twins any longer.

After class, I ran to the front gate where everyone congregated to wait for the giant doors to open. I was the first one to the top of the steps. I looked for my brother through the opening. I heard a cry, "Pinche Yanqui!" It was my enemy's voice. I wasn't going down. The image of the boy spitting in my face with a taunting smile angered me. He had riled up the bull inside me, and I was snorting, waiting to find him. I paced back and forth in my tight cowboy boots, clamoring loudly on the top steps while more kids arrived. I adjusted my Yankees cap, remembering how Gene had beaten up the three boys for me. It was my turn to defend myself.

The mob watched me pace, my nose flaring, and moved away. A group of six boys crashed through the throng of bodies. It was him in the middle of the pack. It was me waiting on the top landing. It was time to prove I was as brave as my grandfather. Flanked by his friends, Skinnynose smirked at me. *"Pinche maricon,"* he spat out. I stared back, taunting him to move toward me, with one hand, then the other. The area cleared around me. He rushed at me with a pencil in one hand, but I was ready. I slammed my right boot in his groin. He keeled over, dropping the pencil. His friends stood back. It seemed so easy to put him down. Why did we have to move back to Mexico?

The boy wriggled up, saying, *"Te mato, pendejo."* He threatened to kill me. This boy wanted to kill me for not understanding his Spanish. Spanish, not English. Here I was back in my own country fighting over nothing. How could this be after going to New York, The Big Apple, without a single word of English, having learned a whole language without a fight? Now here I was back in my own country, and this little asshole wanted to kill me for wearing a Yankees cap, after everything I went through in New York, after having my penis sliced. I may have imagined it, but I saw him reach for his pocket, and I remembered he could have a knife. That wasn't going to scare me anymore. I threw myself on him, punching him with both fists. I thought of my brother and my grandfather gathering strength even though his friends stood watching. I feared for my life and didn't want the boy to pull out a knife, so I kept punching. The crowd started counting, *"Seis, siete, ocho."* They urged for more. *"Dale mas!"* They were rooting for me, cheering me on, urging me to kick their friend. They were on my side. I was afraid to stop.

We wrestled up to our feet. *"Yanqui, gringo,"* he slurred.

"Chinga tu madre!" I yelled in textbook Spanish, trying to emphasize my Mexican, Aztec, Spanish, bullfighter roots. I swung my boot to his knife pocket. He went down. I wasn't going to let him pull out his knife. I kicked again remembering each and every time he'd stabbed me, punched me, spit on me, and kicked me. Every time he tried to get up, I stopped him with a swift blow to his body, then his head once, twice, three times. The crowd roared. I couldn't stop. I kept kicking the boy until his head swiveled about, smacking into

the wall and back to my boot. My enemy lay motionless at my feet.

The blood smeared all over his face startled me. It was ugly and made me realize I didn't have the stomach to be a matador; I wanted to barf. I felt bad for the boy. I wanted to be his friend, not his enemy. I stood on the top step looking down at the boy, then at his friends. I wanted to run away, but the energy from the cheering cries called for more displays of my *machismo*. Instead, I dared anyone else to come up, puffing up my chest and raising my chin. *"Y, quien mas?"* I asked who else wanted me. No one did. *"Ole!"* I yelled, throwing my arms up in victory, feeling like a victorious matador. Then in an instant, the very same friends of my victim picked me up on their shoulders and started chanting, "Charlie, Charlie, Charlie!" They knew my name and paraded me around the courtyard on their shoulders, all the while chanting "Charlie" louder and louder. I saw the director priest and the nun at a window looking out, not interested in stopping what they had witnessed.

Don had been right; no one ever bothered me again at that school, and I was able to concentrate on learning rather than protecting myself. There wasn't any room for Charlie Chaplin/Cantinflas-type humor in a Catholic school. God didn't have a sense of humor is all I could make of that place. I must have earned everyone's respect because after that day, I was the first one picked to be on a soccer team, and boys suddenly started passing me the ball.

That was the start of my return to Mexico. It was all about being macho. I missed Linda and Gene. They taught me so much and were so supportive of everything I had to do to become an American. Now back in Mexico, I couldn't trust anyone, I didn't have any friends, and I spoke Spanish with a *gringo* accent. I lost my appetite and lost a lot of weight. I kept to myself, and no one bothered me. I saw Skinnynose every day in the courtyard. He stayed clear of me. His friend, who had warned me about a possible knife, later told me he had made up the story to scare me. I wanted to make friends with Skinnynose, but we never spoke. He and all his friends stayed away from me, and I never asked anyone anything.

Dad planned an Acapulco vacation. We were back in Mexico, and Dad wanted us to enjoy all of it. Acapulco was perfect for us after experiencing the cold lakes of New York. The paradise-like white sand, clear blue sky, and warm water let us forget New York winters. Our hero had taken us back to our homeland. Together we faced the Pacific Ocean. Mother and Dad held hands as they waded in while Don, Eugenia, and I splashed in. It was the best in Mexico, and no one cared how much Spanish or English I spoke. I forgot about my *gringo* accent and played with total strangers for three glorious days, trying to shed my Americanized mannerisms. It may have been the nature of a beach town that made people so accepting, but I never felt out of place like in school. Mexico was my home again, and Acapulco made me feel a part of it.

Dad took a lot of pictures. The lifestyle, the splendor of the Pacific Ocean, and the joy on people's faces were all captured on his camera and chronicled in his vast collection. He kept a library of color slides that reached back many years and included our New York assimilation experiment. We viewed the pictures of Acapulco one night along with some New York pictures. I was stumped. What was New York all about? Why did we work so hard to become Americans only to come back? "What's my job now?" I asked Mother and Dad. "Mexico, Mexican, English, Spanish, American, Melting Pot?"

"*Que sera, sera.*" Mother smiled.

"Your job is in school." Dad knew what I was asking. "Just like in New York, but now you don't have to assimilate." He seemed happy and definitive with his answer.

We moved into a fancy modern building in an exciting part of Mexico City, Polanco, where Dad joined the Olympic Club Mundet. It was a private club with more Americans than Mexicans and where

English was the preferred language. I could almost hear Doris Day singing "*Que Sera, Sera*" as I walked in. Jai Alai courts, tennis courts—both clay and grass surfaces, swimming pools, baseball field, indoor basketball, and restaurants were the attraction for by-invitation-only members.

Eugenia was happy to be back in Mexico. Don was in his glory, making friends quickly and doing well in school. I didn't have any friends that belonged to the club, so I was always on my own. Mother and Eugenia didn't enjoy sports or the outdoors, so they never attended. Watching Dad swim and exercise in the gym was a lesson in agility. He was slim and trim, had been on the gymnastics team in college, as well as the rowing team, and played intermural baseball. I wanted to be like him and spent my time at the club when I wasn't in school. It was a place away from Mexico that felt so foreign to me. We sometimes walked to the club under a colorful sky at sunrise when the streets were quiet.

On our walk to the club one morning, I asked Dad if he ever got into a fight in school. He smiled in a way that said he'd never heard a more ridiculous question. "No, school is for learning," he answered.

"Would you fight someone if you had to?" I asked.

"Fights usually start with arguments. We have words and manners. One can always walk away." He smiled with confidence. I thought about the boy I'd bloodied. What would Dad have done? Would he have done what I did? He would have told the nuns. I told the nuns and priests, but they failed to stop the skinny-nosed bully from hurting me day after day.

"But if a boy spit in your face, and kicked you, and stabbed you with a pencil," I said, looking up, making a case for my fighting.

"Oh, Charlie," he said, shaking off the thought, "why in the world would that ever happen? Just get rid of those thoughts."

I wished we were still in New York.

We continued walking. I decided Dad would never want to be a bullfighter. His style and grace were better suited for swimming and dancing with Mother. I wished I hadn't fought in school so that I didn't have to have a secret from Dad. I wondered if my grandfather would have done what I did in school. He, too, was tall, lean, wore suits, and probably never fought anything other than a bull. Clouds hovered above darkening the sky.

Swimming in the rain is fun. Hail showered down just as we got to the pool. "Hi-Yo Silver!" I screamed, jumping in the pool, storm pounding the water. Dad jumped in next to me and stayed underwater, holding his breath. I followed underwater and watched hail smash into the water. I tried to keep under holding my breath as long as Dad, but I couldn't. We swam across the pool for cover under the low diving board. Kernels of hail pummeled the board. "It sounds like popcorn," I said.

"Good observation, Charlie," Dad said, treading gently. I punched and kicked the water, trying to stay up with him, all the while breathing in the chlorine. "Slow down, Charlie, relax," he said. But I didn't. Thunder and lightning crackled, picking up momentum as it crossed the sky. I reached for Dad. He took my hand. "My, this is an angry one." He edged toward the ladder, directing me to go ahead. "It's coming in waves. Get ready to run for cover as soon as there's a break." The storm seemed angrier than ever. More thunder. More lightning. I saw how white his skin looked next to me. A thought flashed through my mind. What would happen if I were struck by lightning? Would I turn white like Dad?

Swimming with Dad at the club on Saturday mornings became our time together. He enjoyed telling me stories about his childhood in New York, and I imagined myself doing the same activities with Gene and Linda. I asked Dad a million questions about his growing up there. He had a full photo album capturing his youth. I could see what my life could have been had we not returned to Mexico. There were many pictures of Dad with a prominent looking man. I assumed it was his father, but it turned out to be his uncle, on his mother's side. His father seemed to be missing from the collection, and Dad never mentioned him. I asked about his father and noticed a change, an almost sad expression on his face.

There were pictures of him in school and at Boy Scout activities. One that stood out was of him receiving an honor of some sort. In another image, he was building a model sailboat. I asked a lot of questions about the boat and his Navy ship, imagining myself in a United States Navy uniform. A bookshelf held some of his favorite books. *Moby-Dick* stood out because it was so thick. I asked about the book. Dad quoted the first line, "'Call me Ishmael,'" and said it was about a man named Ahab, battling a whale until his dying breath.

The movie *Moby-Dick* opened at the theater that year, and Dad took the family. The film was in English with Spanish subtitles. I could follow the movie in English, and that made me feel special. Afterward, Eugenia and Mother were exhausted while Don and I wanted to know more about Dad's sailing and Navy experiences, especially the ship he was on—an airline carrier. He said it was nothing like Captain Ahab's ship.

A few weeks later, he came home with a shipbuilding kit with hundreds of pieces for a three-mast schooner. He created a workspace under his cherished framed picture of the three-mast schooner. Night after night, I watched him delicately join pieces together while listening to classical music.

One night I hummed Doris Day's "*Que Sera, Sera,*" and Dad put it on the stereo. That brought everyone to the living room, and we all sang along. It was a family moment that started in New York and came back to Mexico with the same wonderful feeling. Dad loved building the ship, and I loved seeing him work. Watching his gentle hands make something beautiful was a lesson in finesse and patience. I fell asleep several times watching the ship take shape.

After a while, I became his helper. I held the tube of glue upright, leaving a bubble on top. The smell of glue was new and felt vital to me as though it were the same glue used to build pirate ships. One time I fell asleep holding the tube of glue and imagined myself on a ship with Dad navigating across the seas alongside pirate ships. The glue prompted my imagination, and the ride across the waters felt real. Somehow, I ended up laying in the bathtub laughing in a daze. I came to with Dad and Mother hovering over me and calling out my name. I appeared to have one of Mother's blackout symptoms. Mother and Dad worried I might have inherited whatever ailed Mother, and soon I was visiting the doctor along with her. In time I was deemed to be healthy, or at least I was spared from electroshock treatment.

During one of my growth spurts, I got so skinny my ribs stuck out, which concerned my mother. She worried I might develop tuberculosis because her father had died from it. She took me to a doctor who limited my activities, no swimming in the rain, and suggested four meals a day. It may not have been his recommended diet, but Mother insisted on me eating two ham and egg *tortas* with orange juice for breakfast. That required *bolillos*, rolls, from the bakery where we bought all our bread. It became my job to get the *bolillos*.

Every morning I donned my Yankees cap, squeezed into my steel roller skates, and headed to the bakery for *bolillos*. The sound of my steel wheels scraping along the pavement broke the morning silence and woke up every dog along the way. The houses had tall cement walls, unlike the low fences of New York. I enjoyed making the clatter that woke up the dogs along the way as I felt I was on a mission beyond securing a few *bolillos*. Telling by the sound, they were mainly large dogs with distinct personalities. Some were angry, some bored, some irritated, others pissed. But one house had two yapping dogs that carried their warning too far.

One morning I yapped back at the midget dogs with, "Hi-yo Silver!"

Two boys, not visible, yelled back, *"Chinga tu madre!"*

The one thing you grow up knowing in Mexico is if you insult a person's mother, you are asking for a fight. I looked straight ahead and kept going knowing these boys weren't going to stop. On the way back from the bakery, the boys were waiting for me. This time with oranges from their tree that was visible over the wall. They threw a couple of oranges, adding, *"Pinche Yanqui,"* and taunted me until I was out of sight.

The next morning the same thing happened. I announced my arrival with the heavy steel roller skates, and the boys popped up again with the oranges and insults. I skated past, head down, Yankees cap tight, arms swinging wildly, and ignored the loud noise. I dodged everything they threw. It was a victory. On the way back, I secured the *bolillos* under my sweater so I could skate faster. By now, the boys sat on top of the wall. One orange grazed my face. That brought up a cackle of laughter from them and a few more taunts. I was back in Mexico. These guys weren't going to stop on their own.

That night I lay on my bed thinking about yappy dogs and the boys. Don was at his desk doing homework deep in thought. What would Don do in my situation? Just at that moment, he picked up his slingshot branch and spun it around in one hand, still reading his textbook.

The following morning, the wall boys met me with their oranges and now had a couple of lemons to boot. I dodged most of them, but a hard one stung me right in the neck. It ricocheted off and hit a stray cat that was staring down from a ledge. The cat scurried off, and the boys laughed louder than ever. When I got to the bakery, the counter lady asked me what happened to my neck. It was bright red and hurt. I took the long way home around the block instead of passing the wall boys.

That afternoon I stopped at Pepe's bicycle repair shop next to his brother's barbershop where I got my haircuts. The shops and brothers were as different as night and day. The barbershop was spotless, white, and well kept. The bicycle shop was a greasy rat pack of steel gears, parts, and oil cans. I had spent time in the shop, looking around and watching Pepe work while I waited for my turn to get a haircut. "*Hola, Pepe,*" I said, eyeing an innertube hanging from the trashcan. He saw me standing near the trashcan.

"*Que quieres?*" he said with a cigarette dangling off his lips. He knew I wanted something.

"*Esto.*" I held up the rubber tube.

"*Pa que lo quires?*" He asked what I wanted it for. I held up my Y-shaped New York cut future slingshot.

That night I went to work on the rubber tube, cutting and trimming and experimenting with the strength it would take to pull back. First, I came up with two pieces about the length of my forearm so that I could pull it back and have enough power to blast a rock through the Y- shaped branch from New York. Then, I cut two slits, one on each side of the leather, and strapped the rubber through. It was perfect.

After school, I came straight home and went to work. I strapped one end of the rubber to one arm of the wood by wrapping it around and tying it with a shoelace over and over until it was hard as a rock. Then I tied the other side until I had a perfect fit. I rushed out of the apartment and to a vacant lot where there were plenty of rocks. I set up a can to practice shooting my slingshot. I pulled back and aimed. Though I missed, I felt the power of the shot by the sound the rock made when it impaled a box. I shot over and over, never hitting the bottle until my arm tired out. I didn't care that I couldn't hit my target. I just wanted to scare the boys.

The next day I took off for the *bolillos* ready for the wall boys. I had the perfect rock placed in the leather of the slingshot on my left side. I warmed up, like a pitcher, pulling back the black rubber a few times before I reached the wall. I pushed my skates rhythmically forward and back. My arms swung across my body, holding the slingshot tight. My skates clamored on the cement loudly, like a warning bell, a foghorn, a train whistle. I flipped my Yankees cap backward, securing it snugly on my head and gripped the New York slingshot as I approached the boys' house. "*Ole,*" I exhaled, ready for battle. Sure enough, the boys were waiting on the wall sitting with their feet dangling, taunting and throwing fruit. I slowed down and stopped directly across from them. I pulled up the slingshot and let the rock fly in one quick motion. In an instant, the rock hit the boy on the left dead in his face. He fell backward. His head disappeared, and I saw the bottom of his shoes flip up and over the wall. I couldn't believe what had happened. I hit my target. I sped away and made it to the bakery for the *bolillos*. I skated the long way home and hid the slingshot in my mattress.

Mother's favorite Mexican songs were playing on the stereo. I turned the volume up and belted out a *grito "Ay, ay, ay, ay!"* Mother appeared and took a pose for a dance. We swung around the room, singing along with the music. A few moments later, there was a loud banging at the door. This was very unusual because we had an intercom system and it had not rung. Mother asked who was at the door. *"Senora, abra la puerta,"* a crying woman pleaded at the door. I knew I was in trouble. I begged Mother not to open it, but the woman's crying was too loud to ignore.

Mother opened the door to find a hysterical woman holding up two bloodied towels. *"Mire lo que su hijo ha hecho."* The crying woman said I caused this. I walked backward, denying the whole truth, shaking my head no. I couldn't believe I actually hit my target, much less caused that much bleeding. *"Ese nino le pego a mi hijo,"* I was to blame for the bloody mess, and she wanted to know what Mother was going to do about it.

Mother slowly turned toward me with a stern face. *"Es sierto, que tu le pegaste al hijo?"* She asked me if it was true that I had hurt the woman's son. *"Y que causaste toda esta sangre?"* Mother unfastened her designer belt, stepped toward me, slipping off the belt and turning it into a strap. A twinkle in her eyes eased my fears as she snapped the strap before looking back at the woman.

"Perdon, perdon, lo siento, yo tengo la culpa," I confessed, apologizing in the same breath. Mother snapped the belt again and

urged the lady to go home and take care of her child. Satisfied, the lady left still crying. I was ready to hear what my punishment would be. *"Gritas, lloras, como la muerte, a la una, a las dos, a las tres,"* she said. Mother whispered for me to cry when she slapped the table and counted to three. Smack! Sounded her belt, and I screamed bloody murder. Smack! Again, I screamed louder. She repeated, and I moaned louder each time, making sure it could be heard throughout the building. We continued until the woman was visible walking away on the sidewalk. We repeated the belt slap and screamed one more time for good measure. Then I begged Mother not to tell Dad. She demanded an explanation and said she couldn't keep a secret from Dad. I told Mother the entire story about the boys, including the taunts, and explained that I didn't intend to hurt the boy. I just wanted to scare the kids. She understood and said she would have Don go to the bakery from that day on.

Pele

One day, Tia Rosita bought me a professional soccer ball with a Pele signature. It was so special, I slept with it. Soccer balls attract people real fast in Mexico. Sure enough, I took my Pele ball to a nearby park and instantly had teammates in a pickup game. In the excitement of the game, my *gringo* accent didn't give me away, and I didn't have a need to ask what any words meant as soccer is all about speed. Tia Rosita's present worked like magic.

I met a few boys that were more interested in playing soccer than making enemies with me. I started showing up at the park regularly and made friends quickly. The park was wedged between two wide, one-way traffic lanes. A corner grocery store faced the park. It was a place to get a soft drink or water after our pickup games. It was also a gathering place. Before long, I was just another one of the neighborhood boys with a nickname — Hot Dog. It didn't matter what they called me because having any nickname meant being part of the group. Everyone had a nickname like *Gordo* for chubby, *Flaco* for skinny, *Chato* for pug nose, *Nalgon* for big butt — all meant to insult and endear a person. Hot Dog merely said I was being recognized for having lived in New York and speaking English. The best surprise about having met the neighborhood boys was they all hated the wall boys.

Mother continued having blackouts. I was with Mother many times when the spells occurred. We could be walking along a busy street one moment, and the next, she'd lose consciousness. She'd drop whatever she had in her hands and continue along, slurring her words. I'd pick up her bags or purse and hold on to her to keep her from walking into traffic. We'd sit for a few minutes and wait for her to come around. She looked so vulnerable and fragile in that state. She would squeeze her eyes, chew, and swallow air until she regained consciousness. I thought she might be reliving her shock treatment memories. Time stood still for me whenever that happened. I held her tight and told myself I'd never leave her side. It was scary and lonely knowing I couldn't help.

Thoughts of losing my mother always dominated my mind in those moments. One time I came home from school and found her stooped over a kitchen chair in a blackout. The pressure cooker whistled like a runaway steam train, and the record player whirled around, making scratchy sounds. It scared the sense out of me. I turned off the stove and record player. I edged to her side, looking for signs of life. I saw she was breathing and helped her up. She looked tortured in her nightmare, squeezing her eyes shut and gritting her teeth. All I could do was hold her until she fell asleep. I brought my homework into her room and stayed with her until she woke up. A series of teeth grinding and shallow breathing preceded her awakening. I watched her slowly come back to her senses, focusing on my face. I kissed her forehead and picked up my homework. She asked me not to tell anyone. I said I wouldn't do that. We had a pact.

Another time, I came home to find my mother unconscious on the kitchen floor, face down in a pool of blood, her beige dress creased underneath oozing in red blood. I feared the worst. I didn't want my mother to die. I looked for life and saw she was breathing. I caught my breath and held her as she came to. "*Ay, otra ves,*" she said, it happened again. I helped her to her room, leaving a trail of blood, and watched her painful journey into sleep. I sat on the bed, unable to leave her alone, watching her natural breathing until she woke up. She looked helpless, disoriented until she focused on my eyes. I waited for her deep sigh that indicated she was ready to resume life, but she closed her eyes instead. With tears and a quivering bottom lip, she slipped back into sleep. What would happen if she died? Would Dad leave us and go back to New York alone? Or would he take us back to New York? Would Tia Rosita take me back?

"Charlie," Mother murmured, her lip still quivering. I gripped her hand tighter. "Charlie, promise me one thing," she said in Spanish.

"Yes, anything," I whispered.

"Open my drawer," she said without opening her eyes. I reached for her nightstand drawer. "Look inside for my medicine. There's a tin inside the chocolate box. Take it out." Strange place to keep your medicine, I thought.

I opened the heavy drawer to her nightstand. I recognized two old cartons of chocolates from New York. I looked inside, hoping to find an Almond Joy chocolate bar, but Mother used the boxes for sewing materials. I wormed my hand through the spools of thread, ribbons, zippers, patches, and many needles. Finally, I felt a small thin round tin box. I took it out. It was a classic fruit and flower imprinted tin gift box. "Do you want a glass of water?"

"No," she said in a weak voice. I handed her the tin. She opened it and drew a few white pills. "You are the only one I am telling about this. These pills are for me if I don't get better. Promise me that if I ever need them, you will help me take them all. No one can know this."

"I promise." Boys honor their mother's wishes. I had to promise. Terminating one's life was a real option, I learned. Her pain was real. The pills were real. My love was real.

The medical treatments were not working, and Dad worried a lot. I worried every time I climbed the stairs to our four-story apartment, wondering how I'd find Mother. Sometimes I'd relive the image of her passed out on the floor, and I'd blast up the steps, two and three at a time. The urgency to reach her would become a matter of life or death until I opened the door and saw Mother alive and well.

Dad finished the model schooner that stood prominently on a cabinet between the dining room and living room. It was a source of inspiration for Don and me to build model cars, boats, and airplanes. Dad took us to a crafts store, and we each picked a model as a project. Don chose a hot rod car with fat wheels in the back and flames along the sides, while I wanted an airplane, *The Wildcat*. I asked Dad if that was what he flew in World War II. He smiled and nodded that it was. The picture on the box showed a pilot that looked like Clark Gable.

Don successfully assembled the car and painted his version of flames while I struggled with my kit. I developed the habit of sniffing the glue before placing each new piece, and soon I started talking to Clark Gable. I asked him what he liked more—making movies or flying airplanes. He didn't answer but kept a reassuring smile fixed on me the whole time I worked on his plane. I worked on the model every day after school. On the third day, I decided I'd finish putting all the parts together because I wanted to show Dad I could be like him. There were a lot of pieces left, so I sniffed a lot of glue. When I finished, I sat back to admire my *Wildcat* and smiled at Clark Gable, who sat in the pilot's seat. "Good job," said Clark Gable! I nearly fell off my chair. He talked to me, Clark Gable, the coolest man in Hollywood, was talking to me. I didn't know how to respond. I leaned in closer, my eyes wide open. "Movies are fun, but they're not real," he said. "Now flying, that's really fun." I saw his lips move as he talked. I sniffed the glue one last time for no reason.

"Do you know *Cantinflas*?" I ventured a question.

"Sure, I know *Cantinflas*."

"Do you know Annette Funicello?"

"That's the girl your brother's stuck on, isn't it?" I nodded yes. "Why are you so sad?"

"Don likes her more than me," I answered sadly.

"She's got a better-looking chest than you," he said with a laugh. "Probably a better kisser than you, too. Now stand up and show me what you got." I stood up. "That's better. Now take me out for some fun. That's right, Charlie, real fun." I picked up the *Wildcat* and held it close. Clark Gable smiled at me and whispered for me to take him for a flight. I carefully opened my bedroom door and looked around. Mother and I were the only ones at home. I could see she was lying on her bed through the mirror on the wall in her room. Clark Gable said, "The coast is clear." I continued to the front door and up the stairs to the rooftop. It was my secret place where I could see all the way to the Club Mundet and where I often went to look at the clouds and remember New York. "What are you looking at up there, Charlie?" asked Clark Gable.

"Clouds. My *Toro* lives there. I want you to meet him."

"You want me to meet your bull that lives in the clouds, Charlie? Okay, that's fine by me. I want to meet your bull, too."

"*Toro*," I whispered. And just as I said it, *Toro* appeared.

"Charlie, *que quieres*?" the *Toro* said with Tia Rosita's voice. I laughed out loud. Clark Gable didn't, and I realized he didn't speak Spanish.

"Did you see that?" I asked, but he hadn't even looked up.

"Time for some fun, Charlie," Clark Gable said. "Make me fly. I want to fly all the way to The Big Apple." I looked closer and saw his reassuring smile that let me know he was ready to fly. Images of Clark Gable flying in my airplane, gliding across New York City over skyscrapers and Macy's department store, with the friendly policeman standing out in front looking up and seeing my plane, whirled in my mind. I stood up and threw the plane with all my might in the direction of the Club Mundet because I wanted Clark Gable to see where I swam. I let go, and the aircraft flew/fell straight down. I watched, expecting Clark Gable to pull up, but he smashed headfirst straight into the concrete street. A truck rolled over the landing spot, leaving no sign of an airplane. Dust.

"Charlie, Charlie," Don's voice sounded through my vision of Clark Gable dying in my airplane. It was Don calling out my name. I looked down to see Don standing below me, reaching up for my arm. I had somehow climbed to the edge of the guardrail. Don climbed up. "What are you doing? This is dangerous," he warned, taking my hand and leading off the rail. Dad approached from the staircase.

"It's dinner time, Charlie." Dad looked around. "I never realized how nice it is up here. Look at all this space. And this beautiful sunshine up here just going to waste." The rooftop was built for recreation purposes, but no one ever used it.

"Dad, I want to fly like you did in the war," I said, pointing to the sky.

"I think you'd be better off flying without a war," he said.

"Dinner's getting cold," said Don, rushing toward the stairs.

Shortly after building the schooner, Dad set out to design a solar energy model that he theorized would provide enough power to use in homes. Solar energy at that time was unheard of. It was crazy to think of harnessing the sun's heat and put it to use. Eugenia was doing a science report on the solar system, so she understood the idea. Dad set up a drafting table with giant sheets of graph paper and offered one to Eugenia for her report. They drafted their work side by side.

After the drafting phase, he set up a workshop on the rooftop. Eugenia studied the solar system in science and kept a close eye on the sun's pattern from the rooftop. She tracked a couple of shadows on the roof with chalk lines, checking them at the exact time for two weeks. She also made a beautiful paper mâché model, each planet was a work of art. My sister entered it in her school science fair and won first prize. She was back in Mexico, accomplishing exciting things in school with Dad's encouragement.

I watched Dad study his design, cut materials, gather parts, and methodically assemble his masterpiece. He patented his design and proved that energy from the sun could be harnessed and put to use.

Somehow, he wired the panels to supply electricity to a lamp and radio in the study area. He introduced his designs and model to several companies, but there wasn't enough interest to manufacture them on a grand scale. It didn't matter; he proved to himself that it could be done, and that was enough. Dad's determination to make his idea work was inspiring to me. He made his plan work right here on our roof in Mexico. I wanted to be as smart as he. I sat like him and held my pencil the way he did. One night I asked him about the gold knife and chain he used to sharpen his pencils. "This old knife was a gift from my father," he said. I could tell by the sound of his voice that it meant a lot to Dad.

Schoolwork in Spanish came more naturally after a while. I was a Mexican back in Mexico fully re-assimilated into my culture. We studied English twice a week, which was boring for me. I found myself counting tiles along a wall or steel bars on windows instead of listening to the nun's squeaky voice. She must have known I was bored because she called on me a lot. I didn't want that attention. My grades didn't reflect my lack of interest or involvement in classwork at all. I got good grades for doing the minimal amount of work. I hated the nuns. I hated being in the same room with them and tried to get kicked out of class in many ways, but nothing worked. I screamed, walked around the room, pretended to stutter every time I was called on for an answer, asked to go to the restroom every hour, but it didn't seem to matter.

By the end of the school year, I was appointed as the class representative to read the nuns' farewell message to the parents. Mother showed up looking every bit as classy as Katherine Hepburn and even donned a veiled hat with a pearled rose embroidered on the left side. I could tell she intimidated the nuns as they watched the priests eyeing Mother. It turned out the message was to be delivered in Spanish and English. I read the letter in both languages and received a round of applause for whatever I had read. I saw the nun gloating at one point as though I'd learned something from her. Mother stood talking to me afterward, by chance, near the spot where I'd had the fight with Skinnynose. She said she was proud of me for having delivered the message in two languages. If she only knew what I'd done right on the very spot where she stood. "I hate this school," I said, thinking it an opportune time to express my real feelings. "I want another school."

Mother's eyelids rolled shut, she clenched her teeth and tightened her shoulders. I caught her purse as it slipped away. I took her hand and led her to a bench where we waited for her episode to pass. Several nuns passed by bowing and genuflecting in a manner of acknowledging Mother's state. I hoped I'd never see those nuns or school again. I held Mother's hand, watching everyone leave while we waited for her to regain her senses. Director gargoyle snuck up on us and asked if we needed anything. Mother didn't respond. I closed my eyes as she had hers and spit, once, twice, three times pretending I was a gargoyle. The school year was over.

Eugenia got straight tens on her report card and received honors for all her schoolwork. She had written a class report on the United Nations. She learned about the American Friends Service Committee, which was a predecessor to John F. Kennedy's Peace Core. She applied for a summer internship with the Service Committee. Don got good grades and took to the streets for his entertainment. We were firmly back in Mexico.

School vacations aren't fun without friends. Don had a lot of friends but always had his wolf face around them, so I stayed away. It was his way of saying I wasn't welcome in his circle. No matter, I had a soccer ball that I'd named Pele. I played soccer every day at the nearby park, where boys were always ready for a game. I loved Pele and took it everywhere I went until one fateful afternoon.

The closest park was on a corner at the intersection of two vast streets with long views in all directions. Traffic was sparse and slow if there was any traffic at all. Occasionally the ball would roll out on to the street and cause cars to avoid it, either slowing to let the ball pass, stopping, or merely timing the distance to miss the ball. Brown public transportation buses came by every twenty minutes and had avoided Pele as well. I was grateful the bus drivers were careful. But one day, my ball slipped slowly, very slowly, on to the street. Anyone could have avoided the ball's path since it was crawling away like a turtle. A bus appeared down the road heading our way. My Pele reached the curb and came to a stop. I thought it was safe resting against the curb, but instead, the bus picked up speed and veered right purposely aiming its front wheels at my ball. Pop! The bus flattened my ball and sped away. The number thirty-one marked on the back identified Pele's killer. My heart stopped. The ball was my best friend and a part of Tia Rosita's love for me. I pushed my dead ball under my sweater, ran home, and hid the ball under my bed, wishing I'd never gone out that day. The image of the bus speeding away with the number thirty-one left an indelible mark on my mind.

Transportation buses had two identifying numbers on them, one in the front and one in the back. For the rest of the vacation, I played in the park, carefully watching as every bus came and went, desperate to see the number thirty-one again. I remembered Captain Ahab's determination with Moby-Dick and how he waited and looked for the whale. I became Ahab every time I heard a bus coming down the street. I strategically placed a small rock pile at my corner lookout spot. I could see the bus number on the front from a distance and waited with a rock in hand for days then weeks without seeing number thirty-one.

Vacation was almost over, and I had all but given up on ever seeing the killer bus when it appeared on the horizon one late afternoon. My heart raced, I leaped for the closest rock in my view as the bus rumbled closer. I wore my Yankees cap and a bright red sweater that day. The bus approached. I checked, double- and triple-checked the identifying number. There was no mistaking bus number thirty-one that was heading my way. I raced across the street to the spot where it had crushed my ball. The bus slowed as I ran across, rock in hand. I imagined myself a Picador running across a bullring taunting a bull with a cape in hand. *Ole.* The bus was empty and moved in slow motion to where I waited. It grew in size as it neared. It was bigger than Moby-Dick. I reached back, gripping the rock tightly, and threw it with all my might. Bam! Bull's eye! The side window shattered. I ran across the street and away from the thoroughfare. The bus continued for a bit; then, the red brake lights lit up. I made it to my building, screaming for joy and ran up the four flights of stairs faster than ever.

Mother greeted me with a grin, wanting to know why I looked so happy and why I was breathing so hard. I said I scored a goal against a mean team. I sat at the window and pretended everything was fine. In a moment, the bus rolled up and stopped in front of our building. Buses never came on our street. Yet, there it was just like Moby-Dick had shown up in front of Captain Ahab. I ran into my room, grabbed my ball from under the bed, and hid under my sheets. I heard a knock at the door then a man's voice. A few painful moments later, Mother came. "There's a man here saying you broke his window. Come out here," she said. I reached out, holding my dead ball. She took it, "*Ay, Charlie.*" She took Pele and walked back to the living room.

I came out to the living room where a devil-faced man with a pencil-thin mustache and greasy hair stood in the doorway. Mother asked me if I knew anything about a broken window. I didn't answer. "*Como sabe que mi hijo fue el que rompio su ventana?*" She asked the driver how he knew it was me who broke his window.

The bus driver said he saw a boy with a blue hat and a red sweater throw the rock and run away. I was the only boy in the neighborhood that day wearing a red shirt, and the cap was unusual enough on its own. I was guilty. I confessed.

Mother knew my ball had been destroyed by a bus. She placed

the ball in my hand and told me to apologize. Apologize for getting back at the bus that killed my ball? *"Perdon, señor,"* I started, but I couldn't stop myself. *"Pero porque mato a mi pelota al proposito?"* I asked why did the driver have to kill my ball on purpose? I held up my dead ball. The man said he was sorry about the ball, but he wasn't the only driver of the bus. It could have been any number of drivers. The only thing that concerned him now was who was going to pay for the window. I looked at Mother wanting a secret expression or twinkle in her eye to ease my way out of this. She stood stern and said she wouldn't help. I'd have to figure out how to pay for the window myself. I told the driver I had no money. I'm sure now that Mother and the bus driver must have had an understanding because she let the driver take me with him to the bus station.

The ride to the bus station garage was a few miles away. I rode in the front seat, feeling entirely justified in breaking the window. I thought Dad would understand if I told him I was doing what Ahab did with Moby-Dick. We reached a wide-open yard crammed with buses that looked like beached whales. I didn't know what to do or what was going to happen to me, but I was determined to make my case. I was not going to let my mother pay for the broken window.

The whole place smelled of grease and tobacco smoke. Two men pounded and hammered a giant tire into place on a tire changer in the middle of the garage. Ranchera music whined from a cheap radio. Soccer team posters and flags filled one wall in the office area, which I felt would make my case. The driver told me to wait in the office. Another slim man with a mustache and cigarette dangling from his lip appeared. He handed me a paper with a telephone number and told me to dial it. It was my mother's writing. Tia Rosita answered. I explained what I had done and handed the phone to the slim man.

The sun set and a few lights came on. I watched countless buses come in with a driver, fill up with gas, and leave with another driver. Finally, a taxicab arrived with Tia Rosita. She looked out of place in her expensive dress, coat, and shoes exiting the cab at the edge of the asphalt. She wouldn't cross the greasy yard. I followed the driver to my aunt's side. *"Ay, Charlie, travieso,"* Tia Rosita sighed lovingly, calling me a naughty boy. She could call me anything she wanted, but it always sounded like Tia Rosita was saying she loved me. I held her tight while she read the bill and paid it with cash.

We got in the car and drove away. *"Bueno, porque haces tantas locuras?"* She wanted to know why I did so many crazy things. I could tell her anything and everything, so she always got an unfiltered answer.

"No se, Tia, haci naci." I said I didn't know, maybe I was born this way. She didn't like my explanation.

"Y por eso rompiste la ventana?" That was no reason for breaking the window. She went on to say I should have told her about the accident. She would have bought another ball rather than have me break the law and risk my life. We rode quietly for a bit. I sneezed from the depths of my lungs, breaking the silence. Tia reached in her purse and handed me a tissue. Her wallet spilled open; a few pictures fell out. I picked them up. One picture looked like a jigsaw puzzle with missing pieces. Some people had been carefully cut out of the photo. It occurred to me that there were a lot of pictures in the family with people's faces deliberately ghosted. Who could it be? I wondered if the missing person in the photo could have been my biological father.

"Tia!" I had a thought, an epiphany. *"Ya, se porque soy tan loco."* I said I knew why I was crazy.

"No estas loco." She said I wasn't crazy.

"Si, por esto." I pointed to the missing piece in the picture. *"Es mi papa?"*

"No, no, no, Papa Bill es tu papa." She had called Dad Papa Bill ever since her visit to New York, and she was adamant about addressing him, and only him, as my father. I knew she and the whole family wanted me to believe, or live the fantasy, that William Allen was my only father. To do otherwise would have been disrespectful. *"Por que*

dices eso?"

"Quien fue mi papa?" I asked who my father was. She put the pictures back and held my hand. It was the conversation she didn't want to have but couldn't avoid. She said my biological father was a good man. He wanted to know me and have a relationship but couldn't be married to my mom because he had a family. It was unfortunate, but that's the way it was, and Mother didn't want to have anything to do with that relationship. He was a thoughtful man and sent money every month until Bill Allen put an end to it. That solved the mystery of the cutouts in pictures.

Que sera, sera.

Jardines El Pedregal

Dad and Mother purchased a lot in the exclusive neighborhood of *Jardines El Pedregal*. It was known for modern design homes, expansive grounds, and high society residents. Dad wanted Mother to have the best life possible, and a home with a view in this neighborhood would be a dream come true. Dad and Mother drove me through the region often to gather ideas for the house they would design. Mother would point out things she liked, and Dad would take pictures or make a mental note. In time Dad would have a design for the house, and we would visit the land with Mother's dream in hand.

One prominent home in the development was an almost all-glass house. It stood above all the rest, and many people would take pictures. It was featured in a magazine with beautiful people lounging at the windows, but in reality, no one was ever seen in it. One morning, the three of us walked around the area, studying the lot with Dad's drawings. A view was crucial, and Dad suggested an all-glass wall in the living room. Mother looked straight at me with a twinkle in her eye, signaling a hidden meaning. "No, no, glass breaks. We can't have any glass walls," and gave me a wink. She never told Dad about the bus window I'd broken.

Building a house in that neighborhood was a sign of reaching a class status beyond Mother's wildest dreams. She was in heaven researching modern living magazines and architecture periodicals. Dad drew up new plans almost weekly as he and Mother would study designs and imagine our new life. She designed her own modern dining and living room furniture while Dad concentrated on the structure.

One magazine featured an octagon living room with a floor-to-ceiling glass wall and a breathtaking view. This inspired Mother. She drew picture after picture of her vision of modern living. She settled on an octagon table with space-age horizontal spindles all around that matched the chair backs and legs. Eight pie-shaped pieces came together to form Mother's modern vision. She continued with a one hundred and forty-four inch by ninety-six inch sleek, L-shaped sofa with designer fabric. She used the same material on the dining chairs that complimented the table. Later, she designed a dining cabinet, buffet, and coffee table.

Everything was designed with the yet-to-be-built modern home in mind. She studied and refined the design with a parade of artisans that she interviewed for each job. The furniture arrived at the apartment before construction on the house had even started. Plastic furniture slipcovers were fashionable at the time, and Mother ordered some for the sofa. She planned to keep the slipcovers on until the house was ready. Still, Dad would have none of that reasoning. We were a civilized family and would keep the furniture clean. But we found ways to avoid the living room. Mother convinced Dad to keep the plastic covers on the dining chairs as a safeguard against Don or me spilling food on the prized fabric. Without exception, everyone that ever stepped into our home commented on the living room, which brought a proud smile to Mother's face. Afterward, she made sure to tell of her plans to move to *El Pedregal*. She was living a dream and made sure we all felt a part of it.

To be sure, she enrolled me in a French and English Academy, motivated by her newfound status. I was a different kind of Mexican now with my *gringo* accent. I got in trouble right away for making fun of the French teacher's lopsided hair.

The French teacher called Mother and demanded a meeting. The next day, Mother accompanied me to school and sat with the principal and teacher. The principal started explaining my bad behavior, but Mother fell into a blackout spell right in the middle of the office. I took my mother's hand, protectively. I didn't say anything about the condition while I waited for her to come back to her senses. I stared at the teacher and principal, sensing fear and confusion. We left the school without resolving anything about inappropriate behavior. Mother never mentioned the meeting, but within a week, I was enrolled in another school.

School uniforms were mandatory in my new school named after Christopher Columbus. A navy-blue sweater, white collared shirt, gray slacks, and black leather shoes made us all equal. I liked the idea of blending in with everyone, but the minute I spoke, I was pegged as an outsider, especially with the name Charlie. I boarded the school bus every morning before sunrise and arrived back at sunset without exchanging a word with any of my uniformed schoolmates.

My classroom teacher went out of her way to make me feel welcome. She used a little English occasionally and would look straight at me. "Is that clear, Charlie?" She over pronounced every syllable and rolled the R in Char-r-r-r-r-lie long enough to have everyone stare at me. That embarrassed me and I'd put my head down on my desk. Then she'd call me to her side and pull me up on her lap resting my head between her enormous breasts.

Oddly enough, I started looking forward to getting called up because it took the pressure off paying attention to her lessons. I think she must have enjoyed having me on her lap because even when I started pushing my ears into her breasts, favoring one more than the other with obvious deliberateness, she never stopped me. I listened to her lessons with one ear, and her heartbeat with the other ear.

In the comfort of her lap, I imagined being in Mrs. Brown's class in the winter overlooking the snow-covered fields. Then, I daydreamed floating across the playground on a magic carpet and into the sky with my *Toro* smiling in the clouds. I was floating across the sky with Mrs. Brown and Linda. We raced along treetops crisscrossing through a forest when Gene appeared behind us. "Trees, snow, clouds!" Gene's voice screamed. His words repeated over and over, faster and faster, louder and louder until I heard the teacher's shrieking voice guide me back to the classroom. The teacher nudged me, and my mind returned to Mexico.

I found my safe place in her classroom. This was my third school in two years. I still had a slight *gringo* accent but felt it disappearing.

At the club, a *gringo* accent was typical, and in time I met a group of boys I got along with. One boy, Anton, lived a block away, and we often walked home together. He invited me into his home, and I had him to our house, often playing board games in English. Mother liked Anton and encouraged me to keep friends like him since his father was a powerful business executive. I don't know how Mother knew it, but it seemed right. Their three-story gated estate was beyond anything I'd ever been in. The study had trophies and wall to wall pictures of champion racehorses with the family celebrating a victory.

Elvis Presley exploded into the world, and young boys everywhere wanted to look like him. Don slicked back his hair and drew out a black pompadour that Elvis himself would have envied. "Ay, no!" Mother shrieked upon seeing Don slicked-out one morning. "You look like a *pachuco*," she said in Spanish. His shiny black hair matched his tight black pants and pointy shoes. A loose white shirt with the collar up, sleeves rolled past his elbow, and smirk is all he needed to be the coolest guy on the block. With that image, Don made friends quickly—some good, some not so good—and became the leader of his pack.

Dad was a Navy man and, like all servicemen during WWII, had read about and seen pictures of U.S. Navy men in bloody fights with Mexican Americans, labeled *pachucos*. Navy men had squelched *pachuco* lifestyle in Los Angeles in the infamous Zoot Suit riots that bloodied the streets and broadcast a horrible image of Mexican Americans. The image of Mexicans with slicked-back black hair didn't go over well with Dad even if, in Don's case, it was a direct tribute to Elvis, who wore black and red, chewed gum, and wore sunglasses. In a protective effort, Dad set down some rules for Don and me right away. Clean haircuts with the part on the left, neatly shorn, and combed at all times. Clothes had to be neutral colors, neat and clean, no red or black allowed. No chewing gum or sunglasses ever.

The next day Don came home with his angry wolf face and a Mohawk haircut. I stayed away until Dad came home. It was a showdown that neither had faced before. Don didn't say a word at dinner and never looked up from his plate. Dad iced his emotions and continued about the evening as though everything was normal. Still, it was the most awkward dinnertime we had ever experienced. Dad had always set the tone for dinner with music, but not that night. We ate slowly and deliberately, not scraping silverware on the plates. I slurped my drink once, which caught everyone's attention. I didn't take another sip. Dad stared at the top of Don's head the whole time, waiting for him to look up, but Don was resolute in keeping his face out of the picture. He stared at his food while the rest of us watched the standoff. Don's head beaded up with sweat. He wolfed down his food without raising his head and very politely said, "Thank you, Mother, for the delicious dinner. Dad, may I be excused?" He never looked up.

"No," Dad answered, staring at Don's beaded head. "And look at me when you address your father." The room had never been so quiet. I placed my knife and fork on my empty plate ever so lightly, but still, the delicate clink of the silverware broke the silence. "Charlie, you may go to your room. Mary, you may as well." We both eased out of our chairs. He kept his eye on Don, who now had his face up, eyes down on his plate. Mother got up, and we each took our plates to the kitchen. When we returned, Dad and Don were still in a standoff. I ran to my room and buried my head in my homework. A moment later, Don came in and dropped on his bed. I left him alone and sat near Mother in the living room. Dad put on classical music, but it sounded like funeral music.

Eugenia saved the night with some good news. She was accepted into a summer internship with the American Friends Service Committee in the Quaker Fellows group. Dad was overwhelmed with pride. Eugenia knew it and curled up in Dad's arms, reading the letter over and over. I noticed Mother's pride in the relationship Dad and Eugenia had.

The following day Don cut off the Mohawk and borrowed my Yankees cap. Don had a way of losing and forgetting things. My gift from Gene was one of them. Don couldn't remember where he left it or how he'd lost it. We retraced his path back to the park and searched until it got dark. I walked home dejected and sad, thinking about Gene and Linda. Don knew I was disappointed and walked with his hand on my shoulder. But something good came of it because he lost his wolf face with me and carried on at the table as usual, which eased the tension between him and Dad.

Eugenia spent the summer as an intern working with Quaker fellows as part of the American Fellows Committee. She returned with dreams of serving the less fortunate around the world. This put a glow on Dad's face like no other—she was giving to others. She lit up as she told us about her experiences and about someone named Herb. He was the biggest guy in every picture. He had a friendly face and stood a foot taller than Eugenia

My birthday came on Mother's Day that year, and I was given a mariachi outfit. The outfit is worn by *charros*, horsemen who perform in *chariadas*. Their skills are legendary around the world. *Charros* can make horses dance, prance, spin on command, kneel, bow, and stand like Silver. Dad planned a horseback-riding outing on a ranch where we would celebrate both Mother's Day and my birthday. I wore my new outfit. Putting on my mariachi suit with regal lines, intricate embroidery-stitched design from top to bottom, front, back, and on the extra-long brimmed sombrero, empowered me to be a master *charro*. The moment I slipped my legs into the pants, I imagined my grandfather dressing for an encounter with a ferocious bull. By the time I donned the sombrero, I was ready to fight, ride, or tame any animal.

We arrived at a rancho on a bright clear morning where ducks and geese roamed near the stables. Chickens scurried about pecking at the ground near a full pigpen. I felt sorry for the chickens stuck so close to the stinky ground. My new suit and boots glistened in the sunlight and caught a duck's attention. He pinned his sight on me, its bill pointing directly at my nose. Another duck did the same, then another, and another, until the entire flock of geese and ducks started my way. I was ready for a bullfight. "STOP!" I screamed; they stopped. "*Ole.*" I turned. No fowl was going to scare me.

I continued on, marching toward the stables but encountered the papa goose standing in my path. It stared at me, daring me to cross. I stared right back and walked toward the gray-feathered bull goose when a pig oinked. I oinked back—a sound I'd never heard come out of me! The bull goose skedaddled as I continued oinking. I reached the stables looking for the biggest and fastest horse I could find. Don followed, watching me take control of the ranch animals with my newfound oink. Don and I were the only two riders. Four horses pranced toward us from the stalls and were led into a corral where we were to choose our ride.

A black stallion stood a hand taller than the rest. He could have been Silver dipped with black paint. I imagined Gene and the masked Lone Ranger straddling the fence waiting to hear my decision. I pointed to the black stallion and sent an oink his way. He blinked at me. Don warned it might be too much for me. I repeated my authoritative oink under my bright new *charro sombrero*. Don chose a brown horse. A ranch hand saddled up the two horses and led them through a cackle of ducks, geese, and chickens. Don and I followed to the start of a trail.

A wide-open space was visible on the horizon at the end of a barbed wire fence along the left side. Don mounted his horse while the ranch hand hoisted me up to my saddle. I oinked for good measure as the ranch hand adjusted my stirrups. Don's horse circled mine, seeming to favor the walk back to the stalls. I looked into the bright sky wanting to see my *Toro* and screamed, "Hi-Yo Silver!" I dug my new boots into the horse's ribs.

The jerk that followed knocked my sombrero backward. The horse leaped forward like a tiger leaping for its prey and ran away. I held on for dear life, unable to pull my backward leaning torso forward. I lost the reins and gripped the saddle horn with all my might, fighting to pull myself up. I couldn't. The horse picked up speed. My boots slipped away from the stirrups, sending my feet flailing in desperate kicks. I wasn't Tonto. I wasn't the Lone Ranger. I screamed a high-pitched, "Stop, help!" and remembered the horse didn't speak English.

I shrieked, "*Ole!*" The horse kicked faster along the trail. "*Tu madre!*" I cursed. Don shouted my name, chasing after me. He followed my sprinting stallion along the trail heading across to the desert. The open fields at the end of the trail drew closer until, in one quick, unexpected move, my horse came to an immediate halt. That sent me flying over the horse's head and across the trail into the barbed wire fence. I landed upside down impaled on the fence, legs and arms out, held up by my ripped mariachi suit. I didn't feel the barbed wire in my back and legs. Blood leaked from my wounds and into my mariachi suit as Don plucked me off the fence. To me, it was my matador's suit, and I had been gored.

Barbaric Spine Surgery

Mother's electroshock treatments had no positive results. Her blackouts persisted, and she continued searching for help, visiting the best medical centers with the finest doctors in Mexico City. She liked taking me with her and wanted my company. To me, it was an excursion reminiscent of those in New York City.

As fate would have it, Dad had been having lower back problems. An orthopedic doctor prescribed a steel corset. Dad wore it dutifully, but the problems continued. One day, at work, his back gave out, rendering him immobile. X-rays showed slipped discs in the lower lumbar. He had to choose between languishing with the corset or surgery. He opted for surgery. Back surgery in 1959 was barbaric. Two steel rods fused six lumbar in his back. He lay in bed for two sad months, stuck in a three-quarter body cast. His room seemed to always be dark with soft music playing and lots of books by his side.

During those months our voices were reduced to whispers. Don didn't bother to talk at all and retreated to his room most of the time. Eugenia kept her head in her books and helped Mother with everything. I was used to having thoughts about Mother dying and wondering what life would be without her. Now I worried about being without Dad.

"*Que Sera, Sera*" took on a new sense for me. The future always seemed cheery and bright, but Dad's stay in the dark room and Mother's mysterious blackouts created a quiet sadness in all of us. Dad's classical music took on a funeral quality, especially since he played it so softly. I had always approached Dad with a smile and usually made him laugh somehow, but during this time, I simply stayed quiet.

Tia Rosita found me pacing outside the apartment one afternoon. I was trying to block out my fears about finding Mother dead, or now Dad, when my aunt appeared. I hugged her with all my might and buried my head in her arms. *"Tia, quiero vivir con tigo."* I said I wanted to live with her, my voice shaky. She saw I was upset and led me down the street. We walked without saying a word. I squeezed her hand three times, and she squeezed back the same. That was our way of feeling together. She always wore high heels and had a familiar cadence that calmed me. I skipped forward and matched her brisk pace. We continued until I caught my breath and looked up. My *Toro*, angels, babies, animals all roamed the clouds. *"Mira, Tia, el toro, los angelitos, animals."* I pointed them all out. She chuckled, followed my finger into the sky, and said she saw everything I saw.

"Tu mami y tu papi viven por ti," she said. Mother and Dad lived for me. *"Y tu por ellos para siempre."* And you for them forever, she said. She knew what I feared.

Spanish without the *gringo* accent came back to me, and I learned to repel childhood taunts. When someone questioned or teased me about having the name Charlie, I'd answer *"Tu madre!"* with a smile. That simple two-word phrase makes quick friends or enemies depending on how it is said. I made friends at school and the club. I played soccer in a neighborhood league and learned to roam the streets just like Don, without fear.

Our apartment was close to the Plaza De Toros, the national bullfighting ring. Sunday bullfights were held and broadcast live on television. I asked my mother if my grandfather fought bulls there, but the stadium was built after he had died. The stadium is a monument to the macho sport that features an entrance with statues of a bullfighter on one side and a charging bull on the other. I walked there and found an open gate. Bulls were kept in red pens along the entrance, and horses stayed on the other side. The smell of dung, hay, sweaty animals, and wet dirt filled the corridor that led to the ring entrance. I followed a boy, probably a ranch hand's son, into the stadium. Young matadors paired up into four groups and took their spots on opposite sides of the ring. They held a sword and a red cape. The young men took turns practicing with bullhorns attached to adjustable wooden frames, alternating roles between the bull then the matador. I stood at the railing close to one of the matadors and watched the brave man. He studied the horns, shuffled his feet, puffed out his chest, and gripped his cape covering the sword. Then he narrowed his eyes and stared down the wooden bull just like I had faced the goose. The horns drove toward the matador's red cape. He stood his ground and swept his cloak over the charging horns. My grandfather's image charged through my mind. *Ole.*

I walked home through a congested street where young boys weaved in and out of moving traffic selling chewing gum. I jumped in and pretended the cars were my bulls. Their headlights didn't scare me. The ducks and geese were meaner than any headlight. The rumbling engines were all too predictable. I had no fear. I knew what I would do and where I would live if Mother and Dad died. I ran up the stairs to the apartment, convinced I was a natural-born bullfighter. I had successfully shed the *gringo* mannerisms from New York and reclaimed my Mexico.

Dad didn't die, and neither did Mother, although her blackouts continued. The doctors' only conclusion was that Mother suffered from depression. Dad's months-long recovery and rise from the bed felt like Easter in our home. Dad had risen from his bed, and he was prepared to live it up. He made a point of how much he loved Mexican culture, the fiestas, the dance, music, and laughter. The joy he saw in people's lives, regardless of social status, attracted him. He said he was going to capture it with his camera. Everywhere we went, he'd comment on the happiness he saw in people's faces, from the street vendors scratching out a living selling cheap treats, to the tour guides in Acapulco. We traveled outside of Mexico City a lot, Veracruz, Acapulco, Tasco, Guadalajara, Puebla, Lake Chapala. Dad took hundreds of pictures, capturing the theme of people happy at work. I never asked him, but I got the idea that the happy people in his photos were "living the life in service to others." Regardless, we were going to pleasant places to see happy people at work while Mother suffered from depression. I felt an obligation, a duty, to be happy or at least to look happy.

Dad worried more than ever about Mother, especially since electroshock hadn't worked. The movie theater was a great place not to think about death. One Saturday, Dad and I walked to the movie theater after swimming. Posters of *The Old Man and the Sea* were on display at the entrance. Dad said the movie was from Hemingway's book and that it would open in a few weeks. We went in to see Jerry Lewis and Dean Martin's comedy, *Hollywood or Bust*. It was playing in English with Spanish subtitles.

Knowing English in Mexico was suddenly an advantage for me. We watched Dean and Jerry drive their red convertible down a palm tree lined Sunset Boulevard and into the Hollywood Bowl. I was so excited, I nearly jumped out of my seat. Dad leaned over and whispered, "California." Later that night, I asked Dad if he had ever been to California. He said he had and reached for a photo album. A large folder slipped off the shelf. His house designs spewed out on to the floor. He hadn't worked on the plan since his surgery. Mother placed them back without saying a word. The pictures of Dad smiling in California with friends alongside a convertible said it all. We were headed for California. *Que sera, sera.*

Belmont 1960

"Choke up on the bat!" screamed my coach. I pulled my neck in like a turtle and waited for the next pitch. I swung and missed. Strike one. Again, the coach told me to choke up. I pushed my shoulders up, trying to make my neck look smaller. The pitcher threw the ball right past me. Strike two. The coach shook his head in frustration and screamed: "Choke up!" He sidled up to me and moved my grip up the bat, saying, "Choke up." *Tu madre,* I thought. It was my first little league baseball game. The pitcher stared down at me, winding up for his delivery. I gripped the bat and waited for the ball. "Atta, boy!" screamed the coach. I swung with all my might, and much to my surprise, I hit the first and last home run of my little league baseball career. I stood watching until the coach, and everyone, screamed for me to run. Dad, Mother, Eugenia, and Don stood on the sideline, watching me run around the California baseball field.

Tim stood in front of my new class, delivering a current events report. "And the robbers were caught a few blocks away," he said. I raised my hand and asked for the meaning of the word *rubbers*. A few chuckles came as Tim looked at the teacher for help. He patiently explained robbers were bad people that stole things. I got the picture. Tim was a big boy with a big heart who made me feel welcome. I had a lot to learn.

Greg's baseball rolled down the street, heading for the sewer.

"Get it, get it!" he yelled. I couldn't see the ball. "In the gutter!" he screamed. I looked around, not knowing what a gutter was. "Hurry!" he yelled before I saw the ball heading toward a drain. I ran after it and caught it before it reached the drain. I was back in the USA — Belmont, California — and back to learning English.

For expediency's sake, Dad rented a house in Belmont below the railroad tracks. The idea was to stay in a rental home while Mother and Dad found a view lot to build their dream home. Until then, we were in the Belmont flats. The adjustment to being in the USA was a lot easier for everyone the second time around. Schoolwork was a million times easier since we didn't have to learn a whole new language. I jumped into sports.

Eugenia called it a blue-collar neighborhood and made no friends. Don wanted a dog, and soon we had a black mutt that he named Satan. Dad objected to the name, but the dog only responded to Satan. At school, I was once again the outsider with a funny accent, but this time no one teased or taunted me.

Dad and Mother seemed happy with the quick adjustment we had all made being back in the United States. John F. Kennedy was president, and everyone was talking about a nuclear war with Russia. We had air-raid drills in class every day, and air-raid shelters were being built across the country. This wasn't happening in Mexico, and no one mentioned it, but we all wondered why we moved to a potential bombing site. *Que sera, sera.*

Dad loved politics and encouraged us to understand the times we lived in. His views reflected the hard times the country had been through with the depression and a war. It was important for us to know his thoughts and opinions about our new country. I couldn't understand anything about politics. I just wanted to fit in at school and become an American.

Eugenia kept a special relationship with Herb through the mail, and soon he showed up at the house. He filled the doorway at six feet four inches with his broad shoulders and friendly face. He was the biggest man I'd ever seen. He had played college football. Football players looked like Roman gladiators compared to Mexican soccer players. His gentle handshake and warm face made a quick friend out of everyone. Mother and Dad welcomed him with open arms, and Herb became part of the family the minute he walked in the house. He was a perfect gentleman and, to me, a giant version of Dad.

With Herb present, Dad had someone to talk about politics with. Herb laughed easily and had a joyful calm about him that we all appreciated. Soon Herb asked Dad for Eugenia's hand in marriage. Eugenia had barely turned eighteen, and she was getting married to a gentle giant. It happened suddenly with Mother and Dad's blessings. Without much fanfare, they married, and Eugenia moved to San Jose, where Herb worked as a counselor in Juvenile Hall. Eugenia would continue her schooling at San Jose State.

Eugenia and Herb visited every weekend. Mother's relationship with Herb was unique, as they both genuinely enjoyed their time together. He liked engaging in current news and always asked Mother's opinion. They could talk about anything. President Kennedy's impact on the world was a favorite topic. Especially when it came to Jackie Kennedy. Mother loved everything about Jackie Kennedy and often told the story about Kennedy's visit to Mexico City. Mother's mannerisms became part of the story as though she were in the limousine ride in Mexico with Mexican president Lopez Mateo. "President Kennedy complimented Lopez Mateo on the beautiful watch he wore. Lopez Mateo took off the wristwatch, handed it to President Kennedy, and said, 'You have a beautiful wife'." Raucous laughter always followed Mother's performance.

Don felt comfortable in Belmont right away. He was fourteen, but with his barrel chest, black hair, and bristly face, he appeared older. He had a mature sense about him that attracted girls, and he made friends quickly. Dan, Ken, Randy, and Tony were all his age and lived on the same street. For no apparent reason, these friends bonded like Boy Scouts from the moment they met. Don had his

Apache club again, minus the treehouse. Elvis Presley's pompadour had influenced teenagers around the world. The television show *77 Sunset Strip* featured a blond character, Kookie, who pulled up his collar and puffed out the front of his slicked-back hair at the start of the show. Don and his friends all did the same, and Dad learned to accept the greasy pompadour.

Building model cars became a favorite pastime until Ken's father bought a Ford, a fixer-upper, for Ken to learn about cars before he got his license. All four boys abandoned their model cars and never left Ken's garage. The five teenagers were the coolest guys on the block. Don was happier than ever but became rebellious, as was the trend for teens. He shut himself off and put on his wolf face again. Mother called him a rebel without a cause for his silence and mean stares. Don paid more attention to Satan than me and showed no interest in anyone.

Dad's love of the outdoors never swayed, and we picnicked on weekends as we had done in New York. But after Eugenia got married, it just wasn't the same. Don turned into a reticent teenager, and Mother stopped going into the water. Dad and I were the only two swimmers, just as we had been in Mexico. It was sad without Don and Eugenia. I could feel an emptiness in Dad and Mother.

Don's reluctance to participate in family events peaked one Saturday morning while Dad was preparing Don's favorite picnic food—deviled eggs. Don said he wasn't going to the lake. Mother quickly pulled the eggs away from Don's reach and insisted we all get in the car.

Don didn't say a word during the ride to the lake and wouldn't get out of the car when we got there. I swam with Dad while Mother set up the picnic. When we got out of the water, Mother had everything ready. Don never came out of the car, and Dad didn't look in that direction. Mother and I pretended not to notice, but we were both nervous. It was hard to watch Don hurt Dad's feelings. Don ruined the day. Eugenia was gone from the family, and Mother looked weak. I felt it was up to me to cheer up Dad. I waddled and oinked my way into the water, but I failed to put a smile on his face. It was our last family picnic.

School was fun again. I had to catch up on English vocabulary, reading, and writing after two years of Spanish schooling. My fourth-grade teacher, Mrs. Smith, helped me with everything I needed, and Dad made sure I kept up with the work. We were assigned vocabulary words for our reading time that Dad checked every week. Homonyms, homographs, homophones, and synonyms drove me crazy—ate/eight, capital/capitol, principle/principal, dining table/multiplication table, bear/bare/bear, bases/basis. Spelling the word is one thing; knowing the multiple meanings of a word meant asking a lot of questions, and I had the perfect teacher for it.

Mrs. Smith saw me struggle with many words and helped me vocalize them properly. She clarified the use of words before I could raise my hand. I loved reading with her, and she loved teaching. We had three reading groups; red was the slow group, yellow was the middle group, green was the advanced group. I was placed in the red group, but I read too fast even though I didn't comprehend everything. "Slow down," Mrs. Smith whispered time and time again. After a while, she placed me in all three groups to monitor my understanding. The vocabulary word list helped a lot. By the end of the year, I was back on track. I had a lot of friends and, best of all, no enemies.

Dad attended an end-of-the-year school night with Mrs. Smith. She handed Dad my report card and said she was proud of my reading progress. Fourth grade was a success, thanks to Mrs. Smith. She introduced me to my fifth-grade teacher, Mr. Sullivan, that night, saying I would enjoy being in his class because he was also a Little League coach. On the way home, Dad said it was a pleasure meeting Mrs. Smith and how lucky I was to have such a caring teacher. I thought about my kindergarten teacher, Miss Brown. "Dad, do you think I could be a teacher someday?"

"Teachers make this a better world in many ways," he answered. "They secure our future, make leaders, provide a pathway to success."

When we got home, Dad perused his books. Don was reading and mumbled a faint hello. Dad pulled out Mark Twain's *Adventures of Huckleberry Finn* and handed it to me saying he had enjoyed the book at my age. I noticed Ernest Hemingway's novel *The Old Man and the Sea* and commented that we never saw the movie. Dad handed me the book and said it was a good time to read it. He placed it on the table and went on to his bedroom. I picked up *The Old Man and the Sea* and found a folded newspaper clipping. It was an article about Ernest Hemingway having killed himself with a shotgun. I winced at the thought. Don noticed my reaction. "What's the matter?" he asked.

"This writer killed himself," I said.

Don vowed his love for Annette Funicello from the moment he saw her on television singing with the Mouseketeers until the day he met Dolores in Belmont. Dolores was a good Catholic girl with the sex appeal of a young Sophia Loren. Her father owned The Kon Tiki Room, an underground lounge reputed to have Mafia connections. It featured a fish-tank-like view into an adjacent swimming pool along one wall. The cocktail waitresses alternated between swimming in the pool as mermaids and waitressing in the bar with bikini tops.

Don did not know Dolores' connection to the lounge when, on a dare, he dove butt naked into the pool. He swam in and out of the gliding mermaids and along the lounge wall. They seemed amused with Don's gorilla-like version of a mermaid glide and watched him do a full-frontal spread eagle at the lounge window. Dan, Ken, and Tony waited at the pool gate with a towel and shoes while Randy stood at the opposite side, ready to distract everyone with a pack of firecrackers. Don made his getaway successfully.

That week he followed Dolores after school one day as she walked alone on El Camino Real, the main thoroughfare of San Mateo County. Dolores was taken by Don's chivalry when he offered to carry her books and held out his arm. They walked arm in arm, laughing and giggling until they reached the Kon Tiki Lounge. Dolores took her books, ran up the steps and into her father's waiting arms. It was at that moment, Don realized Dolores' connection to the lounge. He knew not to walk her to the door. Instead, he waved and showed his gap-tooth smile. The father didn't waste time ushering Dolores inside.

My fears belied the comfort of our new town when I arrived home one day and found my mother face-down in a pool of blood, lots of blood. I thought for sure she was dead this time. I wasn't ready for it. In Mexico, I was used to preparing myself for a sight like this while I ran up the stairs, every step helping me to build the courage to open the door to our home. That wasn't the case in a single floor home.

It had been months without one of Mother's blackouts. I ran in the door and straight to the kitchen, expecting to find Mother enjoying her new kitchen. Instead, I found Mother sprawled on the floor, a pack of frozen vegetables at her side with the freezer door open. Her flowery green and white dress was stained in blood, Perry Como crooning on the stereo. I instinctively ran for help to my neighbor Skip Beale's house. I pounded on the front door until Mrs. Beale answered. Three TV trays with TV dinners stood in front of the television. I interrupted their meal. I wanted to say help, but my throat burned, and no words came. "What's the matter, Charlie?" she said and cried out for Skip. He came to the front, and the three of us ran back to my mother. She was alive. She opened her eyes. I started to breathe again. "It's okay, Charlie. Your mother is going to be okay." Mrs. Beale kneeled next to Mother. Mother's eyes swept right across me.

"Help," was the only word that came out of my mouth.

An ambulance showed up just as Mother was coming to. She looked at me, still in a daze. I followed her to the back of the ambulance, not sure what I could do. Mrs. Beale took my arm as Mother waved, assuring me she was in good care. Mrs. Beale insisted I not stay home alone and go to her home until Dad came home. Skip pulled out a fourth TV tray and motioned for me to sit. "What would you like, Charlie, meatloaf, turkey, or chicken?" Mrs. Beale asked, rising on her tiptoes and peering into the top freezer. She was the same height as my mother and reached in exactly as Mother had done so many times in our own refrigerator. She held up all three frozen food packages. Mother had never served a frozen dinner and swore she never would. As delicious as the pictures looked, all I could think about was Mother.

"I don't want my mom to die," I uttered, short of breath, and ran outside. Skip followed. His parents stepped to the doorway.

"Hey, catch!" Skip yelled, throwing me a baseball mitt. He had a way of disarming my fears. I shoved my hand in the glove. Skip lobbed a ball toward me. I threw it back hard. My heart pounded. He threw it back harder. I had to concentrate on the ball. We picked up the pace, and after a while, I was throwing fastballs with all my might.

Don showed up just as Dad appeared, walking in the distance. I dropped my mitt and ran to the safety of my father's arms. His face turned pale as I told him the bad news. He hurried into the house. Don took me aside. I couldn't talk. Dad left for the hospital, saying he'd left money on the table for us to get some dinner.

A brand-new McDonald's opened up across the tracks on El Camino Real. We took the money and headed for the golden arches to eat our first McDonald's meal. I timidly teased Don along the way, saying it was probably named after Donald Duck, and we'd be eating duck meat. He didn't laugh. Images of Mother in the ambulance crept back in my mind. I wondered whether she would be getting more electroshock treatments. I imagined Mother in the hospital on a white table wrapped in electrical wires with a man standing over her, holding a power switch. I pictured her face wincing in pain, helpless. I wished Dad rushing in and ripping the wires off Mother's head. I lost my breath. I didn't want to see the image anymore.

"Donald Duck. Donald Duck. McDonald's duck meat!" I yelled and ran away. I reached the tracks, unable to catch my breath. I couldn't get the image of Mother in the ambulance out of my mind. I didn't want to cry in front of Don, and I ran away as he got closer. My shoelace got caught on a rusty nail sticking out from the wood that lined the tracks; I tripped and fell hard on the gravel rocks. Don reached me and knelt next to me. He sat on the track and waited until I could breathe. I saw a smashed penny on the gravel and picked it up.

"Good luck," Don said. "Make a wish." I couldn't look at him, still thinking of Mother.

"I wish for Mom not to die," I said and looked straight at him, tears rolling down my cheeks.

"Mother is not going to die," he said.

"How do you know? What if she does die?" I wiped away the snot and tears on my face. "Sorry, I'm just not as tough as you," I said, referring to the tears.

"Cry, it's okay," he said, putting an arm around me.

"If it's okay, why don't you ever cry?" I asked. I'd hit a nerve. We walked on, listening to the rickety sound of crushed rocks under our shoes. "Why?"

"I left my last tear in reform school," he said with a resentful tone on the word reform. "I wish I could cry. But—" he stopped.

"But what?"

"You can't undo the past."

"Did the older boys hurt you?"

"Not the boys."

"Did the men beat you up?"

He looked deep into my eyes. "That would have been easy." I sensed I'd be better off not knowing. A train whistle sounded in the distance. We stood up and walked. "*Que sera, sera,*" Don said with one arm on me.

Mother's fall turned out to be a miracle in disguise as she was referred to Stanford Medical Center, where she was diagnosed with epilepsy. What a relief it was for Dad to know Mother's medical condition could be treated with medication. Mother received a regimen of prescription drugs that changed her life. I suddenly had an answer to the mystery of her living or dying. Dad built a beautiful wooden pill organizer with hand-carved letters for each day of the week. Mother's painful spells were no longer a mystery. My parents were so encouraged with the diagnosis they decided Mother could now learn to drive.

Mother needed a license, and she would have access to Dad's car. He taught Mother to drive in a nearby industrial parking lot. One day, a HELP WANTED sign caught Mother's attention just as a British couple stepped out of the building. It turned out they owned a fashion business. They started a conversation, and Mother learned the HELP WANTED sign was for a seamstress position. Her secretarial skills didn't translate into English, so she put her pride aside and took the job because she liked the couple.

Before long, they became best friends. The four dined and danced together at different spots that included Mexican and British places. Mother was happier than ever being around people and never complained about her job. Somehow, she passed her driver's test even though she had reservations about it because it was in English. Dad encouraged her all through the process and looked forward to seeing Mother drive one day. She did exactly that.

She drove the car to work the day after passing the test. The British couple was so happy for her, they invited Mother to lunch. It must have been a long lunch because I was home from school, playing in the front yard, when Mother roared up along the street with the window down, her head reaching over the steering wheel. "Charlie!" she yelled with a smile I'd never seen before. I gasped. She honked the horn proudly announcing her command of the car. Her British passengers flashed yellow teeth and waved excitedly. It all looked dangerous. The car never slowed down but instead picked up speed and turned the corner with the pasty couple waving in the rear window. A crash of metal on metal followed. The image of Mother smiling behind the wheel flashed through my mind. Mother crashed Dad's car on her first day of driving and never drove again.

Baseball was a way of life in Belmont. Mr. Sullivan became my Little League coach, and we practiced in our elementary school field. He made everything a lesson in and out of the classroom. He included me in his lesson one time by listing Spanish words on the blackboard. He asked the class if anyone could think of a Spanish word. No one raised a hand. "Come on, think," he urged. "Think about where we live." He went on to say we lived in a state that used to belong to Mexico and Spain, who built the Missions all around us. He mispronounced Junipero Serra and asked me to say it in Spanish. It was the first time I ever dared use the Spanish letter values in class without fear of ridicule. I said the name in Spanish, and everyone clapped. Then he explained about the street names and cities, San Francisco, San Bruno, San Carlos, El Camino Real, and asked me to say them in Spanish. We filled up the blackboard by the end of the lesson. I felt so proud after that, and I never missed a word Mr. Sullivan used in class or on the baseball field.

I became a catcher, just like my favorite player, Yogi Berra. Mickey Mantle and Roger Maris were setting home run records for the New York Yankees, and Willie Mays was the best player in the world. The San Francisco Giants baseball stadium, Candlestick Park, was one short bus ride away. I attended my first Giants game with my neighbor, Skip. He was thirteen and old enough to cut his lawn. Together we mowed lawns in the neighborhood and saved enough money for a Giants double-header. We each bought a whole loaf of French bread, loaded them with salami and cheese. We shared a big bag of chips, and each had two soft drinks. Dad let me use his Navy binoculars for the game.

Skip knew where Willie Mays parked his gold Cadillac, so we went early hoping to get an autograph, but we were too late. The Cadillac was there, and Willie Mays was already in the park. We walked around carefully, holding our lunch bags, and looked inside. It was perfect, just like Willie Mays. The whitewall tires were immaculate and smelled like new rubber. Skip handed me his lunch bag, looking around, and kneeled down to tie his shoe. Then without warning, he unscrewed the tire air cap. Skip stole Willie Mays' steel air cap! He screamed, "Run!" and took off running. I chased after him, with both bags wobbling in my arms and binoculars swinging across my chest. By the time I got to the gate, I'd lost a sandwich and the chips. It didn't matter; we had Willie Mays' Cadillac air cap.

We rushed across the parking lot, and through our gate without looking back until we reached our third deck seats. The bright colors of the baseball field and uniforms took my breath away. Everything looked brand new. Willie Mays warmed up in his crisp white uniform on the greenest lawn I'd ever seen. I thought about the lawns we cut to buy the tickets and knew it was all worth it now.

A barber shop banjo-playing quartet roamed around singing songs I'd never heard. Their red and white striped vests and straw hats reminded me baseball was a national pastime. The players cleared the field, and a lawn crew came out. The excitement in the stadium built up more and more with line up announcements and special guests in attendance. Organ music came up, and a few cheers sounded, unifying the crowd in a roar. Then the announcer asked everyone to rise for the national anthem. Everyone stood up and sang. I mouthed the words pretending to know them. A lump of emotion built up in me as the words, the lyrics, rang through loud and clear. The patriotism expressed in the whole event from the field to the sky was something I felt a part of. I'd learned enough history to understand what being an American meant. I appreciated I was a Mexican on my way to becoming an American.

The thrill of baseball at Candlestick Park with Willie Mays, Willie McCovey, Juan Marichal, Orlando Cepeda, and all the Giants Baseball team stayed with me. Listening to games on the radio became a whole new experience after that day. I was able to imagine the game better, and I was more comfortable playing the game. The New York Yankees still lived in my head, but the San Francisco Giants lived in my heart. Little did I know the next World Series would be between the Yankees and Giants.

I got home at dusk and found Dad and Mother playing badminton in the backyard with the British couple. Herb Alpert's marimba band played on the stereo, and four margarita glasses stood on a table near the barbecue. Their laughter rang over the music with each snap of the racket. I rushed through the entrance without saying a word, not wanting to interrupt their fun. Instead, I opened my bedroom door and found Dolores' breasts glaring straight at me. Don reached for her blouse. "Shut the door," Don snapped. I dropped my baseball mitt and slammed the door. The marimba music played on over the laughter in the backyard. Embarrassed, afraid of the naked breasts that loomed over my bed, I locked myself in the bathroom and tried to rid my mind of the image that would become the standard of perfect breasts.

The following morning, I asked Dad where I could get the words for the national anthem. He whistled the tune as he looked through some books and handed me a copy of "The Star-Spangled Banner." I never wanted to go to another game without knowing the words to the national anthem. I started reading but couldn't make sense out of it. Dad explained the history of the lyrics. It didn't take long to learn the words, and it made me feel a little more complete knowing the song. Every game started with that even on television, so I felt a little closer to the game knowing the words.

Mother and Dad sold the *Jardines El Pedregal* lot in Mexico and started looking for a place to build their dream home in California. On weekends they drove up Ralston Avenue and through the hills looking for a lot with a view. They would stop at every open lot, stand face out, unroll the designs, and assess the space. I accompanied them several times and saw their excitement as they imagined the house. One time while holding the blueprints, I noticed names on the bedrooms. Dad had penciled "Came and Bill" in the master bedroom. Eugenia's name appeared in the next bedroom. I mentioned she was married. Dad shrugged the thought away without responding. "Why don't you have a baby?" I suggested. Again, no response, and we continued to another vacant lot.

Pompadour coiffed teenagers throughout the country watched Dick Clark's *American Bandstand* religiously, and dance parties were the rage in music halls everywhere. Don watched the show in our bedroom and told me about the dances he attended with his friends. He danced to the music, and for some reason, he was much more talkative while moving. He said he met many girls but was only interested in Dolores. She was not allowed to go dancing parties until she turned sixteen. She and Don were fifteen. "She's fifteen?" I said, imagining her breasts right at the spot where I was sitting.

"I'm going to marry her," he said. Bobby Picket's hit song, "The Monster Mash," came on, and Don went crazy. He twisted and gyrated, as I'd never seen anyone move before. He turned forward and back, arms locked in a bent position swinging side to side, then swiveled forward on the ball of his shoes as though putting out a cigarette with one pump then the other. He pretended to light a cigarette and take a puff before throwing it down and stomping it again. His pompadour bounced as he dipped and twisted to the rhythm, head bobbing like Elvis. The bullfighter in him came out in the extra flair in his hips and set him apart from the rest of the teenagers. A full spin around to the left then to the right finished off his performance. I believed he would marry Dolores.

"When?" I asked.

"As soon as we graduate from high school."

"Where are you going to live?" I thought about the house Dad was planning and how empty it would be without Eugenia and Don.

"We'll get an apartment, then a house, and have babies," he said, catching his breath.

"Where?" I asked.

"Someday, I'll buy a house in the hills at the top of Ralston Avenue."

"What about a car?"

"Duh!" He quit paying attention to me and turned up the volume.

A few weeks later, Eugenia came to visit with Herb and some of their friends. They were all college graduates, and to Dad's delight spoke of politics. They had met through the American Friends Service Committee and were excited about President Kennedy's Peace Corps. They all wanted a career in the service of others. Dad showed his support and pride in Eugenia's choices in friends and career possibilities. She was on a fast track to graduating from college early and had several humanitarian career options in mind. The Peace Corps was high on her list.

Mother impressed everyone with her delicious dishes while Dad served up margaritas. I had just started Pop Warner Football and told Herb all about playing. He said he was proud of me but cautioned not to get hurt as he had a bad knee from his days of playing football. His friends shared their stories about college and asked me where I was planning on attending. I said I didn't know, but I was sure it would be a college with a good football team. Don appeared with his shiny black hair and slumped shoulders, looking a lot like trouble. Herb worked with juvenile delinquents and tried to coax a few words from the reticent teenager Don had turned into, but Don didn't answer a single question and kept his sight on his plate. Later somebody commented on what a brilliant student Eugenia was and what a bright family she had. Don smirked. Herb asked what college plans Don might have. Don said he was going to be a plumber like his friend's dad and stormed off. Eugenia was embarrassed, Mother was hurt, and Dad was speechless. Dad's crestfallen look haunted me. Mother and Dad's song, *"Besame Mucho,"* came on the stereo but neither got up to dance as they normally would have.

Late that night, Don confided his feelings to me. "I just want to fit in with my friends. This is where Mother and Dad brought us. Isn't our 'job' to fit in, to be like everybody, to assimilate?" Don whispered. It was late, the lights were off, and we were supposed to be sleeping.

"Yes," I agreed our job was to assimilate, fit in.

"There's too much pressure to be perfect, like Dad. I want to be a middle American, union job, house, car, boat, wife, and kids. What's wrong with that?"

I had no answer but intuitively knew it was not why Dad brought us to America.

Skip came over to our house the following day and asked if I wanted to go to McDonald's. I said I didn't have any money. "Neither do I," he said. "We will after we cut a lawn." We started up the street knocking on doors until we came to Greg's house. Greg was my team's shortstop, the smallest boy in our grade, and a real daredevil. His parents wanted the lawn cut, and Greg wanted to help, so they offered to pay us an extra fifty cents. We finished in record time. We had a dollar fifty coming, but we got a tip, so the three of us headed to McDonald's with two bucks. Skip ordered six hamburgers. He bet he could eat a whole one in a single bite. All we had to bet was a burger. I wouldn't have believed it, but Skip won. Without pause, he then polished off three more. Greg laughed so hard he never finished his hamburger.

We walked back balancing and racing on the railroad tracks until we heard a train in the distance. We rushed to get to the other side of the tracks. Greg slipped on the loose gravel. "You're out!" Skip said in a taunting manner.

"Give me a penny, Skip!" Greg yelled, jumping to his feet. Skip, being an avid coin collector, checked the dates on a few coins before handing us some pennies. We each placed a penny with Lincoln's head facing up on the track, hid behind some bushes a safe distance away, and waited for the steel wheels to flatten Abraham Lincoln's face. The train was still out of sight. Greg, already restless, shot up and ran across the tracks to the other side. "Come on. Don't be a chicken!" Greg yelled, motioning us to join him. Skip didn't hesitate and moved to the other side. I followed. We waited. I wasn't quite sure what being a chicken was all about, but I didn't want to be one.

"What's chicken?" I asked. I had learned to trust Skip ever since he helped save my Mother's life.

"Like James Dean *in Rebel Without a Cause*. You know the chicken race, last one to cross wins." I understood as Greg took a sprinter's starting position. The train came into view far down the track. I took a sprinter position. Greg lay down across the tracks pretending to snore. A train whistle announced its presence. I remembered the movie and the scene where James Dean drives his car to the edge of a cliff and almost gets killed when his black leather jacket gets caught on the door handle. I looked up for my *Toro* to gather strength, but he wasn't there. I thought of Don, Dad, my macho bullfighting *abuelo*. What would they do? The train drew closer and louder. I didn't care what anyone would do, I wasn't going to get squashed by a train. I leaped across the tracks, took a safe position, and watched Skip and

Greg play chicken.

Greg snored and closed his eyes, still on his back. Skip dug his back foot into the gravel and looked at Greg, who got up and positioned himself right next to Skip. The train conductor was in view. He blew his warning whistle. Skip and Greg waved. The whistle blew again, steady and closer. He wasn't going to stop. Finally, Skip bound forward, and Greg followed across the tracks. Greg smirked in victory. The train thundered by shaking the earth beneath our feet. Greg shrieked. Skip screamed like Tarzan. I bellowed like a bull. We all held our primal cries steady until the train passed, then ran to find our coins.

"Chickens," Greg said, picked up his coin, and bounced it like a hot potato.

"Better to be a live chicken than a dead duck," Skip said.

Greg and I were in Mr. Sullivan's class and baseball team. We sat next to each other at school and played baseball after school almost every day. He made everything a competition and annoyed everyone except me. He was a target for ridicule and taunts because of his buck teeth and tiny frame. His classroom antics got a lot of laughs but also got him well-deserved punishment. He was the kid who made fart sounds during every air-raid drill and ended up sweeping the floor or cleaning after school.

I had gained weight and grown to be one of the biggest boys in the class. We became, in a funny way, Mutt and Jeff, as we were always together during baseball season. We got along well with everyone on our team and class, but Greg had a way of making quick enemies with any competition we came across. In spelling games, he'd blurt out letters while other students were up and get disqualified. During hangman, he would yell out answers and ruin the game for everyone. Worse of all was the baseball field taunts and screams he'd get for being tiny. He didn't like it and played with a vengeance.

During one game, an opposing player, much bigger than Greg, kept calling him Mini Mouse. Greg very deliberately tripped the boy when he rounded second base. The other team's coach came storming out of the dugout protesting and screaming while his fallen runner stormed toward tiny Greg. The runner was twice Greg's size. I instinctively ran to Greg's defense. The runner got Greg in a headlock, and the coach was screaming about Greg's dirty play. I rushed in headfirst and knocked the boy off of Greg. Mr. Sullivan pulled me off and stopped the game. A few minutes later, Greg and I sat and watched the rest of the game from the bench. Our team won and lived to play the championship game, but it was a hollow victory.

I was excited that Mother and Dad were planning on attending the big game. Mother made a fat salami and cheese sandwich on a French roll for lunch. I devoured it with a tall glass of milk and headed out when Dad reminded me to brush my teeth. I was already a little late but rushed into the bathroom and pretended to brush my teeth by turning on the water for a few seconds, sticking my toothbrush under, and slapping it against the bathroom sink. I ran out, jumped on my bike, and pedaled furiously up the street. I picked up speed as I headed alongside the parked cars, wheels spinning faster and faster.

I imagined Yogi Berra riding to his first championship World Series game on a bike just like mine. I sped past several long sedans. Then without warning, a long car door flew open right in front of me. I smashed into it and flew right over with my bike. The driver came to my side, apologizing and asking if I was hurt. I didn't know because I couldn't feel anything, and all I wanted was to get to the game. I apologized and asked if I could leave. I didn't stick around for an answer and raced off to the match.

"Sorry I'm late, coach," I said.

"What happened to you," Mr. Sullivan said without a smile. I thought I was in trouble for getting there late.

"I had to finish my meal and brush my teeth." I wished I'd mentioned how big the sandwich was to make a better case for being late. "I'm ready to go."

"No, you are not playing like this. What happened to you?" He pointed to my shirt. "Hon, can you help Charlie." He motioned for his wife. I looked down, felt blood running down my face, and saw my shirt was bloody red. I wasn't crying. *Ole!* The bullfighter in me survived. Mrs. Sullivan rushed to a basket and pulled out a first aid kit. This spectacle got everyone's attention as I dripped blood across the field. I couldn't feel a thing, no pain at all, and asked to play. But Mr. Sullivan wouldn't even let me warm up. I watched warmups from the side. Greg yelled out, "Meatball!"

Dad and Mother strolled over. Mr. Sullivan walked over to Dad. I went to Dad, "I had a bike accident, but I'm okay. Can I play?" Dad knelt down and looked in my eyes. He looked concerned and asked me to follow his finger with my eye. Left, right, around. I didn't play in the last game of the all-American sport I'd learned to love.

Dad was at the forefront of satellite communication with his job at EIMAC, Eitel-McCullough, where they designed and manufactured electron power tubes. He worked on nuclear research and computer data networks. His engineering skills were highly sought after. He had numerous high paying job offers, including one at Texas Instruments with a salary and stock options that would have exceeded Mickey Mantle and Willie Mays' salary, but Dad couldn't see us in Texas.

"How's the book?" Dad asked. *"The Old Man and the Sea."*

"I like Joe DiMaggio," I answered, remembering seeing the name when I thumbed through the book. "I'm still working on it."

"Takes place in Cuba, you know."

"Communists live there," I said, trying to pivot the conversation away from the book. "Are we going to war, Dad?"

"Not likely. There's too much at stake. Communism is a form of government where everyone shares in the distribution of wealth. Everyone works for a common cause." He walked to the stereo and played *"Guantanamera,"* which he had been playing a lot. Now, it scared me.

"Skip said we're going to blow up the whole country."

"No one's going to blow up anything. Cuba's a beautiful country with beautiful beaches. Read the book, you'll see."

"I will, Dad," I said.

"We might move there," he said in a serious tone. "Life will be very different. Everyone is equal there. Food is rationed. Beans, rice, meat, and all food essentials are equally distributed, so no one starves. It's better for the whole population to rise together." He paused, looking for a reaction. I had none. I was thinking about baseball. "Each family gets one cube of butter per week. We will learn to share the wealth of the nation." Still, I had no reaction. "And we will all work in the fields cutting cane."

"Did Joe DiMaggio and Yogi Berra ever play there? Can I play baseball?"

"Baseball is very popular. Fidel Castro plays baseball. You will play baseball there." I sensed Dad's irritation with my questions, but that was better than being quizzed about the book I hadn't read. Then I remembered the paper clipping. "Why did Ernest Hemingway commit suicide?"

"You can go play now," he answered in defeat. *"Guantanamera"* played again and became Dad's favorite song. He seemed to drift into a paradise of thought when it played.

I picked up my glove and ran outside where Skip and a few other kids were throwing a baseball around. I joined in feeling empty, wondering if this would be my last game of catch with my friends. Skip lofted the ball to me. I missed it. Everyone laughed. I ran after the ball and threw it back to Skip just as Don showed up holding hands with Dolores. "What's the matter?" he asked. "You look scared."

I was scared. "Dad says we're moving to Cuba," I said with a quivering lip.

"I'm not going," Don asserted and gripped Dolores' hand. If Don stayed and marries Dolores, I'd be the only one going to Cuba with Mother and Dad. I looked up and saw my *Toro* staring down with a sad face. He didn't see any hope. Later that day, I found Mother and Dad looking through a local real estate booklet. *Why are they looking at that?* I wondered. I went to my room and found Don taking apart his hot rod model. "I'm not going," he said, breaking off a piece. "I'm not going," he repeated with each piece. I buried my head in my pillow and curled into a fetal position. I felt Don sit next to me. "Come on, no *llores*," he said.

"I don't want to go without you," I whimpered. "What's going to happen?"

"*Que, sera, sera*," he said.

Dad's idealistic dream of taking the family to Cuba ended when U.S. spy planes photographed Russian ballistic missiles in Cuba. The United States set up a military blockade to prevent any more weapons from reaching Cuba. The whole world tuned in to watch John F. Kennedy and Nikita Khrushchev battle out a Cold War nuclear threat. President Kennedy demanded the missiles be dismantled and sent back to the USSR in full view. That made headlines and the nightly news. Dad watched night after night as Cuba fell further into Russian control, and his dream faded away. His dream was gone, but he forever whistled "*Guantanamera*."

Dad made an offer and went into escrow on a lot with a panoramic view of the bay. Mother's dream was back. They looked happier than ever, especially since Mother's blackouts had stopped. Mother loved watching Herb's adoring ways with Eugenia and joked about having grandchildren too big to carry. Dad's dream home would have a big family room for everyone to gather on Sundays and a designated bedroom for Eugenia and Herb for weekend visits.

Without the fear of moving to Cuba, I was free to enjoy my all-American life that now included football. Greg was too small for football, but he accompanied me to practice the first few times. He carried my helmet on the way home, jumping up and down reliving the scrimmages I'd run and said he'd be at every game. The second week Greg got teased at practice and flipped off the player. An argument ensued, and Greg ended up getting kicked off the field. I walked home alone and found him sitting on his front porch with two glasses of Kool-Aid. He handed me one. *That is a real friend,* I thought. He promised he'd be at my first game and keep his mouth shut. *That'll never happen,* I thought.

Dad drove me to the first game but didn't stay. I started as a fullback on offense and linebacker on defense. Greg was nowhere to be found. It was a grueling game. My legs felt like rubber at times. I could barely stand up by the end of the game. I fell asleep wondering why Greg never showed up.

A loud knocking on my window woke me up. It was Skip. I slid the glass pane. "What's going on?" I asked.

"Did you hear about Greg?" Skip whispered.

"No?"

"He's dead. Hit by a train."

"What? No!" I said, denying the thought.

"Yes, dead as a doornail," Skip said.

"Playing chicken?"

"He's no chicken. He's a dead duck!" he laughed nervously and ran off.

Skip and I attended the funeral services. I expected a sad priest in a silk cassock and white-collar consoling everyone. Instead, a bright-eyed minister conducted the services in a blue suit. To me, he looked like a salesman. The wood coffin was closed and draped with a silver silk cloth and flowers. An American flag hung behind the arrangement. I was ready to sing the national anthem. "Chuck, Skip, I know Greg would want you to be pallbearers," Greg's crying mother whispered. I followed Skip's lead through the services. The image of Greg running across the train tracks with his goofy smile haunted me the whole time. In the end, six people, including Mr. Sullivan, helped carry the small coffin outside and into a hearse.

Don turned sixteen with one thing in mind. He would get a job and buy a car as a first step toward marrying Dolores. He spent a lot of time at Ken's house with his friends, and just as his father had planned, Ken had a working car by his sixteenth birthday. Ken's father worked as a mechanic and taught the boys about cars and boats. Before long, Don was working on engines. He saved enough money to buy a Black 1954 Ford that needed mechanical work more than a paint job. He wanted it to look as good as his plastic model hot rods. In a short period, Don painted the car, raised the back end, and customized the interior with an eight-ball gearshift knob, steel steering wheel, and a floating dice liner around the back.

Dad didn't like it and said it was a step in the wrong direction. He warned about having friends without college aspirations destined to work with their hands, like plumbers. "They'll have dinner guests that will wonder where those hands have been all day," he said. I got the idea that Don's friends didn't meet Dad's standards of "living in service for others." Much as everyone liked the look of Don's car, it stood in our garage for weeks. Don worked on it day and night with his friends.

One night my parents were out with the British couple. Don had some friends over and loaded four records on the stereo in this order: Dee Dee Sharp's "Mashed Potato Time," Chubby Checker's "The Twist," The Sensations' "Let Me In," Little Eva's "The Locomotion." The songs played over and over nonstop. The "Mashed Potato Time" got everyone going right off the bat. They all stood up and bounced around the room, swiveling their hips while twisting forward and back to the steady beat.

Randy was the best dancer with his long legs that seemed to twist without regard to his upper body. His contortions while drinking, eating, or telling a story defied nature. He had two halves, torso and legs moved independently. They all took turns dancing in the center while everyone else cheered. Out of nowhere, Don shot me his wolf face. I sensed I wasn't welcome as the boys snuck into the backyard and lit up cigarettes. They blew white smoke rings into the dark. Then they started a competition to see who could blow the most smoke rings. Dan shot out a few before busting out laughing on less than ten. Ken blew about twenty good size rings. Randy shot out fifty before falling off. Don came up with his own way with a flamenco finger roll to his cheeks and blowing out Cheerio size rings. It looked like fun until Don blew smoke in Satan's face. He barked and ran into his doghouse. The doghouse was his fort. I knew how Satan felt being rejected by Don. He had his wolf face on.

I left before Don could blow smoke rings in my face. I don't know why, but I walked into my parents' bedroom and opened Mother's nightstand drawer. I looked around for her chocolate box. I pulled it out just as car headlights swept across the window. I opened it and found the tiny tin box with Mother's death pills. I wished I hadn't looked. Her seizures had stopped, but the death pills were still at the ready.

A car door slammed shut, then a girl's laughter rang through the music. I went to my bedroom knowing Don didn't want me around. I turned on the television, but the music and laughter in the living room were distracting. I snuck into the garage to sit in Don's hot rod. I wanted to pretend I could drive, but when I turned on the lights, I saw Dolores' breasts. She and Don were sitting in the front seat. Her blouse was off, and Don's shirt was unbuttoned. I slammed the door shut and ran back inside the house.

Just about that time, the movie *West Side Story* swept the country, and every teenager had to choose a side—either a Jet or a Shark. Don and his friends went to the movie theater near Ralston Avenue down the street from McDonald's and the Kon Tiki Lounge. By chance, I was at McDonald's with Skip when Don's group walked out from the movie. It was apparent that they had aligned themselves with the Sharks. They had slicked-back hair, tight jeans rolled up at the bottom, black leather shoes, matching zipper jackets along the lines of James Dean's *Rebel Without a Cause*, and they all dangled a cigarette from their mouths. They were the coolest guys in town. They walked in unison to their own beat, leaning forward to keep their pompadours flopped forward.

They strutted, danced, and snapped their fingers in unison until they reached a parking lot wall. They slammed forward, kicking one leg up and bounced off screaming, "Sharks!" Of course, Don had to align himself with the Sharks; they were Maria's side, and she was his Dolores. The group continued on down the street. Skip and I followed Don's group as they bobbed down the sidewalk.

Dolores stood outside the Kon Tiki Lounge as Don's group approached. Don saw her and brandished his comb. His friends took their combs out, and they all slicked back their greasy pompadours. They were all in sync, now walking to an imaginary beat heading straight toward Dolores. Skip and I stopped to watch. "This is dangerous," said Skip.

Sure enough, the front door swung open, and Dolores' dad stepped out, flanked by two men in dark suits. Don's group stopped their *West Side Story* fantasy and sauntered on by as Dolores' dad stared at Don while leading her inside.

"What was that?" I said.

"Mafia," Skip answered.

"Like Elliot Ness and Al Capone?" The TV series *The Untouchables* was the most popular show on the air.

"That's it. Just like Al Capone."

Soon after that night, Dad announced that we were moving south. He had accepted a job at Pioneer Electric in Orange County. Dad did not explain the move, but Mother said it was time to find a better place for us to grow up. Sunny Hills in Fullerton, California, was a new and affluent community. She and Dad wanted the best for us, and Belmont wasn't it. "I'm not going," Don challenged at the table when Dad announced his intentions.

"You'll go, and you'll learn to smile," Dad said, referring to Don's wolf face.

"No, I'm going to join the Navy," Don said, looking straight ahead as though ready to salute. "All I need is your signature when I turn seventeen." Mother dropped her fork. My heart raced.

"Then you'll have to wait until your birthday," Dad ended the conversation.

Don woke up with a wolf face on his birthday. He looked miserable all day, and after dinner, he pulled out a U.S. Navy form. He wanted Dad's signature to join the Navy. Dad aged ten years in that one moment. Don's defiance and determination to stay where he'd found his place won out. Dad signed the papers. Don responded with a curt "thank you," pivoted an about-face, and retreated to the bedroom. He was a different person, bent on closing Mother and Dad off. I stayed away.

Sure enough, Don was at the Naval recruiting office bright and early the next morning. But the experience didn't go as planned. The Navy physical revealed a heart murmur. It was the last thing Don expected. A series of doctors' visits ensued which confirmed the heart irregularity. It had never been detected before and had never shown any symptoms. He was devastated. His Naval service and marriage plans were derailed. He was stuck with us and would have to move to Orange County. *Que sera, sera.*

Dad's purchase of the dream-home lot fell out of escrow on a technicality. He, once again, went ahead to set up our new life. Dad bought a brand-new ranch style home in the heart of a white republican neighborhood. A moving company loaded up our household and transported everything except Satan. Mother, Satan, and I jumped in Don's hopped-up Ford and headed to Southern California on the 101 Freeway. I sat in the back with Satan and watched Don navigate the roads with confidence while Mother cringed with embarrassment at the image we represented—three Mexicans and a dog in an old hot rod car.

Don snarled and sped angrily on the open highway. "Slow down," Mother said, trying to calm him down. Don responded by speeding up. I watched the speedometer needle float past the sixty mark and felt the car rattle. Satan barked, but Don didn't care. "We need food," Mother said. Don sped up again. She asked if I was hungry, but I wasn't about to suggest we stop if the wolf face wasn't hungry. Satan barked again. Mother said Satan must have to go to the bathroom. How's he going to flush the toilet? I asked humorously, but no one had a sense of humor.

Don gripped the gearshift knob and pushed the pedal to the metal. Mother sat back while I gripped Satan and watched the speedometer needle turn past the 80. The engine roared. The whole car shook. The windows rattled. We picked up speed until smoke billowed out under the car, and the dashboard lit up. Satan barked louder and louder until the engine screamed its final death cry. Don stared ahead, then at Satan before looking at Mother. She gave him a two-eyed blink. He seemed relieved as we sputtered into Paso Robles in the dark. Luckily, we reached a service station next to a café.

I sat in the back with Satan while Don and Mother talked to the service station attendant. Don appeared to be in a better mood, protective of Mother as they gathered information and phoned Dad. He wanted to be in charge and stood a little taller. Mother suggested we eat in the café, but Don wouldn't leave Satan alone in the car. Back to peanuts and snacks. We waited, eating only what we could buy at the service station. Don insisted that Mother and I get in the car while he stood guard with Satan.

I fell asleep watching Mother's worried expression that reminded me of our train ride to New York. Mother's knight in shining armor arrived in the middle of the night. We arrived in Fullerton at dawn, ready for a new life. *Que sera, sera.*

Fullerton 1963

The house on the hill was enormous for our needs, but Dad and Mother wanted the best neighborhood for Don and me even though Don had pledged to leave on his eighteenth birthday. The pristine community was straight out of a Walt Disney all-white storybook. The Disneyland fireworks show was visible from our dining room window, and Mother served dessert right before the fireworks every night. Everything was new, every day was perfect, everyone was beautiful, and every home had a late-model sedan in the driveway. The streets were without a blemish anywhere. Mother, Don, and I were the only brown people visible throughout the development. To me, the community looked like an extension of Disneyland with June Cleaver running the show. Before the California Fair Housing Act was signed into law, home sales could include race exclusivity. Orange County developments at the time had explicit racial and religious exclusion provisions. When Mother and Dad showed up to sign the escrow papers for our home, he pointed out the provision as distasteful. He signed the papers and handed Mother the pen without anyone objecting. *Ole*, Dad.

Don had no interest in making new friends at school. He wanted to move back to Belmont. He went to school, wrote Dolores every day, and read in his room with Satan at his side.

Mother kept busy in her hilltop palace trying to fit in with the Stepford wives, but she had a hard time making the adjustment. Public transportation was not practical, so she was dependent on Dad for everything. She played English lessons on vinyl records all morning long, but never lost her accent. Mexican music kept her company in the afternoons. I came home from school to her upbeat music and a sandwich most days. It was our time together. Mother lived vicariously through the stories I'd tell her about my day while she prepared dinner.

She told me exciting stories about growing up in Mexico. Her youth was marked by highs and lows of the Great Depression, WWII, and her father's death that left the family of six sisters and one brother to fend for themselves. Yet hearing Mother tell the stories of those challenging times made me wish I'd been there. She spun her tales with simple nicknames, *"Gordo," "Flaco," "trompudo,"* and my favorites, *"cochina," "angelita,"* and *"el diablo."* Although the tales she told were of hard times and often with tragic results, there was laughter and a punch line. Through all the stories, I learned the Perez clan faced life with dignity and ingenuity. Now, in the solitude of the middle American housewife, life seemed too simple for Mother.

Her high-fidelity albums were precious, and she cared for them like fine china. One day two new albums arrived in the mail with mambo music. Perez Prado's mambo came on with a beat unlike any other. My hips and knees started bouncing to the rhythm, and in no time, I was in full swing with Mother. It was an unwilled reaction. I don't know why or how my body knew what to do, but the dance was inside me. Lucy and Ricky Ricardo's music must have done something to me because at that moment, I was Ricky Ricardo.

I entered seventh grade at Ladera Vista Junior School and quickly made friends. It was my first move without having to learn or relearn a language. On the very first day, I felt welcomed by my peers and teachers, especially my English teacher, Mr. Graham. He dressed as though he'd stepped out of *Esquire* magazine in a checkered madras shirt, starched chino pants, brown wingtip shoes, and matching belt. He made it clear at the start of the class that everyone would understand Mark Twain by the end of the year because Mark Twain was the foundation of American Literature. I was glad I knew two

Mark Twain books. I was comfortable in my new school even though it felt like I was in Barbie and Ken's dreamland.

But it was Orange County, and I was a brown-skinned Mexican in an otherwise white community. I rode the school bus to and from school. The first day I took a window seat on the right side, near the back. The next stop, three eighth-grade bullies stormed up to me, sneering, almost threatening me. I looked up. "This is our seat," said the freckle-faced one. The shortest boy angled to my back.

"Move," said the tallest boy. If he hadn't been so nasty, I might have moved; instead, I answered that I didn't see their names on it. The bus driver called for them to take a seat.

"Come on, Jay," said shorty and tapped the tallest boy. I turned away. They said something about "getting me" and took the back row. I got the idea that they were going to be trouble.

On the way home, I purposely did not take the same seat. I sat near the front. When the trio boarded, they each bumped my shoulder on the walk to the back. I knew they were up to something. Mexico City and Skinnynose came to mind. I loaded up my saliva by slushing it in my mouth, building up more each mile, each stop. By the time we reached my stop, I was ready with a reservoir of saliva in my mouth. I got off the bus and walked very close to the windows, expecting trouble from the bullies. Sure enough, the window opened, and all three faces stared out. "Beaner!" they screamed together, and together they all received a mouthful of sticky white saliva. The expression on their faces was priceless. My timing was impeccable. I blew the spit with the precision of an artist's spray gun, hitting all three faces equally. I never stopped or looked back. I sauntered on with my Charlie Chaplin-like swag.

The next day I stood near the gym entrance when the bullies appeared around a corner. The trio flanked out wide and faced me. I expected a confrontation but knew I could quickly rush into the gym, so I waited. "Beaner!" Again, the trio screamed and walked away. I didn't respond.

A full shouldered blue-eyed boy walked out of the gym and stopped me. "Are you going to take that?" the boy asked. His name was David O'Connor.

"Take what?" I answered.

"They called you a beaner," David said, annoyed.

"I like beans," I said.

"But they're calling you a bad name," David said protectively.

"I am Mexican. I like beans. Why is that bad?"

"You better watch out," David warned. "They're not going to stop."

As it turned out, David was right.

He invited me to a popular teen hotspot—an ice cream parlor. It became our after-school meeting place. I met a lot of boys and girls there and learned the ins and outs of middle school social life. I studied the mannerisms and dress code suited for this new life. Before long, I was wearing plaid madras shirts, chino pants, wingtip shoes, and sometimes a tie. I fit in perfectly, I thought. But it was Orange County, and I was a Mexican.

The three bullies showed up at the ice cream parlor one day while David and I were talking to a couple of girls from English class. The trio swept by, purposely bumping me as they walked past one at a time, each calling me "Beaner." Suzy, a tall and popular girl, turned red while the other girl, Linda Ball, gasped. David wanted to confront the bullies. "This is bullshit," he said. "They're cruisin' for a bruisin'." I said I liked beans, and they could call me a bean-eating Mexican all they wanted because it was true. Suzy and Linda cried.

"Sticks and stones can break my bones, but words will never hurt me," I shouted out, sarcastically, staring directly at the trio. They didn't respond. The four of us walked away. I thought about Skinnynose in Mexico and what it took to stop him from bullying me. I wasn't going to let these boys intimidate me any longer. "*Viva, Mexico!*" I shouted toward the trio and smiled.

The next day I walked into the boy's lavatory, where I came face to face with the biggest of the trio, Jay. In a split second, Jay turned into Skinnynose for me. I pushed him. He must have had slippery shoes because he fell, dropping his books. I kicked them across the floor and dared him to call me a beaner. He didn't say a word, and just like Skinnynose, he cowered and crumbled. He started up, but I pushed him down. "Not so tough without your friends," I taunted.

"Fuck you, beaner!" He scrambled for his books. This was Skinnynose all over again.

He looked scared without his friends and never fought back. I turned to leave, but he screamed, "Beaner, fuck you, we'll get you!"

With one swift move, I slammed him into the wall. He crumbled. "You tell your friends to leave me alone," I said and kicked his books into a stall before walking off.

The whole school learned about my "assaulting a boy in the lavatory." Next thing I knew, I had a posse of eighth graders after me. The principal called me into his office. He had a caring manner about him with a soft voice and a friendly face. "Do you know why I called you in?" I told him about the ice cream parlor episode. He said he'd talk to the boys and make sure that never happened at school. He asked about my father and mother, wanting to know about my last name. I told him about the move from Mexico to New York, learning English in kindergarten, and how we ended up in Fullerton. He seemed fascinated by the story. He asked questions about family backgrounds in New York and Mexico. I sensed he wanted to know how my white father met my Mexican mother and ended up with me. I cut to mother's telling of the first day she laid eyes on William Allen in the engineering department. I ended the story by quoting Mother and using her intonation as best I could, "Back off ladies. He's mine!" The principal chuckled, and I continued with, "Are you going to tell my dad?" He didn't answer.

"Do you like sports?" he asked. I nodded in the affirmative. "You're tall; maybe you should try out for basketball." I was six feet tall. I told him about my football and baseball teams in Belmont.

I missed the bus and walked home that hot day, wondering why this was happening. I didn't want to believe all this anger was over my being a Mexican. But there was no other explanation. It was a three-mile, uphill walk that wound through one of Orange County's exclusively white neighborhoods. My madras shirt, new pants, preppy shoes, and schoolbooks couldn't conceal my Mexican roots. The blazing heat bounced off the asphalt like an oven. Sweat dripped off my brow as I turned a corner. A rhythmic sound of garden clippers snapping away spilled across the tranquil garden of the corner lot. A Mexican gardener was busy at work, sweating just like me. We made eye contact. *I must look like a clown to him,* I thought.

The next day the principal waited for me at the school entrance with my P.E. teacher. They had a plan for me to join the track team. I was to report to the gym after school for President Kennedy's Physical Fitness Challenge. David O'Connor happened by and asked to join me. After school, a group of twenty or so boys and girls suited up for the challenge that included sprints, leaps, pull-ups, and sit-ups. I immediately saw the bully trio with Jay smirking and pointing at me. David followed my gaze. I ignored them.

We had to race twice around the track. Boys lined up first. The coach blew the whistle, and everyone raced to the inside of the track. I didn't want to run next to the eighth-grade bullies, so I sprinted ahead of the trio. David stayed with me, shoulder to shoulder until Suzy came upon us and raced ahead. She won easily.

The bullies started toward me as we headed for calisthenics when all of a sudden, Suzy tripped one of the boys. Everyone laughed at the bully. The coach looked over to us and heard the fallen boy yell, "Beaner!" The coach stood next to the boy and told him he was off the squad. The trio left. David and Suzy laughed, and I saw a smile on the coach's face.

I was doing well in school and would soon begin playing baseball in a new league. Nobody was going to stop me from fulfilling Dad's dream of his family assimilating into the American Dream. It's what

I wanted more than anything. But we were in Orange County.

The next time I went to the ice cream parlor, the three bullies were there. I knew they were looking for trouble. "Taco Bell's down the street, Charlie," Freckleface snickered.

"Carlos. Isn't that right, Carlos?" Jay said. "Did you change your name when you crossed the border?" he taunted. How did he know? Isn't that what everyone does? I didn't react. I was with David, Suzy, and a few other kids from class.

"Beaner lover," said Jay looking at Suzy. I rushed toward them. David followed, but the three ran out screaming they'd be back. I believed them.

"I'm sorry," I said. David was pissed, and everyone was upset. No one knew what to do. I called home and told Don what had happened. He told me to wait for him.

"What's wrong with people?" Suzy sobbed. No one answered. We made small talk about favorite ice cream flavors and tried to distract ourselves from the fear in the room.

Don showed up, ordered a drink, and sat nearby without saying a word. He opened a book and read quietly. A few tense moments later, a group of loud teenagers in a convertible pulled up screaming for Charlie Allen. I didn't move. The car was packed, six boys in all, three of them the bullies. Suzy gripped my arm.

David stood up. I looked at Don. He coolly walked straight up to the driver and said, "You found me." The boys wilted. They couldn't believe what they faced. Don was by now a manly-looking teenager with a barrel chest and five o'clock shadow of facial hair.

"You're Charlie Allen?" the driver asked, beads of sweat forming on his face.

"I am Charlie Allen. You looking for me?" And with that, the bullies drove off with their big friends.

"Sorry," I started as we walked home.

"It's not your fault. This paradise life that Mom and Dad want for us is ridiculous. It's stupid. It's not for us. Look at Mom in her palace on the hill. It's a prison, solitary confinement. In Mexico, she had a life."

"*Que sera, sera.*"

"I'm moving to back to Belmont."

Don had no interest in anything other than moving back to Belmont, which hurt Mother and Dad. The new house seemed sad and lonely most of the time, as Don would only come out of his bedroom, reluctantly, for meals. It upset Dad that Don took forever to get to the table. He showed up with his wolf face and said dinnertime would be better if people ate like animals in a stall, so no one had to talk. That statement was the final straw that set up the dismissal Don wanted. Dad gave Don permission to move to Belmont.

It was a Saturday farewell with little fanfare. Don never asked Dad to drive him to the Greyhound station and didn't say a word all morning. I watched him pack, making sure not to show my sadness. Afterward, Don waited outside with Satan and his belongings. I walked in and out of the house, waiting to see if my parents would come outside to say goodbye to Don. A yellow taxi drove up at ten o'clock. I choked back tears and helped Don load his luggage into the trunk. We stood shoulder to shoulder, prolonging the moment before we faced each other. "Okay, this is it," Don said, handing me Satan's leash. "Take care of Satan."

I stood facing him, aware I was taller. I had no words for him. I knew he was making a mistake. He knew he was hurting Mother and Dad. He hugged me tightly and pressed his face against mine. It felt like rough sandpaper.

I walked Satan back to the house while Mother and Dad walked toward Don. I played with Satan for a few minutes and heard the taxi drive away. The sound of Mother's shoes pitter-pattering up the walkway resonated across the yard. Mother and Dad rushed into the house, crying. It would be the first and only time I ever saw Dad cry.

I started into my bedroom with Satan. I heard my parents quietly speak to one another, the sound of tears coming through the wall. The house felt like a mortuary. First Eugenia went and now Don. I saw an envelope on my pillow. It was a letter to me.

Dear C,

As Tony Bennett says, I left my heart in San Francisco. So did I, but I'll always be your big brother. Dolores has my heart, and I'm going to get it. Maybe you can visit when we get an apartment. Keep up the grades in school, and don't let anyone kick you in the face.

I love you and Mother and Dad and Eugenia and Satan. Tell Mother and Dad I love them. I don't belong here. I belong in Belmont. I'll send you my address and phone number when I get one.

Don

The following morning, I found Mother dressed in a new teal pattern dress looking out the kitchen window. The green landscaped front yards seemed to sparkle under the morning sun. She appeared sad. I waited for her to look at me. The house felt empty. I felt my mother's loneliness. "Music?" I suggested. She turned to me wearing a pair of cat's eye-shaped sunglasses and walked toward me. I laughed out loud. "Jackie Kennedy glasses?" I joked.

She took off the glasses and started for the stove. "Don't laugh," she said, laughing harder than I. I covered my face with a kitchen towel. I couldn't look at her without laughing out loud. *"Me veo ridicula?"* She asked if she looked ridiculous, and without waiting for an answer, she picked up the sunglasses and left the room. Neither of us knew what this sudden laughter was about. Ennui had left both of us giddy. Mother's attempt at fitting in Orange County with Jackie

Kennedy type glasses said it all.

We had both been trying too hard to fit into an all-white community. I played Mother's hip-moving Mexican Cumbia music. If she couldn't be in Mexico, I could bring a little Mexico to her. I let the music take over the room, starting with my hips and moving my legs across the room into the kitchen. Mother returned, prompting my Charlie Chaplin/*Cantinflas* imagination.

A good breakfast would cheer us up, I thought. But *Cantinflas* wanted to dance and swiveled my hips back and forth out of sync with my legs. I took one step forward and two steps back, then one step to the left and two to the right. My hips and legs bounced to the music, sending me in all directions. I opened the refrigerator, danced with the open door, swinging it open and shut, and pulled out eggs and tortillas. Mother laughed; I deadpanned the whole dance. I turned the stove on and poured a little oil, the whole while keeping my legs wobbling to the music. There were only three tortillas left. No respectful cook would offer anything less than equal portions. I carefully folded one tortilla in half and held it up. I was in sync with the music. I was *Cantinflas*. She shot me a quizzical stare, wondering what I was up to. I folded all three tortillas again and again to the beat and dropped them in the pan. I scrambled four eggs in a saucer while the tortillas cooked and mixed them all together. Mother came over, sprinkled some salt into my improvised concoction, and grabbed two plates. "What is this?" she asked.

"It's the Jackie Kennedy special," I deadpanned.

MY AMERICAN PIE

In the next few weeks, I learned to lead my own life without my big brother. I played Pony League baseball on the Angels team with a red, white, and blue uniform. I wasn't a standout player, but I could play left field and make contact with the ball at the plate. A few of my teammates were in my classes and became my best friends. I was taking a new American identity.

Tom, a friendly boy with a flawless face and quick smile, was a shortstop who attended summer baseball camp. He scooped up ground balls like a pro. His father owned an insurance company. Stuart, a lanky boy with a perpetual smile, played first base and played baseball as well. His father was an executive with The Carnation Company. Mickey was a redhead freckle-faced Irish boy who barely made the team. His father was a loudmouth who screamed at the referees and coach. Mickey's face turned red at the thought of his father. He secretly told me he feared making an error with his father in the stands. I couldn't imagine what that fear was about, but hearing Mickey say it explained a lot of his nervousness. He also went to church a lot with his mother and siblings. The biggest boy, Mike, was an exceptional athlete whose father was a coach at another school. He had a set of weights in his garage and pictures of high school football and wrestling teams. We all lived close enough to walk to one another's houses. I now had my group in Fullerton just like Don had his in Belmont. He had the Boy Scouts, the Apaches, and the Sharks. I had the Angeles and an all-American uniform.

Together with my new friends, I played sports, went to movies, and had "chaperoned" dance parties with girls. Sue Arnold had the best house for parties with lots of rooms, including a game room complete with a popcorn machine and pool table. Her father was too busy running his restaurant businesses to chaperone us, and her mother was drunk by nine o'clock. Suzy showed up with the most popular girls. She was a good dancer and pulled me onto the floor whenever she wanted.

None of us knew how to dance except Suzy. She held a lesson for everyone, using me as her partner. Stand together facing each other, one hand up, left right left, left right left. We were doing the waltz. It didn't matter, everyone followed. Sue's mother, Mrs. Arnold, walked in just as everyone was stumbling through a dance lesson. She complimented us on how nice we were and left the room. Mickey snuck a bottle of gin from the long bar and poured some in the punch. All the boys rushed the punchbowl. In a short while, we were dancing up a storm to the Beach Boys and Duane Eddy. "Surfing Safari," "Surfing U.S.A.," "409," and "Wipeout" played over and over until we couldn't move.

I collapsed on the corner couch with Suzy. She threw her long leg over mine. I squirmed, wondering what I should do, but before I could decide, she screamed, "Pancake!" Everyone piled on the couch, grabbing and feeling and smooching. I had Suzy in my arms, her head buried in my chest, unable to move until the pile lifted.

The music blasted, and everyone screamed louder than ever, and still Mrs. Arnold did not come back in the room. Sue said her mother was drunk by now and would not wake up. Boys and girls had paired up around the room, making out. Mickey was pushed away by one girl. Stuart was wrapped in another girl's arms. A girl slapped Tom's hand without unlocking her lips from his. Mike wrestled with a girl on a rug. I sat with Sue and Suzy awkwardly, avoiding sitting too close to either girl. I was the only Mexican in the room.

Football season came around, and I played fullback and linebacker on Mike's Colt League team. His father was the coach. Mike was a good quarterback and team captain. We lifted weights in his garage while Mike's Dad preached football strategy for offense and defense. By the time we got into games, Mike had full command of the huddle. I learned what plays to look for in different situations. I learned when to expect a rush, a forward pass, and to wait for the play to develop — in theory.

On the football field, facing a growling lineman set on knocking me over, was about staying alive. I knew that on pass plays, the linemen would stand and block, so I'd wait for the play to develop and follow the flow. A rush would send linemen forward. I must have inherited a bullfighter's instinct of some sort because I got in the habit of going up on my toes in some kind of dance right before the snap. I didn't do that in practice at all, but in a game, I got anxious. It felt better to be in motion when the play started than to wait. Instead of trying to go straight through the linemen, I took a matador's approach—sidestepping and pushing their helmets downward as they rushed forward. And it hurt less. I made enough tackles to catch our coach's attention. We won a few tough games, and we lost a couple.

Our next party was a pool party at Stuart's house. The pool ran the length of the house and overlooked a sea of modern homes. I thought about Mother's dream home in Mexico and wondered if this is what she imagined. It was a night party with loud music and a spiked punch. Stuart's Dad was out of town; his mother was happy to sit in the den smoking and drinking with a friend. Once again, kids paired up on the lawn furniture for some smooching. Duane Eddy's "Wipe Out" got everyone moving. A few of us were in the water when one of the girls screamed and jumped off a chaise.

David O'Connor stood up, smiling with his penis sticking up out of his swimsuit to the top of his stomach. The screaming girl dropped in the water, telling David to get that thing away. In an instant, everyone ran over to look at David's imposing penis, remarked in some way, and fell in the pool. David pretended not to know what everyone was reacting to. Suzy and I were at the deep end, laughing when I felt her slide behind me and wrap her legs around my waist, then her arms. My back arched, and I got goosebumps. I was ready to turn around for my first kiss in life when David fell into the pool. Someone screamed "Shark!" and everyone scattered, screaming the same.

We had one more football game to play when Mike's father learned he would be the first coach at the new high school. Mike and I were in his garage working out when his father told us. He wanted Mike and me to know we would be on the team. We challenged each other on the weights the rest of the afternoon with dreams of playing on the big field. We visualized our next opponents, counting out our reps, and screaming how we were going to tackle them and smash them into the ground and win tomorrow's game. By the end of the workout, we were gladiators ready for the coliseum. I had a new sense of belonging to something bigger than me and part of the U.S.A.

The next day was Friday, November 22, 1963. President Kennedy was killed in Dallas. The world stopped. Our game was canceled, and the season ended.

Teachers and students were in tears. Disneyland closed that day, along with countless businesses. Television broadcast news nonstop. Dad consoled Mother while we watched. Dad spoke to several people as calls came in from around the country and Mexico. His face got whiter with each phone call. The tragedy carried on all weekend, seeming to enter every aspect of our lives.

The whole neighborhood was in mourning. None of the fathers played the usual loud music during the Saturday morning car washing ritual in the driveways. I helped Dad wash his car, and the only sounds were water hoses and newspapers squeaking on windshields. It was a solemn Saturday morning. Then one woman brought out lemonade for everyone, and another brought out fresh baked cookies. Soon the cul-de-sac filled with crying wives and consoling husbands. Mother came out and joined the group in tears, but I suspected her tears were more an effort to fit in rather than genuine grief because I caught a wink from her.

Monday in school, the tragedy of President Kennedy's death was on everyone's mind. Mr. Graham talked about the historic times Mark Twain lived through, including the Civil War and the shooting of Abraham Lincoln. We would look for similarities in our time of the civil rights movement starting and JFK's assassination. He quoted both Lincoln and Kennedy's inauguration speeches. It made sense to him, but he was addressing a group of hormonal eighth graders. No one responded to anything. All the classes were about the same, as each teacher tried to make sense out of this heartbreak. Mr. Graham and the history teacher came up with a joint project for anyone interested in doing an in-depth term paper. The plan was about putting John F. Kennedy's presidency in historical perspective. How would his presidency affect our history? *Our* history? Was I part of this? Was I now an American? Mr. Graham encouraged us to form study groups to have in-depth, honest discussions, and express our thoughts.

Right away, Suzy formed a study group with me and five others. I didn't know whom she had invited until I rode my bike to her house; I was the only boy. We sat around the dining table with her new almanac and history book. A trophy-filled curio cabinet stood in plain view. Her brother had earned a track scholarship to U.S.C. and had amassed dozens of medals. Suzy's mom was a teacher and watched with pride as her daughter led our discussion.

Although I didn't say much in class, Suzy asked my opinion on every point. Every time I spoke, someone would chirp "Shark!" and a chorus of giggles would follow. Suzy's mom came to my rescue with a wink and a nod, letting me know the girls were being silly.

Lincoln's death was reasoned to have been because of slavery and the Civil War. It was easy to understand Lincoln's death, but forming an opinion on Kennedy's was too recent. The new almanac included President Kennedy's wartime Naval record and congressional service, so we had something to write about. We needed reasons for his death. The news on television and radio was confusing everyone. We weren't in a war, and the civil rights movement was fresh. It was reported that Lee Harvey Oswald was a communist sympathizer who'd lived in Russia and married a Russian.

We were at a loss for discussing what Kennedy's death meant in history other than he was the fourth president shot and killed in office. We had nothing more to say about John F. Kennedy's impact on history. We all stared at the wilting flower arrangement in the centerpiece of the table. I sensed everyone's eyes on me; it felt as though I'd stopped progress with my wandering thoughts. I wanted to leave. I remembered the Cuban Missile Crisis. Dad subscribed to *The New Republic*, and I remembered seeing a headline about Kennedy and the Cuban leader Fidel Castro. I said I'd ride home and come back with an article that would help. Suzy agreed it would be helpful. She headed out the garage door for her bike as the rest of the group giggled.

Suzy headed out ahead of me, yelling she'd beat me. It became a race. I caught up with her and raced ahead up a knoll along an elementary school. Suzy cut across the parking lot. Somehow she knew the shortcut. I continued on. I turned the corner and found her waiting at the end of my cul-de-sac gleaming like Jackie Kennedy. I rode up and circled around her. "How do you know where I live?" I asked, still balancing the bike.

"A birdie told me," she said.

"Which house is it?"

"The big one right in the middle." She smiled, looking at me rather than the house.

"Come on," I said and sped up to the house. Suzy followed. We parked our bikes and walked inside. Mother was in the backyard pruning roses. "*Hola, Mami,*" I said. Mother looked up through the window and smiled. Suzy looked around, studying the furnishings.

"You speak Spanish?" Suzy seemed surprised.

"Yes," I said, realizing I had never uttered a Spanish word in front of my friends.

"I'm jealous," she said. "I want to learn Spanish. Can you teach me?"

"Sure, I can. It's easier than English, that's for sure."

"You need a year of a foreign language for college. It'll be fun if we do it together."

"I'll get the article," I said, offering a glass of water. I poured two. Mother stepped in. "*Hola, Mami.* This is Suzy." Mother looked up at Suzy, who stood a head taller.

"*Hola*, Mrs. Allen," Suzy said. "I'm Suzy, a pleasure to meet you." Mother gave me an approving wink and went back out.

We rode away, taking the shortcut. The school parking lot was empty. Suzy stopped in the shade under a tree. I circled around, balancing myself carefully on the bike. "This is where my mother works. She's a teacher," Suzy said with her Jackie Kennedy smile.

"Are you going to be a teacher?" I asked, wondering what Jackie Kennedy felt when her husband died in her arms.

"No, I want to work with horses. What do you want to do?" She watched me balance myself without pedaling around. I didn't have an answer. "Are you going to circle around like a circus clown all afternoon?" The image of the Kennedy's in the convertible riding through Mexico and Dallas swirled in my mind. I tried to figure out a historical statement to make of it, but clowns appeared in my head. I looked for my *Toro* in the sky.

"*Payasos*! Clowns!" I felt a tugging on my shirt. Suzy grabbed me. I stumbled off the bike. She still held my shirt. I saw the same expression she had in the pool when we almost kissed. Goosebumps came as I drew closer to her.

"You want to be a clown?" she said.

"No. I want to be a shark!" I shouted without thinking. She giggled. I giggled. We pulled away. I balanced myself on the bike again. She waited for me to stop acting like a clown. Patient, calm, smart, fast, sophisticated, curious, driven, fourteen-year-old Suzy scared me to death.

"Get off the bike and kiss me," she said.

I circled around faster instead. "I have to go!" I shouted. "Don't tell anyone I didn't kiss you." And I raced away embarrassed. Why couldn't I kiss her? Wasn't my job to assimilate and do as Americans do?

The news was nonstop reporting on President Kennedy's killing and Jack Ruby shooting Lee Harvey Oswald. There was a lot made of Kennedy's PT-109 boat and his Navy career. I took down Dad's Navy photo album from his bookshelf and looked at his pictures. They looked a lot like Kennedy's pictures that were being broadcast on television. I studied the similarities between Dad and J.F.K., imagining them as friends. *The Old Man and the Sea* caught my eye on the bookshelf. I decided to write my paper on Cuba and J.F.K. Dad and Mother were in the living room watching the somber news. I asked Dad to help me understand *The New Republic* and concluded John F. Kennedy's presidency would be remembered for stopping communism from reaching the U.S.A. Afterward, Dad assured me we would not be moving to Cuba. He could see my concern.

Thanksgiving weekend ended with a phone call from Don. He had been detained by the police in Belmont. Dad's hair seemed to turn gray overnight. Don arrived a few days later and told me what happened in Belmont. "We jumped the gun," he started in a regretful tone. "I got a job, got a room, enrolled back at Carlmont High School, bought Dolores an engagement ring, and then everything blew up."

"Did the mafia come after you? Scare you?" I asked.

"Dolores' father is not a real mobster. He uses pictures from movies and newspapers to give his bar a personality. The problem is he goes to the same church as the police commissioner. He scared me."

He went on to tell me the whole story. Don and Dolores would see each other on Saturday nights. Dolores would tell her Dad she was going to the movie theater with her friends for the double feature. But she and Don had a plan. The movie theater was on the corner of El Camino and Ralston Avenue. The entrance was on El Camino Real. Don parked his car around the corner. Dolores snuck out through the side exit and jumped in Don's car. They would sneak over to Don's room and make it back to the theater by the end of the night. One time, Dolores' father went over to Don's place on Saturday night with the police commissioner. They got the landlord to let them in and discovered Dolores naked in bed with Don. That was Thanksgiving weekend, and the last time Don saw Dolores. Don's romantic dream of marrying his high school sweetheart came to a bitter end. After that, he quit talking and stayed in his room reading literature, mostly tragedies and poetry. "Romeo and Juliet had it right," he'd say when Dad or Mother tried to talk to him.

Our joint History/English papers were graded. Everyone got papers back except me. Suzy received an A grade and gave an oral presentation. She wrote about Kennedy's term being remembered for the civil rights movement and the rise of Dr. Martin Luther King's dream. I figured I was in for an F. I asked Mr. Graham about my paper. He said I got the only A-plus and kept the report because he was sharing it with the principal. Suzy held her paper up, showing me the A grade and winked when she heard I got an A-plus. I never knew why, but it was Orange County, and Barry Goldwater was running for president on an anti-communist platform. *Que sera, sera.*

Mexico Lindo

Don returned to the school he hated and continued on without friends. Mother and Dad decided we needed a family vacation in Mexico. Don's dark days of sitting in his room reading tragedies and not communicating had to stop. On the first day of winter break, we had the car packed and ready to go on a long drive. Dad set a schedule to maintain an average of fifty miles per hour, including stops. We would stop for gas, food, one brief stay in Guadalajara and still make it to Mexico City in forty-eight hours.

He placed a letter in the mail and said we'd beat the message to our destiny. Don and Dad shared the driving time, and we drove into Mexico City on a bright sunny day at the forty-seventh hour. Dad drove to *La Reforma*, Mexico's central street that features fountains, gold statues, monuments, high-end stores, a tree-lined paseo, and a host of historical landmarks. It was now Mother's favorite street for the fact that John and Jackie Kennedy had ridden through the same route just two years earlier. I remembered learning the history of Mexico while walking with Dad as he told it. We arrived in front of Tia Rosita's house just as the mailman was delivering Dad's letter. Dad's prediction was right. To me, he was the smartest man in my world, and this was just more proof.

Tia Rosita answered the front door wearing a blue suit, looking every bit the executive she had become in a worldwide import/export business. But to me, she was my Tia who expressed love for me, peeling grapes and laughing about it. The smell of mole wafted from the kitchen where my *abuela* would be. I followed the scent straight into the kitchen and found *Abuela* exactly as I had her in my memories. She stood over the stove wearing an embroidered apron, hair braided up, long dark dress, stirring her magic mole. "*Hola, Mamacita chula,*" I said, kissing her on the cheek as had been my custom. She looked up once and smiled, accepting my kiss without saying a word. She didn't have to say anything; her smile while cooking meant more than any words could express.

"*Que es lo mas importante en la vida?*" I asked her what the most important thing in life was.

"*La familia,*" she said without looking up and tasting her creation. "*Y mole,*" she smiled, satisfied with the taste of her mole.

"*Y que mas?*" I asked what else.

"*Que sera, sera,*" she said, finally looking straight at me. I was glad to be in Mexico, where life seemed so clear. The extended family arrived: — aunts, uncles, cousins — who all seemed content to be doing well. Life was good for them; they knew who and what they were without the anxiety of fitting in. I felt at ease, knowing I could easily have fit in with this large group had we never gone to the United States.

Don took off for the streets with his wolf face. I stayed close to Tia Rosita every day. Being back on the streets of Mexico with the sound of mariachi music and the savory smell of food on the streets was a real contrast to the new life in Orange County. Poverty revealed itself in people's faces as it never had before. Especially in old women's faces. Dad's words about a life purpose being in the service to others crystalized with the image of the women's desperate eyes. Living a life in the service to others, the less fortunate, was easy to figure out in Mexico. I could do a lot to help people here with so much poverty everywhere. Eugenia had married a good man who was doing just that, and she was determined to work in social services.

We spent a lot of time in Chapultepec Park, where crowds of people filled the pathways, and hawkers screamed for attention. Don didn't like being back in Mexico. He seemed nervous until we stopped at an alley store. He bought a knife that he could open with a snap of his wrist. He was a shark with a wolf face and a knife. He relaxed and put the knife in his jacket pocket. Would I be carrying a knife if we never left?

"What's the knife for?" I asked.

"If you can't see the knives in those guys' pockets, assume they're there anyway," Don said, motioning to a group of shifty-looking teenagers who gathered at the alley entrance. He had cautioned me many times about the dangers of the streets in Mexico. We walked toward the teenagers. They stared at Don then me. Don gripped his knife and stared back. They opened a path for us.

"Scary," I said.

"It's not Disneyland," Don said. He kept his hand in his pocket as we walked. He didn't have to tell me not to say anything.

"You want to move back here?" I asked.

"We don't belong here anymore," he said.

We celebrated the New Year in Mexico City's famed light display at the Palacio National. It is a fiesta like no other with food, music, dance, and the glorious building on display, dressed in white lights. The palace is on the original site of the Mexican ruling classes since the Aztec Empire and where Moctezuma II, Hernan Cortez, Benito Juarez lived during their reigns. It is also the site where Mexico's first bullfight took place under Spanish rule. Memories of playing in the courtyard, learning about the palace of fine arts, attending an opera, and feeling the pride of Mexican patriotism felt good. If we moved back here, I knew what I'd be doing every New Year's night. Dad and Mother strolled, arms wrapped around each other like young lovers. Tia Rosita and Eugenia walked arm in arm. Don and I straddled behind.

"*Charlie, cuando regresas a vivir conmigo?*" Tia Rosita asked when I'd move back, wistfully. Without warning, fireworks lit up the sky, just like Disneyland's parade. Dad moved closer to me and put his arm on my shoulder. I was glad I didn't have to answer Tia Rosita's question. I knew, I felt, my loyalty and patriotism were now for the United States.

We headed back to Fullerton the following morning. Dad drove down the mountains into the picturesque countryside. I thought about the train ride we'd taken a few years earlier that seemed so different. I had been scared to leave Mexico, uncertain of what was ahead in New York. Now I was glad to leave for the comfort of California.

Nighttime came, and Don took a shift at the wheel while Mother and Dad slept. I sat in the back, watching the oncoming headlights pass by in the dark roads. I caught Don's eyes when he opened the window. He signaled to be quiet and took out his knife. And with one quick motion, he tossed the knife away.

The Beatles invaded the nation with their hit songs—"I Want to Hold Your Hand," and "She Loves You." Suzy decided Tom, David, Stuart, and I would make the perfect foursome for lip-syncing the songs in a talent show. How she talked us into doing it, I'll never know, but we reported to her house for our first rehearsal without objection.

Guitar in hand, I twisted, sang, and moved my hips like Paul while Tom, David, and Stuart played their parts. We wiggled and bounced our way through "I Want to Hold Your Hand," and "She Loves You." Suzy's mother applauded. But when we finished, she walked to me and whispered, "Tone down the hip moves. You don't want to look like a jungle bunny." I had responded to the Beatles as I'd done to mambo.

"Okay," I responded wondering what a jungle bunny was. She lit up a cigarette.

"Charles, I understand you are a Mexican," she said, exhaling a cloud of smoke.

"Yes," I said.

"Well, that's nice. And what are your career plans?" she asked with joy in her tone.

"I want to live a life of service to others. Perhaps teaching as you do," I said what I'd rehearsed a million times.

"Teachers don't make enough money. I'm a woman. I have a husband with a good job. Teaching is for women with husbands." She looked agitated as she inhaled with a vengeance before looking away. Orange County values spewed out of her front and center as she exhaled.

Our talent show was a success. We had future cheerleaders, a ventriloquist, a Jerry Lewis impersonator, one boy played a saxophone solo of the hit song "Tequila." He warmed up the audience and set the stage for us, because the minute our group came up the students roared. The American hysteria over The Beatles came alive in our little auditorium. Girls screamed just like on the *Ed Sullivan Show*; they wanted to believe we were the real group. I tried to deliver. I shook my head and moved my lips to every syllable, just like Paul. David, like John, strummed the guitar with the same intensity. Stuart stood like George, and Mike accidentally hit the drums a few times, trying his best to look like Ringo. We swung and rocked through "I Want to Hold Your Hand" picking up audience hysteria with every beat. Then we went right into "She Loves You." The place exploded. Girls rushed the stage, teachers jumped in between, and boys clamored for more. Somehow, we reached the end of the song without causing a riot. Afterward, we headed for Disneyland.

"Get in," Suzy said, taking my arm and pushing me into place. I was not expecting her sudden moves, but she secured herself between my legs and settled into the Matterhorn ride. We jerked forward, sending Suzy's back into me. I eased back and felt the tracks rumbling under me as we headed up the mountain. Suzy's hair flew into my open mouth. She leaned back and moaned. My heart raced.

Assimilation meant fitting in with the culture, and this was a test of my fitting in. I slid my arms around her waist as she had done with me in the pool. She didn't resist. We headed up a ramp slow and steady. I just as slowly slid my hands on her breasts, right hand to her left breast and left hand to her right. We headed straight down. I cuddled and held her tight. She pushed back, and we rode the rest of the way coiled together. I was living up to my assimilated expectations.

Suzy's mother had coordinated a carpool with Linda Ball's mother and a friend. They made an evening of it and waited in the Disney Hotel, so we had a no-holds-barred night of teenage make-out sessions on every ride. Tom Sawyer's Island was a perfect spot for kissing and petting, and that's precisely where we all spent most of the night. Linda Ball was Sue Arnold's neighbor and rival. Their parents spent money lavishly on everything, including horses and cars. Linda Ball announced her birthday party date to christen the pool that was under construction at her house. She talked about it as though it was going to be the event of our year and kept looking at Sue. Sue Arnold's parties were hands-down the best of the year. Not to be outdone, Linda Ball was determined to one-up her neighbor. After our evening at Disneyland, we gathered in the parking lot where Linda Ball's mother waited with a notepad. She wanted everyone's address to send out birthday party Invitations. We all wrote our address in the notebook.

"Sonny Liston's going to kill that loudmouth nigger," a high-strung teenager screamed behind us. His friends agreed with brash cheers. It was Orange County, and Muhammad Ali, then known as Cassius Clay, was set to fight Sonny Liston. The civil rights movement brought out the ugly truth that racism existed in the country, even in Disneyland.

That weekend, Don took me to a closed-circuit viewing of the Liston-Clay fight. It was a drive-in movie theater location. That night thousands of people watched, standing instead. It was scary. People yelled, "Kill that nigger!" in unison as the fighters were introduced. Don had predicted an upset, saying speed wins. I rooted for Cassius Clay because I always liked the underdog. We watched as he danced around the muscular Sonny Liston. Everyone waited for Liston to knock the young dancer out and cheered with every punch he threw. Don cheered along with Cassius Clay's quick moves and showboating. Don laughed when Liston's punches missed, and Cassius Clay answered with sharp blows to Liston's head. Incredibly Sonny Liston quit mid-fight. Fans were upset around us, screaming that the fight was fixed and calling for Sonny Liston's head.

Don and I started away, but Don's excitement was evident. He was rooting for the wrong guy. Three white guys pushed forward to Don and me. "Fuck that nigger and fuck you, Mexicans!" screamed one. The three guys had picked on the wrong Mexican. Don answered the guy with the fastest punch of the night. The guy dropped like a bad actor, spinning around and falling flat on his face. The other two guys froze with mouths open, staring at their fallen loudmouthed friend. Don pushed me away, just as two officers rushed forward and stood next to the two white guys. "That's him," one guy said, pointing at Don. "He did this. He started it." The other guy helped the fallen one.

"That's a lie," said Don. "He started it, I finished it." With no further explanation, the officers handcuffed Don.

"Fucking nigger, Mexicans! Fuck Sonny Liston, too. It was a fix!" yelled the downed guy, still dazed.

"See, officers?" said Don.

"They started it," I said, pointing at the three.

"Fuck you, beaner!" The guy was still screaming. His friends helped the guy up, and the three ran off screaming, "Niggers! Mexicans!" louder than ever. The policemen did not stop them. All I could think about was how Dad would have reacted. What would he have done? What were Don and I supposed to do? It was wrong,

wrong, wrong.

Luckily, a uniformed vendor stood up for Don and me, explaining that the threesome had been the aggressors with foul language and rudeness. After a while, the officers thought better and took the handcuffs off Don without apologizing or mentioning the racists' remarks.

Linda Ball's party was scheduled for the second weekend of Easter vacation. Her father bought her a blond horse that was delivered to her backyard stables the first day of the vacation. She invited David, Sue Arnold, Mickey, and me to her house during the week. She was so excited and sure the party would be the highlight of the school year. But she downplayed her enthusiasm with, "I really don't want to have a big party, but Dad and Mom insist." No one believed her as she paraded around in a perfect western show outfit that Dale Evans would have envied. She led the way to the stables.

"Poor little rich girl," laughed David. Linda blushed and walked away.

We followed past the expansive new pool area. A loud thump sounded nearby, *"Ay, con cuidado!"* Someone said "be careful" in Spanish. Three Mexican workers were placing new patio furniture and flowerpots. Two hoses gushed water into the model pool. The stables were below, along with a trail that bordered Sue Arnold's house. Linda's German Shepherd ambled behind, tongue draped to one side.

We all walked to the trail and watched as Linda slipped up on her new horse. She took off down the path and out of sight. David tried to kiss Sue Arnold, but she pushed him away and rushed off toward her property. "Good going, David," I said.

"It's a pool party." Mickey opened an envelope. It was an RSVP to Linda's party. Linda struggled back with rosy cheeks and dilated pupils. She saw the envelope and took off again without a word.

Linda stepped out to her new pool the following morning and

read a NO MEXICANS sign posted above the pool safety rules. It was a hot and sunny day. She cried as she rode her bike furiously to my house.

The doorbell rang. I opened the door and saw Linda's steamy red cheeks and sad eyes. "What's the matter?" I asked, surprised to find her standing in my doorway. "Come inside. It's hot. You want some water?" She followed me into the kitchen, where I poured a glass of ice water. She sipped it nervously. "What's wrong?" I said.

"I have something to tell you," she started. She choked up and took a sip of water. "I can't say it." She looked weak and put the glass down. I offered a chair. She walked toward the living room instead and dropped on the sofa, crying.

"Why are you crying?"

"You can't come to my party," she said.

"Okay."

"I hate my dad."

"Okay."

"I wish I didn't have a birthday." She looked up.

"Why?" I asked.

"He said no Mexicans in the pool," she said through tears with snot running down her face. I laughed nervously and reached for the tissue box.

"No Mexicans?" I said. What would Dad say? What would Dad do? I laughed louder, almost hysterically. Should I be angry, hurt? "No Mexicans in the water. Now, that's funny. I won't go. I promise." I'd been in Orange County long enough to not be surprised by this, and I couldn't take it personally. It wasn't Linda's doing, and I felt her sadness.

"I hate my dad. I hate my dad. I hate my dad." She blew her nose and cried, holding my mother's prized pillow. I hoped the snot wouldn't get on the pillow.

"It's his pool. He sets the rules," I reasoned.

"He thinks he's a big shot because his grandfather was Jesse

James."

"I'm related to Tonto," I said playfully.

Linda's crying echoed through the house. Mother walked in, startled to see Linda. Don came out of his room. Linda looked up at the three Mexicans staring at her and buried her face in the pillow. There was no avoiding the snot on the pillow this time.

I rode my bike alongside Linda toward her house through a trail I'd ridden a hundred times before. The sun blasted down the whole way. It felt different that day when we reached Linda's street, as though I was being watched. Her father's white Cadillac stood at the house entrance visible through the white fence. The front door opened, and out stepped Linda's father. He was a short blond man who seemed in a hurry. I circled up to the gate and watched Linda ride through to greet her dad. He looked my way. If he didn't want me in his pool, I wasn't about to stick around to find out why. "Hi-yo Silver!" I shouted in my best cowboy tone and rode away.

Dad and Mother were planting spring flowers along the entrance walkway to our home when I returned. I watched for a moment, appreciating the delicate manner they handled the baby plants. Dad kneeled next to Mother, a nursery box between them, each placing flowers in the ground. The yellow pussy willow, purple daffodil, and azaleas were in good hands. The tenderness of our home felt very different from Linda's place.

"Did your friend get home safely?" Mother asked in her sweet accent. She had been speaking English a lot more since moving to Fullerton. It was different and special to hear Mother's efforts at assimilation. It was a humbling experience for her to not have command of the language to tell her colorful stories. But now, in this upper-middle-class neighborhood in Orange County, it was time to make every effort to fit in.

"Safe and sound," I assured. Then I clarified the idiom. "Safe and secure."

"She likes you," Mother teased gleefully.

"That's impossible!" I objected too loudly. I blushed and laughed. Dad joined the laughter. The three of us shared my teenage coming-of-age moment of lust. I didn't realize it, but I was drenched in sweat from the bike ride and my embarrassment.

Satan barked wildly in the backyard. Don called out his name. Dad rushed to the yard. Satan was up to something, a possum most likely.

"*Ay Charlie, no digas que no te gusta esa rubia,*" Mother spoke in Spanish the second Dad left. She told me not to deny the idea that I liked that blond.

"*Imposible, porque su papa puso un deletreo* that said 'no Mexicans' in the pool," I said in Spanglish.

"*Pobrecita.*" Poor girl, Mother said, her eyes on a flower she was preening. "*Y tan joven.*" Mother felt sorry for Linda. The idea of someone not accepting us simply for being Mexicans was an anomaly to Mother. "If they don't want you in their pool, it's their loss." She moved on to the next flower. She truly felt sorry for anyone of that mindset. I liked the way she dealt with racist behaviors as insignificant aberrations.

Pony League Baseball tryouts started that week. Nothing is more American than baseball, and that's what playing meant to me. The competition was crowded with the best players in Orange County for my age group. Eliminations were swift and fast, but in the end, Mike's father drafted me into his team, the Indians. We practiced all week and had our first game scheduled against Stuart's team, the Dodgers. I wanted my family to share the big event with me because it was the next level baseball league with a beautifully kept field. Dad, Mother, Don, and I got in the car and headed down the hill to my first game in our new town. Mother searched the AM radio; a few Spanish stations played. She stopped when Peter, Paul, and Mary's song

"Puff the Magic Dragon" played. It was at the top of the charts and played everywhere. Memories of singing "Row, Row, Row Your Boat" in the car with Dad at the wheel crossed my mind. "Puff the Magic Dragon" blared in the car, and I sang along, then Dad and even Mother joined in while Don simply frowned. We passed by Disneyland, singing the simple tune. It was the perfect upbeat song for finishing junior high school.

The baseball field looked like the San Francisco Giants' field to me, with smooth green grass and patted down infield dirt. For a moment, in my crisp white uniform, I felt like Willie Mays standing in center field. *"Oh, say can you see by the dawn's early light . . ."* Lyrics to the national anthem rang through my head right before the first pitch. The Dodgers were up first. Mike pitched and had a quick inning with a strikeout and two ground balls. Bottom of the inning, Mike was first up. He swung at the first pitch and made contact with the ball, but the ball slid right up the bat and into Mike's forehead. I was on deck and watched an enormous bump swell up instantly over Mike's eye. He went down like a rag doll. I heard Mother's distinctive scream in Spanish. Mike's father ran to his son and hovered over him for several minutes. I wondered whether he would still attend Linda's party. Mike had to leave the game.

I was up next and could only imagine the ball smashing into my face. I struck out on three straight swings. I heard my mother's gasps on each pitch. I was left to make good for Mike on the mound. I managed to get through the first four batters without giving up any runs. Then I faced the pitcher that caused Mike's bump. He stood right over the plate, daring me to throw a strike. I wound up, kicked my leg up higher than usual, gripped for a two-seam fastball, spun around and sent the ball right into the batter's ribs. I loaded the bases with two outs. Mike's father ran out to me. "That was not necessary," he said with a wink. "That was a linebacker move."

I was the only pitcher left, so win or lose, I had to finish the game. Stuart came up to bat with his perfectly pressed Dodgers uniform. I thought he could attend Linda's party without changing his clothes. He had been to baseball camp two summers in a row and had the confidence of Mickey Mantle and Willie Mays. I looked in for my catcher's pitch sign. I only had one pitch, so it was more of a formality than a strategic move. Stuart stood straight up, waiting for me to wind up. I wound up reaching for all the might I had and delivered the fastest ball I'd ever thrown. He hit my first pitch right out of the park. We lost the game by a score of twelve to one.

After the game, Mike's father told Dad he was looking forward to coaching me in high school football. Baseball, football, both all American sports as far as I was concerned. I was still living the American Dream and had high school to look forward to. Dad stood, smart as ever, holding Mother's hand. She looked regal as ever in a stylish yellow satin dress, matching shoes, and a white sweater. It was her effort to fit in with the Orange County wives. Despite my failure as a pitcher, I felt Dad's approval for participating in America's favorite pastime.

Dad barbecued steaks in the backyard for dinner. I was exhausted. "Cheer up, Charlie. Winning isn't as important as how you play the game," Dad said. I smiled, hoping to divert attention away from my thoughts about Linda's party. "Your will to finish the game is what came through."

"Am I an American now, Dad?" I asked.

"Yes, you are." He looked up.

"Okay." I smiled. He smiled. We all smiled. We had learned the Allen way of mollifying difficult issues.

Later that night, Don came into my room. "We are Mexicans, always have been, always will be," he insisted.

"Okay," I said, wondering why Don was so adamant about the issue.

"Why would you ask Dad?" Don said.

"Because I got uninvited to a friend's party. Her Dad said Mexicans weren't allowed in their pool."

"If they don't want you in their pool, it's their loss," Don said, relieved.

David telephoned, saying he wasn't going to Linda's party because he heard I'd been uninvited. He had invited anyone who didn't want to go to Linda's party over to his house. I rode over on my bike. His parents had set out snacks and games. David's older brother, Bob, and their father stood on the porch as I approached. Together the three spanned the entire porch with their broad shoulders. All three had dark brown hair parted on the left with matching chins. We walked to the backyard where they had set up a dartboard and horseshoe game. Two punching bags hung from the patio cover. David's father sent the speed bag rattling with one punch then smacked the big heavy bag with his other fist. "You ever feel like punching somebody, Charlie, you take it out on these and avoid a whole lot of trouble," he said.

"Okay," I said. I imagined the guy's face that Don had punched at the Liston/Clay fight and punched the speed bag, sending it rattling. It felt good. Then I saw each of the three kid's faces who'd greeted me by calling me a beaner upon my arrival at the school. One by one, I punched them silly, and it felt good. Finally, I imagined Linda's father's porky face and body on the heavy bag. Bang, bang, bang. It worked. David's Dad was right. I left my anger on the punching bag. I looked up and saw a grin on David and his Dad.

"Good work, Charlie," he said. We walked inside the house. Several boxing trophies and pictures filled one wall over a desk in the study room. David said his Dad had boxed professionally before going into business. That explained his father's sideways nose.

"Anybody in your family ever fight?" David's father asked. "Mexicans are tough lightweights."

"My grandfather fought bulls," I said, wondering what I'd be doing had I stayed in Mexico. I knew I wouldn't have been excluded from attending a pool party.

"Charlie's going to play high school football," David said and led me toward the backyard.

"Your dad's pretty cool," I said as we walked.

"He's also an asshole," David said, shaking his head. "He's fucking our neighbor's wife."

"Shit," I muttered.

"And he's got a girlfriend at work," David said, shaking his head in disappointment. "He's always fucking around." Then he smiled as a blond girl turned the corner. "Hey, Barbie," he greeted his sister. Then turned to me, "This is my sister." She didn't look at all like the boys. "Mom got her revenge." The girl stared, holding a rag doll, blurted out a hello, and ran off.

"What?" I said, confused.

"Mom had an affair with our blond surfer boy milk delivery man," he said with a straight face. "Barbie's proof."

Suzy walked in with a cake and a bag of chips. "Puff the Magic Dragon" hummed on the radio, and more friends filled the backyard. It turned out that Suzy found out about Linda's father not wanting Mexicans at her party and organized another party with David. I had no idea and felt terrible for Linda. Mike walked in with a bandage on his forehead. He punched the bag and said the other guy looked worse. He danced around, imitating Cassius Clay. Mickey spiked the punch with a bottle of rum, and David turned up the music. Before long, David was doing handstands, bouncing to the music, while the rest of us danced around him.

A full springtime moon smiled down on us like magic. Soft dark colors outlined friendly smiles all around that gave me a sense of belonging. I was an American for the night. Everyone sang along with "Puff the Magic Dragon" and "I Want to Hold Your Hand." A silver glow outlined Suzy's face every time she got near me. We danced and sang and giggled without a care in the world, and before the night was over, our lips were locked together. I never felt better in my life than that very moment when everything around me made sense. I was a part of the American Dream that Dad envisioned for his family, and I was lost in the splendor of a hormonal surge in Suzy's arms.

Monday morning at school, Linda rushed up to me with her new Polaroid camera and snapped a picture of me. She ripped out a sheath of plastic paper and waved it around. "I'm sorry about Saturday night," I said.

"Don't be," she said and blew on the paper. "I got this new camera. You want to see the pictures?" She handed me a stack of pictures from her party.

"I didn't know about David's party." I looked at the sad pictures feeling guilty that very few people showed up. One photo showed Linda flipping her middle finger under the NO MEXICANS sign.

"I don't care. I was glad no one came," Linda said. "I thought about you all night." She blew on the film. "I wanted you. I wanted you to come over and jump in the pool."

"Happy birthday," I whispered, imagining John Wayne walking into Linda's backyard, guns drawn, finding me naked in her pool. "I hope your dad doesn't see this picture." I handed back her pictures.

"Do you want to come over to my house and swim in the pool?" She separated the plastic film cover off the Polaroid picture and smiled. "Look, you don't look Mexican," she said, holding up the photo she took. "You don't have a Mexican name. I'll tell him you're Italian."

"I am a Mexican, always have been, always will be," I answered, looking at the picture she'd just taken. Here I was in the Polaroid, a young man in a new Arrow button-down shirt and silk tie, under a cardigan sweater looking every bit as well-dressed as any Orange County teenager. After ten years of working toward being like William Allen, I felt very much assimilated into American culture, and now Linda wanted me to be Italian. Italian?

"How about this weekend?" She smiled.

"Are Italians supposed to be better than Mexicans?" I wished I'd worn a matador suit.

"Well . . ." she hesitated. The bullfighter blood in me ran fast through my veins. Linda wanted me to pretend to be Italian for the privilege of playing in her pool. *Tu madre!*

I was not about to deny my existence. I may have been trying to fit in too much, but to deny my roots was a hurtful notion. I saw my mother's face and my entire family in Mexico, Don, Eugenia, Tia Rosita—all hurt by this crazy idea. Then Dad's face floated in my head.

"Please!" Linda said. "Pretty, please."

"We are Mexicans, always have been, always will be," Don's words answered in my head.

"Allen isn't Italian," I pulled away. "Sorry about your party."

John F. Kennedy's springtime fitness challenge was in full swing all around the country, honoring his legacy. Suzy led the girls in all events with her long legs and lean muscles. I watched her push herself through every challenge with an endless determination. Seeing that forced me to work harder. David won the pull-up contest easily with a school record of fifty-nine pull-ups. I beat Mike at the finish line by a hair in the hundred-yard dash while he took the fifty-yard dash in record time. "People are talking about us," said Suzy as we approached the starting line for the mile run.

"What are they saying?" I said.

"We're going steady." She flashed a huge smile. The whistle blew, and we were off. Suzy had won every mile race the whole year and wasn't about to let anyone ahead of her. I stayed at her pace through the first three laps, but she kicked into another gear around the final lap and won.

"I'm going to run track in high school, and so are you!" Suzy screamed in my face as I finished second.

That night, I told Don about Suzy's going steady comment. I

didn't know what I should do about it. "Give her this," Don said, handing me a gold Saint Christopher necklace. He said it was what was left of his relationship with Dolores.

"Suzy, will you go steady with me?" I said, standing next to my bike on her bright porch the next day. I handed her a satin jewelry box.

Suzy opened the box. "Yes, yes, yes," she said, admiring Don's pain-filled gold chain. She snapped it around her neck, and I watched Saint Christopher glitter on her skin. I was going steady with the smartest girl in the school. Mexico was receding into a distant memory.

Before I knew it, graduation day was upon us. The commencement ceremony was short. It was a hot day, and speeches were sadly marked with the assassination of John F. Kennedy. The whole country was still in shock, and graduation ceremonies everywhere were bittersweet. Afterward, Dad announced he had accepted a job with a company in Northern California. "Berkeley?" I asked, holding my junior high school graduation certificate. Dad announced we were moving to Berkeley, California.

"It's across the bridge from San Francisco," he said, handing me his heirloom gold pocketknife and a card. "Congratulations, son." I felt disoriented. Moving away after all the struggles to fit into this place was not good news. Was this pocketknife supposed to ease the hollow feelings I was having? I looked around the sea of white faces feeling emptier than ever. I was suddenly an outsider—again. I wanted to disappear.

"Congratulations, Charlie," Mother said in her sweet accent and gave me a hug.

"*Muchas gracias, Mamacita*," I said loud enough for everyone to hear my perfect Spanish intonation. I wanted to run away. I faced Dad. We stood in the middle of the ceremony under a bright sun, shoulder to shoulder in blue suits and matching ties. He looked so happy and proud, I didn't want to upset his day. Families and friends

I'd been a part of for two years celebrated the occasion, taking pictures, holding flowers and gifts. I was numb. I would not be with them next year. Junior high school may as well have been a dream. We may as well have been going back to Mexico as far as I was concerned.

Suzy called me over for a picture with Mr. Graham. I hesitated, feeling a lump in my throat. "Proud to have been your teacher, you two," said Mr. Graham. "I know you will both lead good, productive lives." He reached out to shake my hand. I barely lifted my arm. Suzy's mother positioned the three of us and snapped a picture. "Any idea what you want to study?" Mr. Graham asked. My throat tightened. I couldn't talk.

"I'm going to U.S.C. and then veterinarian school at U.C. Davis," Suzy answered confidently.

"I'm moving," I said, lip quivering. "We're moving to Berkeley."

"Great school, U.C. Berkeley," Mr. Graham said. "Thinking man's school." I couldn't get another word out.

When we got home, Don was packed and ready to go. "What's with the face?" he said. "You should be happy. You just graduated."

"Berkeley. Did you know about this?" I asked.

"It's closer to Belmont," he said with a grin.

"And a million miles from Fullerton."

Berkeley: 1964

Berkeley stands across the Golden Gate Bridge on the east shore of the San Francisco Bay. It is cold and foggy compared to Orange County. We moved into a hillside home overlooking the bay and the whole expanse of the Golden Gate Bridge. Mother and Dad had found their palace with a million-dollar view.

I entered Berkeley High School at the height of the civil rights movement. Dad was active in the campaign through the Unitarian Fellowship and was deeply concerned with the injustices Black Americans were experiencing. Berkeley began a progressive integration program, known as the Ramsey Act, that put black and white students together on the Berkeley High School — West Campus. The nightly news kept the country abreast of the movement. We watched demonstrations, speeches, Southern police officers turning dogs on citizens while fire hoses knocked people off their feet. Martin Luther King, Malcolm X, and Mohammad Ali were center stage, raising awareness on racial issues. Dad's reaction to the news was always one of despair. Mother sat next to him. After the news hour, they would both sigh, look at one another, and inevitably say they could always move to Mexico. The thought of moving to Mexico triggered pangs of fear and angst that created a wave of anger I didn't recognize. "Mexico?" I questioned one time.

"Sure, look at what's happening here," Dad answered, pointing out a newspaper photo of three Mississippi civil rights workers, James Chaney, Andrew Goodman, and Michael Schwermer, who had gone missing and were assumed killed. "All this happened in

Germany," he continued with a somber face. "Japanese internment camps are part of this country's history. What's next?"

"*Nos vamos a Mexico.*" Mother said we'd go to Mexico. She gave me a two-eyed blink. I took it to mean it was dangerous for Mexicans.

"I can't continue paying taxes to a government that treats its citizens like this," Dad said. I noticed his dream-home blueprints on the shelf behind him and pictured us moving back to Mexico.

Although it was an exciting time to be in Berkeley for black and white students, I couldn't feel a part of it. Willie Mays, Muhammad Ali, Harry Belafonte, and Ray Charles were all I knew about Black Americans. I was once again the outsider. I stuck out like a sore thumb with my not-white nor black skin dressed in an Orange County preppy outfit. The whole environment seemed dark compared to the Disneyland-like landscape I'd just left. I resigned myself to the idea that we were moving to Mexico. I kept to myself and watched on the sidelines as Black and White students mingled throughout the days. Public transportation was my means to and from school. I rode the Colusa Street bus to and from school with white students to the West Campus. One day the biggest boy of all caught my eye as he passed my seat. His name was Paul Guernsey. His shoulders spread across the aisle, which explained why he took the center seat in the last row. He wore a light-blue shirt with navy blue pants and brown loafers. He would have fit right in with the Orange County group of friends I'd left. Excited students quickly filled the seats between us, and I turned away. I felt a tap on my shoulder and turned around to see the big boy's eyes staring at me. A moment of déjà vu stirred in me. Was I sitting in the wrong seat? "Would you open your window?" he asked.

I opened it without saying a word and looked away. I wondered what Dad's life would have been like with a blue-eyed family. Would he be thinking about moving to Mexico now? It didn't matter; I didn't belong. I wasn't white. I wasn't Black. *Que sera, sera.*

For all practical purposes, Don was home again. Belmont is

thirty-five miles from Berkeley, a one-hour bus ride. But all his friends had cars by now, so it was easy for him to fall back into his Belmont life. He was happier and seemed content with only seeing his friends on weekends. He was a senior and still had to finish high school. His future was with his Belmont friends. "What are you and Dolores going to do?" I asked one school night while doing homework in the living room.

"Dolores," he paused, choosing his words carefully, "and I are finished. She moved to Boston," Don said, putting the thought to rest. "We're better off this way. We're way too young." He marked a play he was reading.

"Funny coming from you," I said, surprised at his self-analysis.

"Life is a comedy or a tragedy. That was a tragedy. Right now, it's a comedy."

"If you say so." He didn't sound at all like the big brother I'd known in Fullerton.

"The world is a stage, and we're merely players in it," he said, holding up a Shakespeare play, *As You Like It.* "A reversal of fortune turns comedy to tragedy and vice versa. So beware of what you seek."

"The world is a stage, and we're merely players in it," he said, holding up a Shakespeare play, *As You Like It.* "A reversal of fortune turns comedy to tragedy and vice versa. So beware of what you seek."

Mr. Brown was my English teacher. He wore a brown leather jacket, graduated from Brown University, and rode a motorcycle to school. He, too, was a Mark Twain fan and quoted the work often. His manner and knowledge of the work made learning easy. He read passages from different authors daily and had a story to tell about the work that made it enjoyable. He spoke about the Elizabethan Era as though we were a part of it. He asked me once to demonstrate how Sir Walter Raleigh doffed his hat and placed his coat over a mud puddle to protect the queen's feet. I stood, tipped my invisible hat, and waved my imaginary jacket like a bullfighter's cape swooping over sharp horns and placing it at a shy girl's feet. Mr. Brown led the applause as I took my seat.

We went on to read Oscar Wilde and somehow make a connection with Elizabethan times and Mark Twain's work. His scope of literature was endless, and we all listened when he opened a book to read. One time we read the last scene from Oscar Wilde's *The Importance of Being Earnest*. I read the role of John Worthing and fell into a high-tone English intonation. Mr. Brown explained the play was about false impressions and how people of that era were captives of society's social obligations. I wondered what requirements I'd have back then, being a Mexican. He called the work a farce, but I took it personally when my character was confused about his identity. By the end of the reading, I had more questions about where I belonged. Berkeley was on the national radar for integrating Black and white Americans in schools. It was a symbol of justice, and civil rights, in a black-and-white world. My classmates were a living example of what was an answer to society's problems, while I was not part of the equation.

Mr. Populus was my first Black teacher. He wore brown suits that matched his shaved head. He'd lost three fingers somehow and proudly displayed the remaining portion of his right hand. I stood alone at the edge of the food court during lunch watching the courtyard dynamics; two groups split right down the middle; Black students congregated on one side, white students on the other. I didn't sit. I didn't belong. I ate, standing up, wondering what group I'd be sitting with had I grown up in Berkeley. Either side would have been beautiful. Students on both sides seemed so happy while I felt out of place—again. Why did we ever leave Mexico, or New York, or Mexico again, or Belmont, or Fullerton? I wasn't interested in making friends. I was pissed.

Mr. Populus walked up to me and asked why I wasn't engaging with anyone. I told him I was new to the school. "You're a pretty cool cat. You'll fit right in, Charles," he said. "Make friends while you can. Look around right now. A lot of people are curious about you. Look at everyone checking you out." He pointed his stubby hand to one side, and some white students looked over. He gestured to the other side, and a few Black students looked up.

"I don't belong," I said.

"That's not a good feeling." He paused. He understood my situation. A Black girl with the most beautiful white smile, big bright eyes, and high cheekbones came close enough for me to smell her perfume. It sent a shot of adrenaline through me. Her name was Wanda.

"NAACP meeting after school?" Wanda stated with a sexy intonation. Mr. Populus nodded in the affirmative. Wanda caught me staring. "You have some color," she said and sauntered away, her tight red skirt calling my name. She turned back. "See you there." I felt obligated to attend.

"What were you saying about not belonging?" he said with a devilish grin. "Wanda is the president of our NAACP club. You're welcome to attend," he said. "You know what the NAACP stands for?"

"National Association for the Advancement of Colored People," I said proudly. "Right?"

"I have some advice for you, Charles," he said. "Somehow, this whole experience here is going to go into our history books. Black and white students are integrating voluntarily while the rest of the country is fighting it." He held up his hand. "I have the title of that book. I'm not going to write it because of this hand," I looked carefully his disfigured hand. "All Bones Are White."

"All bones are white," I repeated. I had my first Black friend in Mr. Populus.

"Yes, only a cool cat like you can write it," he said and walked away through the black students. I watched him stroll through the congestion. One student looked over and caught my eye as he talked with Mr. Populus. The student walked over to me with a big smile. He dressed like a gangster in Elliot Ness' show *The Untouchables*, complete with a black vest and shiny leather shoes.

"Hey, you're new here, aren't you?" he said, reaching into his pocket. He wasn't Black or white and stood at an angle. I thought he must be Italian. He spoke rapidly and looked around as though passing on a secret.

"Yes," I answered.

"Well look here, I'm thinking you're going to need some protection." He pulled out a wallet proudly displaying a condom-ring imprint on one side. "I see all the girls looking over here. Check it out." He smiled at a Black girl with shimmering hair looking our way. "See that? You're going to need one of these." He pulled out the condom from his wallet. I hesitated and looked away. A white girl smiled at me. "Looks like you're going to need more than one," Wayne said, opening his coat. "Fifty cents for one, but you're going to need my three for a dollar pack." He dangled three Trojan condoms in my face. "Welcome to Berkeley. Girls here are horny," he said, smiling toward some onlookers. I snatched the pack out of Wayne's hand and reached in my pocket for the only dollar I had.

"You be careful, Charles," he said, and I realized Mr. Populus must have sent him over. He took out his wallet and showed me the rubber indentation, saying it was essential to have the rubber ring visible for the girls to know I would be safe. He asked for my wallet, ripped one of the condoms from the pack, and placed it dead center. He put the remaining two condoms in my shirt pocket and started off. "Wayne Westley Garcia's the name. If anybody bothers you, you mention my name."

After school, I walked to the NAACP meeting in Mr. Populus' classroom. I entered a packed room. Wanda and Mr. Populus stood in front of the class and greeted me. By the end of the meeting, I was a full member of the Junior NAACP student committee. It was a new form of being an American I never expected.

I had to walk home because Wayne had my bus money. I headed up University Avenue. The University's Campanile tower was visible in the hills. I felt Dad's presence and wondered if I'd attend the college there. I turned the corner and saw Paul walking alone in front of me. His broad shoulders and six-foot-two-inch frame made it easy to recognize him. He turned around for no reason and stopped when we made eye contact.

"Hey, I'm Paul," he said. I didn't answer. "You live this way?" He pointed in the direction we were walking." I mumbled a "Duh." "You angry?" he asked. I didn't answer. "What's your name?" he persisted.

"Charles Allen," I said.

"You're new here, aren't you? So am I. We just moved here."

I didn't know what to make of this big guy. Without much thought, I reached in my pocket, pulled out two condoms, and waved them in his face. "You're going to need these. Girls are horny in Berkeley."

"Rubbers?"

"Two for a buck," I slipped them in his shirt pocket and stuck out my hand. He pulled out his wallet and handed me a dollar. I tried to show off the rubber indent on my wallet, but it hadn't worn in. I made sure he saw how I had placed the condom when I slipped his dollar in my wallet. He set one in his wallet just as I had mine.

Mr. Populus handed me a basketball the next day and told me to make friends on the court. I made my way to the basketball courts and played HORSE—alone. A minute later, a gangly boy with a big grin emerged from behind a steel container. I bounced the ball to him as he crossed toward me. He took a shot at the free-throw line and made it. "Horse, you go first," I said. His name was Archie, he had a perpetual smile, and he giggled with every statement he made. We spoke, not caring about the game. It turned out he was friends with Wayne Westley Garcia. I told him I was born in Mexico and would be moving back soon. He missed every shot he took but kept his silly grin the entire time. Wayne showed up and asked how many rubbers we needed. Archie confessed to having used his rubbers to jack off in. He didn't want to buy anymore because a sock is cheaper. I said I had one left and wouldn't need it anymore. I asked Archie if he jerked off in the rubber.

"Everyone does," he answered and missed another shot.

"Practice runs, is what I call it," said Wayne. "But you have to be ready when the real deal comes along. Better safe than sorry."

I didn't fit in with the Black groups nor the white groups in my new school. Archie and Wayne seemed like outsiders in a way, and I felt comfortable with them.

One morning I stood outside the school staring at the red brick wall holding my new umbrella. I waited for a minute, wishing I were anywhere else. Archie stepped up. "Charles, you want to cut out of this joint?" He read my mind. "San Francisco's fifteen cents away," he said, holding up a dollar. "You in?"

Dark clouds hovered overhead as I was about to make the biggest mistake of my life. The last thing I wanted to do was sit in school on a rainy day. "Come on," he said, rushing across the street as rain burst out of the clouds like in Mexico City. I caught up with Archie and took cover under a Foster's Freeze patio cover across the street.

A blond older boy stood under the cover blowing smoke rings into the rain. He wore a blue denim Levi's jacket over an army-green t-shirt, black pants, cowboy boots, and black belt with a cow-horn buckle. He greeted Archie and introduced himself with a firm handshake and a pumpkin smile with three missing front teeth. His name was Bubba. He lived in the apartment complex next door with his mother. He pulled up his sleeve excitedly and showed us a tattoo of a bleeding heart with a ribbon and letters spelling MOM on his forearm. He said he'd gotten it the night before in San Francisco. "San Francisco's where we're going," said Archie.

"Cutting school?" Bubba asked, then proudly stated, "I'm not."

"He dropped out," Archie said.

"Joining the Army. Going to see the world," Bubba said.

I felt out of place with this urban cowboy and goofy Archie laughing at every word he or anyone said. I knew I should have gone to class that morning, but the thought of trying to fit into the great Black and white student experiment on a rainy day where we would be indoors the entire time was too much. Bubba made more sense at that moment than school. He said he wanted to go to San Francisco with us but needed to get some cash and cigarettes. We went to his tobacco-wreaked apartment with him. It was a one-bedroom apartment with an unmade pullout hide-a-bed sofa in the front room. I could see why Bubba wanted to leave.

"You ever sniff glue, Charles?" Bubba asked, holding up a tube of glue before placing it in his jacket. He grabbed an opened carton of Lucky Strike cigarettes on the coffee table, slid out a pack, swooped up a handful of coins, and threw up his hands like a rodeo star — all in one swift motion.

"No," I answered. Archie giggled, indicating I'd missed out on a good time.

Bubba was different from anyone around, just like me. The only difference was, he didn't care about fitting in or want to fit in, while I couldn't stop thinking about it.

We took the bus over the Bay Bridge. San Francisco's silhouette of skyscrapers reminded me of New York and Mexico City. I wondered what my life would have been like had we stayed in either place. We walked toward Fisherman's Wharf under a clearing sky through the busy downtown streets. I welcomed the noise and smell of the traffic and people moving through the crowded streets.

Everyone seemed content in making their way through the quagmire of big city life regardless of color. "You ever have a blowjob?" Bubba broke my attention with his deep voice, bellowing cigarette smoke. Archie giggled and tripped, not answering the question.

"No," I said.

"Queers will pay you twenty bucks for it," Bubba continued. "You let them suck your dick for a few minutes, and you got yourself a twenty spot." Archie and I both burst out laughing, not believing what we'd heard. "Don't knock it till you try it!"

"That makes you a fag," I laughed nervously, hoping I wasn't going to be put to the test on whether I was homosexual. I looked around for a woman to take my attention off the gay thoughts and images that flooded my mind. I fended away my sexual insecurities with the knowledge I had felt Suzy's breasts and kissed her endlessly at parties.

"Twenty bucks is twenty bucks." Bubba smiled with clarity in his eyes that said his sexuality was not at stake in the moneymaking blowjob he knew.

We walked to Fisherman's Wharf commenting on every short-skirt-wearing girl Archie and I saw, while Bubba smoked and laughed at us. The Golden Gate Bridge stood on the left, reaching Marin County. On the right, Alcatraz Federal Prison was famous for housing Al Capone and the Bird Man of Alcatraz. It had recently closed after inmates Frank Morris and the Anglin brothers escaped. Now giant faced telescopes lined the pier, and tourists crowded around to get a closer look at the monolith structure that exemplified the country's worst criminals. Bubba jumped at an opening on a telescope and put in a quarter. We each peeked at Alcatraz and agreed the swim was impossible, as sharks would have eaten the inmates before they reached the shore. I felt macho having seen the inmate housing, wondering how I'd fare against hardened criminals. I'd fight any of them if they tried to have sex with me—no place for sissies.

"Time for some glue, no?" said Archie, picking up an empty popcorn bag and handing it to Bubba. We walked to a parking lot across the street and hid between two large sedans. Bubba pushed the glue into the bag and sniffed in and out before passing it to Archie, who did the same and handed it to me. The smell was the same as Dad's model glue. I inhaled a couple more times. Archie's giggles got too loud for me. I stood up and walked toward the pier. The bright colors of the boats and water under a blue sky looked like a fairy tale of sorts. A three-mast schooner was visible on the left that reminded me of Dad's meticulous project and his framed picture. The clouds swirled overhead, casting shadows across the boats. I looked up and almost fell in the water. My bull, my *Toro*, peeked through the cluster smiling at me. "What are you doing here?" I asked.

"What are you doing, Charlie?" my *Toro* said in Spanish. Tears rolled down my cheeks. "Your fears are my fears. Don't live in fear." The sounds of *Fantasia* swept into my head, spinning me around and around until I reached a pier where fishermen unloaded full crates of live crabs. Crab legs reached out for me, sending my heart into panic mode. Boats started clamoring, ropes swung like nooses overhead, while water jumped to the sound of *Fantasia*'s thundering drums with the Golden Gate Bridge in the background. "Get the fuck off the pier, kid!" a gruff fisherman yelled. I snapped to and ran up to the walkway where a laughing Archie and Bubba watched.

"Don't live in fear," my *Toro* whispered from above. A shiny sedan with big headlights rumbled up the street and turned into a charging bull. *Tu madre!* I stepped off the curb and into my bullring. My matador blood rushed through my veins. The sedan slowed down. Was it the bull digging his hooves? I raised my umbrella like a picador and held an imaginary cape aimed at the oncoming sedan. The driver honked and swerved away just as I was about to make my kill. I spun around and found another car/bull charging toward me. I righted my umbrella and held firm for the car. The car sped up and honked. I kept my ground and twirled a perfect *Veronica, Ole!* I was ready for my pretend kill, feeling my grandfather's blood. A car screeched and stopped, but another vehicle slammed into the first car as I crossed my bullring. More horns and tires shattering cut through my senses.

Bubba grabbed my arm and pulled me away from the rear-ended car. The three of us ran as fast as we could toward the skyscrapers until we were safe. I didn't say a word as we walked on without a destination. We came to a movie theater where men loitered outside smoking and staring our way. "Now's the time if you want to make twenty bucks," said Bubba. "Just ask one of those guys to buy you a ticket." Archie giggled and turned red in the face. I covered my penis and walked away backward. Bubba approached a man that looked old enough to be his father in a sweater and tie. The man bought tickets and walked in with Bubba.

"Are you going to do it?" I asked Archie.

"I will if you do," he said. A shiver of fear ran through me. What if I liked it? What if I discovered I was a homosexual?

"No. I'll stay poor," I said. Archie agreed. We waited for Bubba across the street. After a while, a brand new black 1964 Ford Galaxy 500 roared up, Johnny Cash's "Folsom Prison Blues" blasting away through the wide-open windows, and stopped in front of us. Bubba was at the wheel with a cigarette dangling from the side of his mouth.

"Get in," Bubba said, showing off his pumpkin smile. I hesitated. "Hurry up!" Archie jumped in the back. I got in the front. Bubba lit up a new cigarette and said his uncle wanted him to deliver the car to his aunt in Texas. I would learn later that he walked out of the theater through the back and saw the car parked with an open window and keys in the ignition. "You guys up for seeing the world?"

Archie opened the glue bag and took a few sniffs. I followed. We drove to Bubba's house, where he got some more money and cigarettes. Archie got some cash from his home around the corner. I was already in trouble, and I didn't want to face Dad when he found out I skipped school. I didn't want to go back to a school where I didn't belong, and what was the point if we were moving back to Mexico? "Texas is big. My aunt has a ranch. We get a room, meals, and the life of a cowboy," said Bubba.

The life of a cowboy spun happy memories in my head of The Lone Ranger and Tonto. That meant adventure. I imagined myself riding, and roping, and racing, and jumping horses all over Texas without a thought of reality in my glued-up mind.

Two glue-laden, country music blasting days later, we reached Flagstaff Arizona at night, where we pulled in to a two-pump service station for gasoline. A sleep-deprived attendant was closing shop for the night, putting away displays and rolling down a steel garage door. He took our money and filled the gas tank while I washed the window. Bubba and Archie went to the bathroom next to a Coca-Cola machine, crates of empty bottles stood on one side. We rolled away as the attendant turned off the lights.

Bubba drove away, saying we were halfway to Texas. We drove in silence. Then he announced, "We need more money." We stopped on the side of the road to count our money. A moment later, I saw the attendant drive past.

"Quick, go back to the gas station!" I yelled. We did. I jumped out of the car and grabbed a case of coke bottles. Each bottle was worth three cents. Bubba opened the trunk, and we stuffed eight cases of coke bottles in it. With a car trunk that big, we could go anywhere we wanted. Archie sniffed the now dry glue bags and giggled as we drove away. Bubba screamed in laughter for the next mile. Roger Miller could have been singing "King of the Road" on the country station. I pictured myself singing with the hobos on a train. I didn't know what lay ahead for me in Texas, but if I couldn't have my life in Fullerton, it didn't matter.

A red police car light appeared behind us. Bubba pulled to the side and lit up a cigarette. "Smoking helps make you look more responsible," he said. A Flagstaff police car pulled up behind us and stopped.

A policeman waited in his car for a minute before coming to the window. He was a huge man with giant hands. "License and registration, please," the officer said.

"I lost my license, officer, but here's the registration," Bubba said, unfastening the registration on the steering column and handing it over.

"Where are you fellows headed?" the officer asked before reading the paperwork. Bubba inhaled his cigarette then blew smoke straight down and away from the window so as not to hit the man.

"We're going straight to Texas to my aunt's ranch."

"Is that so?" The officer looked up, studying the three of us. "And who does this car belong to?"

"Oh, this is my uncle's car," Bubba said confidently. "He's driving the truck and six-horse trailer."

"Is that so?"

"Yes, sir. He's about an hour ahead of us. You may have seen him in a white truck and trailer—"

"You have a Chinese uncle?" He waited for a response. Bubba chocked on his cigarette. "This car is registered to a Henry Wong in San Francisco."

We were arrested for interstate transportation of stolen property, a federal offense.

It was November, and we would spend twenty-eight days, through Thanksgiving, in jail.

Day One

Dear Mother and Father,

I'm so sorry to have to tell you I am in jail at the address on the envelope. Please don't tell Tia Rosita. I'm sitting in a cold steel cage with two cots, an old coffee can, and magazines for toilet paper.

Please tell Mr. Wong I didn't know his car was not Bubba's uncle's car. I'm sorry.

Day Two

Dear Mother and Father,

The weather here is cold. There is no glass on the window. Only bars. I miss your food. We get three tiny meals a day. This place stinks.

Day Three

Dear Mother and Father,

Please don't tell Aunt Honey, Aunt Florence, Tia Rosita, Mama Chula, or anyone else in the family. I think about you all day long. I'm sorry I ran away from home.

Day Four

Dear Mother and Father,

Berkeley is not really my home. When are we moving to Mexico?

Day Five

Dear Mother and Father,

I hope you are okay. I hope Don is not mad at me. Please, please, please don't tell anyone from Fullerton what a terrible person I've turned out to be.

Day Six

Dear Mother and Father,

They are moving me to a new place today.

Day Seven

Dear Mother and Father,

I have to wear a uniform here. I have a new friend. He is an

Indian and looks like a Mexican. He doesn't talk much. He said he was in a cave at night with some friends and alcohol. Someone got killed, and he doesn't know if he did it.

P.S. This place is warmer. There's glass over the steel bar windows.

Day Eight
Dear Don,

I screwed up. I bet my pancakes and hash browns in a card game. I lost. That's not what I screwed up. I stole a car. I guess you know. There's a queer here who keeps talking about sex. He's creepy. He's big and talks like a girl. He sings Wayne Newton songs all day.

Day Nine
Dear Mother and Father,

A fellow here says "good night" to everyone right before he takes a run across his room and smashes his head into the steel wall. He says that's the only way he can go to sleep. He has his own room. There's another guy screaming all night about being in the Korean War. He says he's a hero with medals.

Day Ten
Dear Don,

I got into a fight and won. I couldn't help it. We had an inspection today. We were all lined up outside our room, against the wall, facing our cots. This guy called me a spic and said I was a dirty Mexican. I pulled the element of surprise trick and punched him in the nose right in front of everyone, and before I knew it, we were punching like crazy. He stopped, and everyone cheered. NO, I DID NOT START THIS FIGHT, AND I AM NOT PROUD. Please tell Mother and Dad. I didn't cry. HAVE NOT CRIED AND WILL NOT CRY.

Day Eleven

Dear Mother and Father

Happy Thanksgiving! Cold turkey and powdered mashed potatoes for me. I deserve this. I am sorry. Don't feel sorry for me. I made my cot, and now I'm lying in it.

Day Twelve

Dear Mother and Father

I got a haircut today by a man who cut someone's throat. He's staying here for a long time. He said I was lucky and should go to college instead of what everyone here has done.

Day Thirteen

Dear Mother and Father,

Two huge soldiers came in today. They went AWOL because they were forced to fight their own men. They were placed in a pit and told to fight it out for the toughest man. The survivor would be the leader. These guys are all muscle, big guys, so it wasn't a fight. They won, but they didn't want to go to Vietnam.

Day Fourteen

Dear Don,

My legs hurt. Movie night. Another fight. A fat guy tried to touch me. He wanted sex. I won.

Day Fifteen

Dear Mother and Father,

A minister or priest came today and asked if I wanted to pray or talk to him. I didn't. If there is a God and a Heaven and a Hell, I know where I'm going. Sorry. Sorry. Sorry. Sorry. Sorry. Sorry.

Day Sixteen

Dear Mother and Father,

When I grow up, I can't vote, go in the Navy, work for the government, become a policeman, a fireman, a teacher, doctor, or lawyer. I have to figure out a new life. When are we moving to Mexico? I promise to be really good in Mexico and never ever break the law. I think I can be an engineer just like you.

Day Seventeen

Dear Mother and Father,

I hope Eugenia and Herb can still talk to me in my new life whatever that will be. I'm sorry Eugenia has to have a criminal brother as the only bad thing in her life. She's a saint, and I'm a devil. I'll miss her if she never wants to see me again.

Day Eighteen

Dear Mother and Father,

There is only one book here, The Bible, *magazines are personal property, and I haven't asked anyone for one yet because I'd owe them something. Cigarettes, candy, or sex are the money they use here.*

Day Nineteen

Dear Mother and Father,

The Indian was moved today. He left me the book The Trail of Tears. I didn't cry. At the end of the day, I got a new roommate. He's a big guy with a funny voice.

Dear Don,

The Indian left. I got a new roommate — the queer. He wants me to fuck him in the ass. He says it will feel like a pussy. I can't sleep.

Day Twenty

Dear Mother and Father,

A Black man gave me an extra cinnamon bun when he was

passing them out. I ate it. I don't think it was for a favor. He just threw it on my plate without even looking up. One thing I see here is how everyone is the same, no matter what color we are. We're all wearing the same uniforms, eat the same, sleep and shower all the same. I wish I could join the Navy, but that's not possible anymore. Sorry to be such a disappointment.

Day Twenty-One

Dear Mother and Father,

I think people who smoke are stupid. That's all they do here is smoke. People live to smoke here. Thank you for not smoking. And thank you for teaching me to be a good person, and providing food, clothing, and shelter. I am sorry I didn't appreciate what you've done for me all my life. I really, really, really made a mess of my life with all the good things you had for me. There are people here who never had anything. Some people have bad fathers or no fathers and mothers. Some have no homes, food, clothes. No one here has gone to college. Everyone brags about their criminal records, robbers, armed robbers, drugs, battery, one bank robber, weapons, wife beaters, a lot of men blame drugs and drinking for the crimes. I have no excuses, Dad and Mom, I did this horrible crime to myself. I'll make it up somehow, even if it's in Mexico. I'll be a better citizen.

Dear Don,

You wouldn't believe some people here are crazy. One guy plays cards all day and tells stories about his pool hustles and card games. His mother taught him everything. His mother has a tattoo over her pussy that says OPEN FOR BUSINESS. *He tattooed his sister with* MERRY CHRISTMAS *on one leg and* HAPPY NEW YEAR *on the other, and above the pussy, it says* INVITE THE BOYS UP BETWEEN THE HOLIDAYS. *He plays for pancakes here. I lost mine to him once. He's been here three times. I'm sorry you have a bad younger brother.*

225

Day Twenty-Two
Dear Mother and Father,

I can do fifty pushups and fifty sit-ups faster than anyone here.

Dear Don,

The queer keeps talking about sex. He wants to blow me. I can't sleep. He says it will help me sleep. I can't talk about it. I have the top bunk, so it's easy to kick him in the face if he tries anything.

Day Twenty-Three
Dear Mother and Father,

Auto mechanics, woodshop, welding, kitchen workers, construction, farming, dry-cleaning, and truck driving are all jobs I can apply for. They're all in a way of service to others. So sorry.

Day Twenty-Four
Dear Mother and Father,

If you want me to go back Mexico with Tia Rosita and Mama Chula and everyone there, I can go as soon as I get out of here and not be the disappointment that I am to you any longer. I'll be eighteen in three years and can stay out of your way if you don't want me back.

Day Twenty-Five
Dear Mother and Father,

I reread the book. I don't understand why Indians didn't just go to Mexico. I miss tortillas.

Dear Don,

The queer blew three guys in the bathroom today. I was on the lookout. I didn't get a hard-on. He doesn't ask me to fuck him in the ass anymore.

Day Twenty-Six

Dear Mother and Father,

I wish I knew when and where they are going to send me and for how long. Other people get visitors here. Don't worry, I'm not asking you to embarrass yourselves by driving into a prison. I just wish I knew what was in my future.

Day Twenty-Seven

Dear Mother and Father,

I guess I'll never be a teacher now.

Day Twenty-Eight

Dear Mother and Father,

See you tomorrow if you still want me.

At last, I received one letter from home addressed to Master Charles Allen.

Master Charles P. Allen,

It is with deep regret that we must communicate in this fashion at your current residence. This family has never known or associated with a criminal element. It will take some time to adjust to this sort of character in our presence. There will be new rules and boundaries in our home that we will all learn to live by.

The act of stealing a horse in the past was punishable by death through hanging. Today's cars are yesterday's horses. Your criminal behavior could have cost you your life had you lived in a different time. Perhaps you would not have ventured out on an escapade in times past when the youth had chores and challenges at home that would have filled the urge for excitement. In the past, nature provided plenty of challenges for a healthy boy like you to challenge and explore your limits. In a sense, this episode may be viewed as a reaction to society's limiting a young boy's activities. Today's world is very different. Society places young adults in a closed environment for the majority of the day and expects calm behavior that merely goes against nature. No son, do not take all the blame for this episode. You have failed, but so have we. We are the adults, and we should provide more avenues, perhaps more parks, for you to use your energy in a more productive manner. Your Mother cries every night, as do I. Wishing you were here with us.

Mom and Dad

Shame

Facing my parents after that letter was not easy. Dad and Mother picked me up in downtown San Francisco. I stepped out of a room and met both their sullen faces. I stood before the great white saint, ashamed to be alive. Dad stood expressionless without reaching out to shake my hand or hug me. I didn't reach out to him. His face looked gray. His hair showed signs of gray. It was my doing, and I regretted causing his worry. Mother stood embarrassed, unable to reach out to me, next to Dad. It was an awkward feeling for all three of us. Dad was driving a criminal in his car. An assimilated, or Americanized Mexican criminal going home with the great William Allen. I had to be the biggest disappointment in his life.

We drove home in silence. It was dark by the time we arrived back in Berkeley. Dad told me to go to my room as we entered. Don peeked his head out as I walked past his bedroom. He handed me a letter without saying a word. Dad must have prepared Mother and Don for my silent homecoming. I waited in my bedroom, not knowing what my consequences would be. I was ready for any punishment Dad could think of.

I opened Don's letter.

Dear Charlie,

I'm sorry you had to live through this horrible time alone. I wish I had been a better older brother and kept you out of trouble. I'm sure you learned a lot about life you may not have learned anywhere else. No matter what happened, you will survive and grow. Be glad you did not end up in a Mexican jail. That could have been the end. You can still have a beautiful and fulfilling life ahead. Mom and Dad will always be here for you. Eugenia and I are too. I love you and will always help in any way possible. Do well in school. Make us all proud. I love you. Don

I picked up the book *Moby-Dick* and tried to read. I couldn't.

A painful hour passed with the most delicious smell of roast and potatoes, homemade bread, and apple pie seeping through the walls before we sat for dinner. It was horrible. Mother had gone all out preparing a roast beef dinner straight out of a *Better Homes and Gardens* front cover magazine, complete with a checkered tablecloth. Considering I'd had nothing but bland food served on a tray for a month, Mother's meal was a feast fit for a king. I wanted to eat the whole roast, but I was a stranger, an outsider in my own home. I waited for my serving, anticipating a savory bite of the roast, checking my best New York learned manners. I kept my hands at my side, watching and waiting for Dad to pick up his fork. He didn't. He stared at his fork. I waited. Don waited. Mother waited. "*Billcito?*" Mother prompted. He took a deep breath, eyes still on his fork.

Finally, he looked up. "This family has never had a criminal at the table," he said, eyes on me. I sat on trial facing Don, Dad, and Mother. Dad picked up his knife and fork.

I lost my appetite.

I had disgraced the perfect man, Mother's knight in shining armor. Mother couldn't give me her calming two-eyed blink. Don stared at his food. I was a pariah in the family. I couldn't take back my stupid mistake that caused all the pain present at the table. All of Dad's good intentions, his efforts in making a good citizen out of me, had backfired. I had failed at being the American he wanted me to be. How would I ever atone for my sins?

I pecked at the food, unable to eat. I drank a glass of milk and waited. "Well, Charles," Dad started. He hadn't called me Charles since he gave me the name. Was he about to disown me? "This episode certainly is not what any of us had in mind for you in your new home, but here we are." At least he still considered this my home. Mother and Don stared at the table. I listened, feeling Dad's pain as he spoke. "You will follow a simple schedule that involves nothing other than school. You will report to school in the morning and home no later than three-thirty. School gets out at two-forty. That should give you ample time. You shall maintain good grades and stay in your room after school until your homework is finished. You may make one phone call per day with either your mother or me present. You will remain on this schedule for one full year. Do you understand?"

"Yes," I said, wishing I had died in Arizona rather than face Dad's disappointed look. Mother and Don picked up the dishes. I saw Mother crying in the kitchen. Don comforted her and held her. She buried her face in his arms. My stomach turned. Don walked Mother to her room.

Dad pulled out the few letters I'd received from my friends in Fullerton while I was gone. "Your Mother and I read these letters from your friends," he said. A letter from David said something about a blowjob. "We have a question about your preferences. As you know, I was in the Navy. Homosexuality is known to happen aboard ships. I have homosexual friends, as well. As far as I'm concerned, it's a free country, and people have the right to their own lifestyles."

"Dad, are you asking me if I'm a homo?"

"Well, Don's called you a 'maricon' many times, these letters are all from boys, and they're mentioning oral sex," he said with a dire look. An unopened letter dropped off the table. It was from Suzy. I held it up.

"This is from a girl." I opened the letter and found the Saint

Christopher necklace and a note wishing me good luck. I put the necklace on without looking up. Don had called me a *"maricon,"* as older brothers often do to their young siblings. It's part of the macho culture. I didn't know what to say or how to prove I was not, but I knew I had never had sex with a boy. "I am not a homosexual, Dad," I said, blushing. Having to defend myself against that thought made me blush even more. "Really, I'm not."

"Do you have any questions?" Dad asked.

"One year?"

"As long as it takes for you to regain our trust. Any more questions?"

"No, Dad, sir," I whispered, hoping the word sir affirmed my subordination.

The rules were set, and I stuck to them like a new cadet. I got good grades, never missed a class, and joined the drama club. I still didn't feel comfortable enough to sit during lunch and stood on the side, trying to be invisible. "Heard you had a rough go out there, Charles," Mr. Populus said after class one day.

"I guess the whole world knows," I said, surprised that he knew anything about my mess. "I messed up my life forever."

"It's a lesson you can learn from. You can still go on to do great things."

"I can't vote, can't work in government, and can't become a doctor, lawyer, cop, fireman, or teacher. May as well go back to Mexico."

"Nonsense," he said, adamantly holding up his deformed hand. "You see this? It came from a similar experience with the law when I was a little older than you. I paid a price, and I am still paying. You're lucky."

"Holy shit. Did you kill somebody?" I asked, remembering the man who cut my hair in Arizona.

"No. It doesn't matter what I did. Everyone gets a second chance, and so will you. As a juvenile, your record will be sealed, and you'll start all over with a clean slate. You just have to stay out of trouble until you're twenty-one. Choose your friends wisely." Maybe I wasn't as screwed up as I thought. Wanda slinked over from the doorway, looking me up and down with her sexy eyes. I turned red. She walked past, leaving my mouth rubbery and my heart pounding. "Be careful with the girls, Charles." He walked away.

Paul startled me at lunchtime with a big smile. "I need some more rubbers," he said. I noticed a few girls smiling and looking over from where Paul had been sitting. Lucky guy, I thought. "Can I get a dozen?"

A dozen? I looked at his friends wondering which girl, or girls, he was having sex with. "Sure," I smiled.

"Ha!" Paul turned and called out to his friends, "I did it." The girls laughed. "They said I couldn't make you smile." One girl, a tall brunette with piercing brown eyes and high cheekbones, motioned for me to join the table. Her name was Karen, and she seemed to be the leader of the group. These kids were just like my friends in Orange County, so American. John, a blond skateboarder with buckteeth, sat next to Karen. Sue, a Jewish girl in a tight blue sweater, seemed bored and made room for me to sit. I didn't. Darlene, a blond Barbie type, fiddled with her hair. Steve, a skinny pale boy, slouched nervously in a checkered shirt. Jim, a six-foot-four boy with Clearasil caked over his pimples, and a few other kids that seemed happy and secure, looked me over. I wasn't comfortable. I didn't want to make friends and have a repeat of Fullerton.

I walked out of school that day to a clear blue sky with my report card in my pocket. I took in a deep breath of crisp springtime air. It felt good—clear, unlike my thoughts. Mr. Populus had given me hope. I skipped the bus and walked toward the hills. I needed to be alone with my thoughts. A vigorous walk would have me home in forty-five minutes. I was under the impression that my police record was going to keep me from doing anything meaningful for mankind; a life of service to others. I picked up my pace wanting to leave that thought behind.

The university, nestled in the fertile green hills, loomed large over the city with political protests. It seemed like the civil rights movement was changing the world right there, and we were all a part of it. Many of the adults I respected, Dad and several teachers, including Mr. Populus, had all gone to U.C. Berkeley. With the knowledge that I could redeem myself and go to the same college, I broke into a sprint. I shot straight up University Avenue, passing college and high school students along the crowded way until I reached the gates of the U.C. Berkeley campus.

Catching my breath, I threw my hands up and spun around. A motorcycle rider passed by. He slowed to a stop and turned around. It was Mr. Brown in his brown leather jacket. He looked a lot like Marlon Brando in *The Wild One,* but with a white shirt and tie. "Hi, Charles," he said. "You look like you could be a freshman here."

"Hi, Mr. Brown," I said out of breath. "I will be."

He swung one leg over, took a sidesaddle position, and pulled out a pack of Lucky Strike cigarettes. "Smoke?" he offered. I didn't know how to say no to my English teacher and reached for the unfiltered cigarette. "What are you going to study, Charles?" He flipped open a Zippo lighter and cupped the flame for me. I puffed the cigarette until it lit. "What does your father do for a living?"

"Engineer," I said and took a puff. "Makes electronic stuff like calculators and things. He says someday computers will fit on a desk."

"Smart man, your dad. What are you interested in?"

"I'm interested in being of service to others." I surprised myself with the quick response, and it felt good. "You know, to help make this a better world."

"That's noble."

"What made you become a teacher, Mr. Brown?"

"Jack Kerouac, Allen Ginsberg, jazz, and Lenny Bruce are all related in a cosmic venture that I'm drawn to. It's all happening right over there." He pointed toward San Francisco and took a deep, satisfying inhale of tobacco. He exhaled a defined stream of smoke.

"San Francisco?" I'd missed the cosmic for the criminal venture. "Beatniks?"

"That's right. That's where it's all happening. I live there. After that, it's Mexico and South America."

"On a motorcycle? I want a motorcycle. Someday I'll be riding just like you, Mr. Brown." I inhaled the cigarette without coughing and watched the smoke dissipate over the Golden Gate Bridge.

"Right now, I'm going to the Free Speech rally. Mario Savio is speaking. Hopefully, I'll make my Spanish class. If I'm going to Latin America, I have to speak the language."

I looked lost. "It's all over the news, part of the civil rights movement. Exciting times."

"I speak Spanish. I was born in Mexico."

"No, shit?"

"You like teaching, Mr. Brown?"

"I like meeting people, seeing and experiencing new places. Read Kerouac's *On the Road*, it'll give you an insight into an un-boring life." He paused, taking a deep drag of his cigarette, crunching out the butt under his hush puppy boots before exhaling. "I know you like Mark Twain, Charles. I think you're a good candidate for the teaching profession." He kick-started and revved the engine. "But first, go out and see the world."

That night I handed Dad my report card. "My teacher says I can still be a teacher, Dad," I said. I had more As than Bs. "He said my record can be buried, and I can be a teacher or anything I want."

"Let's hope you can stay out of trouble," Dad said, unconvinced, still in his white shirt and tie. He sighed at my grades. He had straight A report cards all his life.

Mother stood at the window wearing a modern satin dress and light blouse, reading a magazine and doing light leg extensions and dips. She loved her palace.

"I'm trying out for football next year," I said. Don came into the room and sat at a table with Mother's and Dad's dream home blueprints.

"Friday night football? I'll be there!" Don said.

"Let's hope that doesn't take away from your studies," Dad said and stepped toward his bedroom. Mother dropped the magazine she held and faded into a seizure. I hadn't seen her in a seizure in a few years. Dad gently guided her into their bedroom. I went to the table where Don sat.

"Mom must have forgotten to take her meds," Don said, concerned. "I hope." I knew he meant to calm our fears.

"Could be those exercises and yoga stuff she's been doing," I said.

"It's supposed to help."

"I hope."

"Mexico is the only thing that's going to help Mom."

"No way." I feared the thought of having to move to Mexico. "Not again."

"They want to build a house in Guadalajara," Don said, pointing at Dad's blueprints. "Guadalajara, Guadalajara, Guadalajara," he sang. "They bought this," he said, showing me a few pictures of a hillside lot I'd never seen. "I'm not going." He slammed the photos down.

"Can I live with you?" I asked. Don shrugged without answering and walked away, singing the same lyrics.

Easy for him to sing away the notion of moving. He had a license, could find a job, had all his friends from Belmont that he could count on. The house design was clearly Mother and Dad's future. Their new lot in Guadalajara was situated on a hillside above a medical school.

"Are we moving to Mexico?" I asked Dad during dinner.

"Possibly. It's not certain, but we will have a home there if and when we need one." He comforted Mother with a nod. She looked weak, vulnerable from the seizure. Had I caused her seizure?

"When you turn eighteen," Mother said in Spanish, making it easier for herself. Eighteen? *Just what is that supposed to mean?* I thought. *I'll still be in high school. Does that mean I'm on my own then? I better get my act together. I don't have much time. Better make plans. Maybe this is my fault that Mother and Dad want to go back to Mexico. This is part of my punishment. I deserve it. Shit, I have to come up with a plan.*

Later that evening, Mother fell into another seizure. I led her to her room. She cuddled a pillow on the bed and closed her eyes. I held her hand, watching her mouth churn with tight lips. Her face jolted back, and tears welled before a calm came. I opened her nightstand and handed her a tissue. She rested her hand on mine. I saw the chocolate box and wondered whether her death pills were still in place. I checked; they were.

The following day I ran into Wayne Garcia at a bus stop. I hadn't seen him since I'd run away. He said Archie had moved away then laughed at my attire. I'd put on a madras shirt and tie, trying to feel as I had before my criminal adventure. He handed me a condom saying it was on the house, and we both headed to the El Cerrito Mall. A few of Wayne's friends were waiting for him at the stop. They all dressed similarly and had slicked-back hair that reminded me of Don's friends. I walked with them toward the main entrance, where another group of slick-haired boys stood staring at us. They all scowled and wore buttoned-up Pendleton shirts with khaki pants.

I sensed trouble and thought about turning away, but I thought I saw a familiar face, so I paused and smiled. The boy, Richard, blocked my path. "Why you smile, faggot?" he said. Mexico, thoughts of having to move to Mexico angered me. I pushed him out of my way, ready for a fight. He didn't fight.

"I'm not a homo."

He stood back with both palms out. "Let's take this somewhere else," he started. "I don't want to go back to jail. I'm on probation."

Probation? Shit. This wasn't the way my assimilated Americanized life was supposed to turn out.

"Fuck your probation. Fuck my parole." *Ole*, I thought. I started toward him, but I thought better of it, having remembered Dad's and Mother's faces filled with worry. Wayne and his friends stood behind me; they had my back.

Richard smiled respectfully. He was impressed with my criminal past. This was a different kind of an American boyhood. My dad would be horrified by, but that didn't matter right now. He was moving to Mexico, and I had to find my way here. For now, all that mattered was me proving I wasn't a homosexual by kicking this guy's ass. "I'll meet you in the field behind the bowling alley," Richard said. Wayne accepted, saying we'd be there in ten minutes. Richard's group walked away around the corner. I had no idea what I was getting into, but I was angry and confused. I welcomed a good fight that would prepare me for whatever was in store for me in Guadalajara or anywhere.

Wayne managed to round up a few more friends as we weaved our way through the mall and toward the field. By the time we reached the area, Wayne had wrangled ten boys. Wayne had a way of winning people's loyalty. We turned the corner into the field to find Richard's group. He had twenty boys and men, some with mustaches, waiting for us. Two members of his group had bats, one — a bicycle chain. I had stepped into the lion's den of future gangsters. *Chinga tu madre!* There was no turning back. This was just like *West Side Story*. Only it wasn't a movie. These guys had real weapons and mustaches.

"It's a setup," Wayne whispered.

"Tough shit," I said and broke away from the group.

"We got your back, Charles," Wayne said.

I faced Richard as he moved into the open area, coolly unbuttoned his flannel shirt, and tossed it to his mustache-faced partner. They both wore sleeveless wife-beaters. I took off my tie and tossed it to Wayne just as my bullfighting grandfather would have done. Richard came to me. I was ready for whatever was coming. I dodged his first swing and bounced back, feeling a lot like Muhammad Ali. Richard came again, throwing light jabs that couldn't reach me. I checked with my own left jabs. He stepped in, throwing a combination of left and right hooks that didn't reach my face. I knew I had this fight easily won whenever I wanted, but the mustache wearing men around gave me pause.

I bounced on my toes and circled around just as I'd seen Muhammad Ali in his fights. Richard came at me again, finally catching me on the chin. His friends encouraged him with some war-like grunts. The chain-carrying fellow smacked it on a rock. The bat-wielding thugs slapped their palms with their wooden weapons. Richard gained confidence. "Parole for what?" he mumbled and attacked with a flurry of soft punches. He couldn't hurt me. "Parole for what?" He was too curious. I moved back, planting my feet. He moved in as I expected. I delivered a perfect right cross that sent him to the ground on his back. One good blow is all it took. A boot-wearing man with mustache blindsided me with a kick to my ribs. I buckled sideways and took a blow on the nose. I faced the dirty fighter, a man in his twenties. "One at a time," I said, my bullfighter blood spewing down my face.

I was in the center of a bullring ready for anything. Richard jumped up with blood on his wife-beater. "I got this, *Tio!*" he shouted. *Tio?* His uncle had jumped in. He backed off. Wayne and his friends stood at the ready. Richard's group let down as *Tio* moved back. Richard now had all of my attention, and I had his. "So, you're on parole for reals." He took a swing and missed. The way he said it, the tone, seemed too friendly for someone fearing "going back to jail." No matter, I punched him, and he hit me until our arms gave out. We were both left a bloody mess, and I felt great. I was ready for Mexico, if that was where Mother and Dad were taking me.

Don caught me sneaking into my room with a blood-stained shirt.

I told him about the fight. "You have to be better than that. You can't afford to get in any more trouble," he said.

"I know. I know. I don't know what got into me," I tried to justify my stupidity.

"You're lucky we're not in Mexico."

"That's where Mother and Dad are going."

"Exactly. Don't make it any harder on yourself. School is the only answer. It's the only thing that stays with you forever, your education."

Coming from Don, those words hit a nerve. I was lost.

Wake-up Call: 1965

I needed a change. I didn't like what I had become at Berkeley High. My life in Fullerton would have been about sports and school. I decided to attend a different high school where I could get a fresh start. I enrolled in El Cerrito High School, joined the football team, and made the honor roll. It was a successful first semester, and Dad seemed to approve of my changes.

Our last game of the season was the homecoming game with Berkeley High School. I was elected defense captain for that game and played linebacker. Paul was one of the captains on Berkeley's team. I hadn't seen him all year. He looked a lot bigger when we shook hands for the coin toss. I wished him a good game, but he only growled. He meant business, as football was his ticket to college. Growling must have been part of the Berkeley training, because the linemen growled on every down. It was irritating to hear and may have contributed to their loss. We won by two touchdowns. Paul stood out as the best player on the field. Afterward, I extended my hand to him. "Good game," I said, glad our uniforms were equally grass-stained and mud-soaked. His teammate, Mark, a chiseled face lineman, stood next to him growling as he'd done all game. I reached out to shake his hand, but he walked away.

"That's Mark. He's an asshole right now. Parents are divorcing," Paul said. His friend Karen walked over in her cheerleader uniform.

"Pizza. Eight o'clock. LaVal's," she said to Paul.

"Good game," I said.

"We lost," she said flatly. Then looked at me, "Pizza. Eight o'clock, LaVal's." I didn't know what to make of it. Paul noticed, somehow.

"You look really dumb right now, *amigo*." *Amigo*? He called me *amigo*, his friend. "Either you got a hard-on for Karen, or you don't know where LaVal's is." He laughed so profoundly; I couldn't help but laugh at myself.

Paul and I walked together to LaVal's Pizza Parlor. We crossed the adjacent parking lot, where an animal-like growl and crunching glass sounded. "Shiiiiiiiit, muthafucking, gr-r-r-r," Mark stumbled out from between two cars, glassy-eyed, with shards of a broken car mirror in his hands. He was drunk and bleeding.

We walked Mark quickly into the pizza parlor outdoor patio area. He stumbled through the red and white tablecloth covered tables and sat with Karen and a friendly-faced boy, Ben, with braces. Karen and Ben handed Mark a few napkins and tried to contain the bloody mess. Mark blurted out a few painful grunts that ended with, "Fuck Vietnam."

Karen jumped away, bumping a man at the next table as he poured his pitcher of beer. The man wore an Army jacket. "Vietnam can kiss my ass," the Army man said. He rolled back from the table in his wheelchair. "What's your beef?" he asked Mark. That got Mark's attention. He focused on the wheelchair, a little too obvious. "Shit happens."

"My brother's in the Army," Mark slurred, then continued, "on his way to Vietnam right now."

The disabled soldier nodded and went back to his beer.

Paul and I became best friends after the pizza party. We shared a warped sense of humor about everything, and both had older brothers that somehow bound us together on needing to prove ourselves. By month's end, we pledged a lifetime friendship. One afternoon at his house, Paul wrote up a blood brother pledge that we both signed. His idea of blood brother pledge was not what I had expected. Instead of a pinprick, he brought out a hunting knife. He said it was the manly thing to do, and to prove himself, he held his arm out and handed me the knife. It was a sharp pointy knife. I reached for his finger, but he stopped me and held out his wrist. "Go ahead, right there. Just stab it," he ordered. I couldn't do it. "Go ahead. Don't be a chicken shit."

"Okay, okay. I got this, just be quiet." I pricked his wrist ever so slightly but just enough to see red. *Phew*, I thought.

"Gimme that knife," he said, snatching it from me. I held out my wrist and closed my eyes.

Whack! He cut my wrist and laughed so hard I didn't feel the pain. His rich, deep laugh was contagious. We slapped our wrists together and took a solemn oath to be blood brothers forever. I felt a little bit more American than I'd ever felt before. I transferred back to Berkeley High before the next semester.

Paul had been approached by senior football players to join a fraternity, the Athenians. His father had attended Berkeley High and was an Athenian alumnus. The club had a history of civic duties, charitable events, and roguish drinking parties. It was, for all intents and purposes, a stepping-stone to one of Berkeley's college fraternities. Athenians alumni included teachers, policemen, doctors, lawyers, judges, and business owners. Many of them were Chamber of Commerce members and maintained close relationships.

I transferred back to Berkeley High and attended the Athenian "rush" with Paul. Membership in the Athenians would be a rite of passage into the American Dream. Rushing a fraternity included a formal introduction to the club's members and the forty-year history. It was held at a home on Grizzle Peak Road with a grand view of the bay. Two brand-new cars, a Ford Mustang and a Corvette, were parked on the street along with several expensive sedans. I stopped at the red Corvette. "This is Kurt Sproul's car," Paul said.

"Kurt Sproul as in Sproul Hall?" I asked.

"The one and only. He was born with a silver spoon in his mouth."

How did I get here? I thought. One year ago, I was in jail, believing I'd blown my chances of going to college, and now I'm about to join a college-bound fraternity. I'd better make a good impression. Paul and I walked to the house and were greeted at the door by two senior fraternity members. They wore black varsity jackets with the Athenians logo, a white block A. "Welcome to the house of ill repute," joked one. The other handed us a beer and led the way to a rec room where twenty fraternity brothers stood gladiator-like in a semi-circle, all wearing Athenians jackets.

Another eight prospective members arrived shortly. One by one, we were introduced and asked to say a little about ourselves. Paul spoke of his football participation and aspirations. One boy mentioned his legacy in the club through his brother. Another boy mentioned his father's and uncle's alumni status.

I was prepared to say something about my football experience but instead blurted out, "I was born in Mexico, and I want to live a life of service to others. Perhaps teaching—" I stopped. The room went quiet, and all eyes were on me. I was thrust back to my first day of kindergarten. My throat tightened. I held up the beer. "Chug, chug, chug!" and chugged it down. Hoots and hollers. That single act of bravado won them over.

We mingled informally, mostly hearing stories about wild parties. A couple of thick scrapbooks with club members in school and community activities—sports, honors, thespian shots, political rallies, and rallies were on display. The most impressive of all was a picture of members up close watching President John F. Kennedy on his campaign trail through Berkeley. At the end of the night, the president of the club handed out a pamphlet that included a list of members going back to 1930. Being a part of this all-American group would set the foundation for the rest of my education and maybe my life. I was on my way back to becoming the all-American son Dad wanted.

Being an Athenian member had its perks besides the

brotherhood; it had an established reputation of civic service, and most importantly, The Thebans, a sisterhood club. They were future sorority girls and partied with Athenians every weekend. The girls were cheerleaders, and drama, student council, and chorus members. I was in a safe place with the Athenians and knew I'd be attending U.C. Berkeley. Paul was on his way to a football scholarship, and we were already attending fraternity parties. I was in a place I could call home that felt right.

I'd stayed on track and out of trouble through my "rehabilitation," as I called my tenth-grade school year. It was time to show Dad my report card. I reminded him I'd played football without it lowering my grades. I was proud of my work, and I wanted him to be proud of me. "You seem to have learned a valuable lesson from your escapade," he said, looking up from my grades. "And this Athenian group of friends, are they going to help you stay on track?"

I whipped out the Athenian pamphlet listing the alumni's accomplishments. He read the list. "This is an impressive group," he said. I'd cleared my criminal profile.

Mother sat near Dad. She took the report card. *"Felicidades, buena suerte,"* she said. The tone in Mother's voice sounded like a cryptic message that we were moving back to Mexico.

Cars were mandatory in my new social group. Everyone had either their vehicle or the use of a family car. With my criminal record, I didn't have the gall to ask Dad for the use of his. I quit football. I found a job at a senior retirement center cafeteria as a kitchen worker. I threw on an apron and learned how to wash dishes, pots, pans, stainless steel appliances, tables, and floors in a one-day training session on a Saturday. The following Monday, I signed my timecard and punched it in the time clock at the entrance. Just then, a brown arm reached across with a familiar fragrance. "Hello, Charles," Wanda purred with a smile. I blushed. "Are you working here?"

"My first day," I said. "I'll be in the kitchen, washing pots and pans."

"Everyone starts there," she started. "But you will move up to dishes in no time. Just don't piss off my mom."

"Your mom?" I said.

"She hired you." I met the small kitchen staff. Everyone was Black. James Brown sounds competed with the clattering of dishes, pots, and pans. Wanda's mother was the day-shift manager in charge of all three meals, and Daryl was the night manager in charge of cleaning and stocking. Daryl carried himself with dignity and dressed like Frank Sinatra. He was in his twenties, carried a briefcase, and attended junior college. He and I were the last ones out every night.

I'd walk to his bus stop with him and listen to his philosophy about life. He was interested in the civil rights movement and saddened by Malcolm X's recent assassination. I looked forward to hearing his unique view on the news. His Black perspective always surprised me. He took pride in everything he was responsible for, including the way I mopped the floor and wiped down the stainless-steel equipment. "Put a little more emphasis on the corners," he'd say while inspecting my floor mopping duties. Then he'd show me how to sanitize the stainless-steel appliances with vinegar and washcloth. "First, you rub it left to right, then you stroke it up and down just the way your lady likes it."

Wanda re-introduced me to her mother as *the new-boy-who-never-sat-down-at-lunch*. I laughed, but the mother never called me anything but that. My shift was from four to nine and started with delivering food trays to seniors who needed assistance at their tables or to the rooms. I had a mantra regularly offered: "Go to college, sweet boy," they'd tell me. Sweet boy. If they only knew I was a criminal. It was my secret, and I would not ruin their image of me.

One day when Wanda was busy inside the walk-in refrigerator, I stepped in behind her to grab a can of tomatoes. Boxes everywhere made for tight quarters and made it difficult for me to pass by her. I waited, giving way, for her to walk past, but she didn't move. She smiled, pumping up my heartbeat. The door closed behind me, turning off the light. We were alone in the dark and cold. She giggled. I melted. Our lips came together. I pulled her hips into mine. We stayed lip-locked, twisting around, feeling each other in the cold, until we knocked over an open box of butter. She rushed out, buttoning up her blouse.

Daryl winked at me as I walked out. Later that night, Wanda stayed with Daryl and me until closing time. Wanda turned up her mother's radio and blasted James Brown's "Maybelline." "You want to dance?" Wanda asked but took my hand, pulled me out of my seat. We danced on the freshly mopped and still wet floor holding each other up. Daryl reached in his briefcase and rolled up a joint. Wanda gave me a doe-eyed look. "Are you going to smoke?" She wanted me to decide whether to take a hit of the joint. I felt empowered, in control of our destiny, and inhaled my first marijuana. Wanda followed and brushed up against me. I pulled her closer. Daryl gave us an approving smile, made some comment about being careful, and turned the lights down as a slow dance song came on the radio.

Night after night, Wanda and I met in the refrigerator and mauled our youthful passions in the dark. One night my Saint Christopher necklace ended up outside of my shirt and fell between her breasts as we kissed. She ran her fingers through my hair and purred from deep down. I instinctively pulled the chain off and placed it around her neck. We stayed longer than usual in the cold that evening.

I collected myself and stepped out of the refrigerator to "New-boy-who-never-sat-down-at-lunch" — it was Wanda's mother — "you better sit down now." She was as serious as my probation officer. I took the nearest seat and wiped Wanda's still fresh lipstick off my mouth. But it didn't matter; Wanda's blouse was askew with the necklace dangling on one side. In our haste, I had buttoned her top lopsided. Now she too was wiping off lipstick from her cheeks. I never entered the refrigerator again, and ten years would go by before I would kiss Wanda again.

Eleventh grade started, and had I saved enough money from the kitchen job to buy a 1953 Chevrolet convertible that I saw parked at a Union 76 service station. I paid fifty dollars for the white convertible. The owner, Joe, was concerned about my buying the car alone and asked whether my parents were aware of it. Dad agreed to my purchasing of the vehicle and placing it on his insurance. I asked Joe for a job before leaving. He told me to come by on Saturday to see if I liked the work. I showed up bright and early, ready for the day. The first thing I did was polish the stainless-steel gas pumps and every stainless-steel door, "the way the ladies liked it." Then I followed Joe around until I could anticipate his moves. I'd wash the windows and check the radiator for water on cars quicker than Joe. At the end of the day, I mopped the floor, making sure Joe saw my way of "putting emphasis in the corners." I got the job. I was scheduled for Saturday and Sunday morning shifts at eight o'clock. Dad came to the station at the end of the day to pick up the car. He warned me that it could be dangerous for me to have my own car. "Why?" I asked.

"It's a bed on wheels," he said. I remembered him asking me whether I was gay. He must have read my mind because he added, "With the girls." He sounded like Mr. Populus.

The Vietnam War was building up, and eighteen-year-olds had to register for the draft. Some of Don's friends had joined the armed services, some were drafted, and some didn't make it back alive. He still had the heart murmur and was a full-time student, so he didn't have to go. Don spent most of his time in Belmont with his group of friends who were now in labor unions and settling into blue-collar family life. He didn't seem content with that lifestyle and never joined any of the union jobs available to him. He enjoyed his time with his friends but had a thirst for learning.

Don loved reading Shakespeare and literature. He took up theater arts at U.C. Berkeley with an eye on directing films and buying a house in the hills off Ralston Avenue, where he'd left his heart. He spent hours and days in his room reading and philosophizing about the meaning of life. He took it to the extreme, sometimes saying life was meaningless and staying in his room, curtains drawn, for days. His existential interpretations pulled him away from any religious beliefs, but he seemed to fight inner demons left from childhood. Mother thought Dolores had broken Don's heart because he was drawn to tragic and dreary stories. Don's dark life worried Mother and Dad.

At the same time, Eugenia's marriage had failed. One day I came home one day to a loud rattle coming from Mother's bedroom. I rushed in and found Mother's nightstand drawer on the floor, the contents strewn all around. Mother knelt in front crying and searching around frantically. "*Mama, que pasa?*" I caught her eye.

"I was a bad mother," she said and looked down again. I saw the death pills. She saw the death pills. I beat her to them. "Take it, throw it away. Flush that down the toilet."

I pushed the bottle of pills in my pocket. "You're a great mother," I said, holding her tight.

"It's my fault. I am a bad mother. It's all my fault." She cried deeper than I'd ever felt her cry in my arms. All I could do was hold her. After a while, she said Eugenia had attempted to end her life with Herb, the only way she knew how. It was an apparent suicide attempt. It didn't make sense. "Why? He was perfect," I paused, searching for the right word to describe the giant I loved, "an all-American man."

"I don't know. I don't know. I don't know."

"What can I do? We do?"

"God is cruel. Unforgiving. He's punishing Eugenia for my sins," she said.

"*Ay, Mami.* No, you're a good mother."

"Our sins pass on to our children." She buried her face in a pillow.

I walked to her toilet and flushed her death pills away.

Eugenia's all-American marriage fell apart. Mother and Dad were inconsolable. They loved Herb but accepted the reasoning behind the decision. Herb and Eugenia were simply growing in different directions; he wanted a simple family life; she sought intellectual pursuits. Eugenia moved to Berkeley to attend graduate school and be near the family. I'm not sure why Mother and Dad kept such a close relationship with Herb, but it seemed as though he came for dinner more frequently than Eugenia. I never talked to my sister about her dissolution with Herb, as it appeared to be too painful. But she seemed more at ease with her new life at the university.

I accompanied Paul to football tryouts one Saturday morning even though I wasn't going to play. I had decided to start earning money to be ready for when Mother and Dad left for Mexico. Cheerleader tryouts were in progress at the student quad. Karen led the drills for the thirty hopeful girls. One girl caught my eye with her high kicks. She was a senior with classic features and rosy red cheeks. Her name was Katie. She was a competitive gymnast. I stopped to watch the girls while Paul went on to the football field.

Katie bounced and kicked and spun effortlessly through the drills. During a break, she started down the quad and shot out a summersault, followed by a backflip. No one followed her. She walked back chin up, auburn ponytail bouncing, without breathing hard.

I wanted to meet her and loitered around, making eye contact with her the entire session. Afterward, I followed her to the parking structure. "Are you following me, Charles?" she said. A gust of wind blew her auburn hair up, highlighting her jaw and rosy cheeks.

"Do you mind?" I didn't pretend to be doing anything else.

"Karen said you're a nice guy." Katie smiled and opened the door to a convertible Volkswagen. I noticed she parked in a reserved parking spot, reserved for Armstrong College staff. It was a private business college across the street. She popped the front hood and threw her gym bag inside. An Armstrong College parking sticker became visible on the front window. "Are you interested in helping me with our rush party Saturday night?"

"Sure. What do you want me to do?" I answered.

"Chaperone the newbies."

Saturday night, I showed up at Katie's house right on time, dressed to impress. She greeted me with a smile and a yellow rose. A subtle scent of springtime perfume excited me as she placed the rose on my sports jacket lapel. Katie's parents were pillars in the community, listed in the Who's Who in America, of German ancestry. Her father, Dr. K, was a surgeon and Cal alumni. He had played linebacker on the football team and was a middleweight boxer. Now he was a team doctor. Katie's mom, Mrs. K, was an heir to the Armstrong family estate that included Armstrong College.

A black Steinway piano under an arched window was the primary focus of the living room. A fresh flower arrangement and a Beethoven bust rested on top of the Steinway. Classical music scores and albums filled two shelves on a wall. Another rack had a row of intricate steins and other German artifacts. Framed pictures of Katie in ice skating competitions stood among other competitive ice skater's photos. Katie introduced me to her mother and father.

Her father sat stiffly, holding a tumbler full of scotch and milk while the mother took a deep drag of a Viceroy filtered cigarette. Dr. K asked me to excuse his not standing as I shook his hand. Katie would later explain he had steel rods holding his neck in place as a result of a car accident. His strong jaw and deep blue eyes mirrored Katie's. Her older brother Victor walked in. He held a baby like a football in one arm. He was an Athenian alumnus and had the same jawline as Katie and their father. He shook my hand with a friendly grin and poured himself a drink. "Welcome to the house of ill repute," he said, offering to pour me a glass. I declined. Victor was only two years older than Katie, but with a wedding ring, baby, and drink in hand, he appeared much older.

"Is that your car outside?" asked Victor. "You have the stock engine in it?"

"I don't know," I answered. I didn't know Victor was referring to the engine.

"If you don't know, then you do." He downed his drink, handed the baby to Katie, and headed for the front door. "Let's take a look."

"Not now, Victor," said Katie. But it was too late. Victor was out the door. "He's a car nut." A parade of girls started through the door. They were Katie's club sisters, and all wore navy blue sweaters. Paul, Ben, and Mark arrived along with three senior football players—all wearing lettermen jackets. Katie passed off the baby to Dr. K and Mrs. K, and they headed upstairs. Katie turned on the music and instructed the boys to form a line on the left side, and the girls lined up on the right. We were to greet the "newbies" as they arrived and led them into the refreshments and dance floor. The door swung open, and Victor walked in, leading a group of excited girls.

"That's a two-ten six-cylinder engine," Victor said as he passed by. He weaved through the assembly and refilled his drink. More girls arrived in small clusters. The greeting line ended, and the party revved up. Victor had set up giant speakers and a dance floor outside. A punch bowl spiked with plenty of alcohol flowed freely, and the Rolling Stones music blasted "The House of the Rising Sun." Katie pushed me on to the dance floor with a newbie, and soon the floor was packed with everyone bouncing to the beat and singing. Mark got drunk and stumbled into the bushes. Ben helped Mark out of the

252

bushes, and they left the party. Paul and I danced with two and three girls at a time until eleven o'clock when the punch was drained, and the music stopped. Before long, a line of cars formed outside with parents picking up the newbies.

Victor poured two drinks and handed me one saying he couldn't drink alone. "You bought that car from Joe Graff at the 76 gas station, didn't you?

"How did you know?" I asked.

"I saw a FOR SALE sign on it there," he said, downing his drink. "I'm holding out for a Fifty-Six Bel Air."

Katie stepped down the stairs with the baby wrapped in a blanket. "Your 'wife,' mother of your baby, is calling for you," she said, handing the baby to Victor, who shrugged.

"Thanks for reminding of my royal fuck up, sister," he whispered and left quickly.

Katie and I started cleaning up. "He doesn't like his wife," she emphasized "wife" again. "He's a Virgo. She's a Gemini. They're opposites. What's your sign? When's your birthday?"

"May eight," I answered. "When's yours?"

"You're a Taurus, a bull. I'm Aquarius, February 2nd."

"*Ole.*" I had no idea what she was talking about.

Sunday morning, I was on duty at the gas station alone in uniform. Katie drove up in her car and handed me a mint green paper bag with a note attached. "I thought you might be hungry."

"I am," I said, opening the note as she slid out of the car and stood right next to me. A subtle fragrance tingled my senses, and I read the note smiling with her face next to mine. She had written my horoscope ending with a heart and a lipstick kiss. I kissed her right there in clear view under a blue sky next to the gas pump. It was the first of a long chain of horoscopes she would hand me on her perfume-scented stationery.

Paul drove up in his parents' car with a cigarette dangling from his mouth. He blurted out the news that Ben's father had killed himself in Hemingway style right in front of his family. The father had shot himself the night before in the living room that overlooked the entire bay area. Katie keeled over, vomiting her breakfast, and cried. "Geez Louise, Katie, I didn't mean to ruin your breakfast," said Paul, reaching into my lunch bag. "I'm just reporting the facts, ma'am." He took a bite of the bologna and cheese sandwich Katie had brought me.

"Ben's dad was so nice. I've known him since kindergarten." She and Ben had lived on the same street their entire lives. Katie picked up her keys, trying to contain herself. I put my arms around her. She sobbed. "Poor Ben and his mom." She kissed me, then held a look into my eyes. "Men," she said, still looking deep into me as though searching for an answer to this horrible news.

"Suicide in front of the family? Fuck me," said Paul. It jarred Katie.

"I have to go," said Katie and jumped in her car. Paul finished off my sandwich while I washed away the vomit.

Suicides rarely made the front pages unless the person was famous. Jumpers off the Golden Gate Bridge seemed redundant. A tenured law professor blowing out his brains in an upper-middle-class home made headline news. "He was depressed," said Katie looking at the newspaper in front of us. There were no pictures in the article nor mention of a "Hemingway style" suicide in front of the family. It didn't matter. We had driven to a lovers' hideaway spot known as Athenian Hill, another membership benefit. "Just like Steve's father," she continued. Steve lived a couple of streets up the hill. He, too, had grown up with Katie and Ben. Steve L's father was a successful executive with Chevron Oil who had killed himself the year before without explanation. "Steve's father was a nice man, too."

"I don't get it," I said.

"What's this all about?" Katie said. We both stared blankly at the paper, then out at the skyline view of San Francisco. Our existential moment gave way to the radio playing The Turtles' number one hit

"So Happy Together." We sang the lyrics, *"I can't see me loving nobody but you for all my life. So happy together."* We groped and ended up in the back seat feeling each other's trembling bodies. From that moment on, that song lit our hearts.

Katie was the first girl I invited to a family dinner. It was a Saturday night. I had planned a dinner and a movie. Mother made her signature mole dish complete with homemade tortillas. Dad prepared virgin margaritas while Don set up the music, both classical and Mexican albums. Dad embarrassed me with his camera, insisting on taking a picture of the colorful dinner on the table. Naturally, he managed pictures of Katie, Katie and Mother, Katie and Don, Katie and me, and finally set the timer for a group photo. I was bright red by the last shot but not as flush as Katie got after tasting the mole. Her nose looked like Rudolph's. Katie tried her best to use her two years of Spanish classes to converse with Mother. Mother was amused but responded mostly in English. After a while, Dad brought out pictures of Mexico and mentioned a Christmas vacation he was planning for the family in Guadalajara. That was news to me as well as a reminder that Mother and Dad's dream home was in the works.

I had learned enough about earning and saving money from my job to not worry about having to move back to Mexico. Mother and Dad could go live in their Guadalajara dream home without me. I was determined to stay in one place forever. I wouldn't need Don's help. I was working thirty-five hours a week plus making extra money buying, fixing up, and selling cars. Katie's brother, Victor, came by the gas station one day in a hot green 1956 two-door Chevy coupe. "Charles," Victor started with a jubilant voice, "this is the deal of the century." He slid out of the driver's seat with the engine roaring and opened the hood. "This is a 327 engine." The excitement in his eyes and voice was contagious. I looked closer, wanting to feel something more than the rumbling.

"When did you get this?" I asked.

"It's not mine. It's yours for eleven hundred bucks." A FOR SALE sign on the window stated fifteen hundred dollars. "My friend knocked up his girlfriend. He's got to sell this. He'll take payments." I calculated the risk and realized this was the deal of the century. He didn't have to say another word, but he did, "It's the fastest car in Berkeley."

Joe drove up in his golf outfit. Golf was his passion, and he had two standing games a week that he hadn't missed in eleven years. Every Wednesday and Sunday, he would be on the golf course rain or shine. "Hello, Victor. How's your Dad?" Everyone knew Dr. K.

"Fair to middling," answered Victor, still admiring the engine of the Chevy. Joe leaned in, trying to seem interested.

"Isn't this the car your friend Lloyd has been spending all his money on?" Joe said.

"He's got a baby coming. He has to sell it," Victor said.

"No mulligans in sex," Joe said.

"This is Charles' new car," Victor said.

Joe nodded, not surprised. "You be careful in this car, Charles." They both smiled. Their approval meant a lot to me. I was keenly aware that Mother and Dad were making plans to leave Berkeley, and I wanted to stay and be a part of something permanent. I wanted to feel as secure in one place as Victor and Joe and all the Athenians who seemed so settled, and stable, and safe. I wanted that feeling.

I took off the FOR SALE sign and shook Victor's hand. It felt good. Buying a Chevrolet felt as good as buying a ticket to my first Giants baseball game. I could have sung the national anthem. The 1956 Chevy coupe became my symbol of belonging, having ownership of the American Dream. But my school grades went down. I'd spend too much time working and not enough on schoolwork. I was more interested in learning to survive after Mother and Dad moved to Mexico than keeping my grades up.

Dad and Mother made plans for Christmas vacation in Guadalajara, where they would break ground on their dream home. By then, Katie and I were a couple. She wrote out my horoscope on her perfumed stationary seven days a week. We had spent every Saturday night together, had gone to every party together, and always ate lunch in the school quad. I told Dad and Mother I didn't want to go to Mexico for vacation.

"You don't want to leave Katie for two weeks, do you?" Mother said.

"No, I don't," I said.

"Your grades don't reflect much interest in having a relationship with a girl of Katie's upbringing," Dad stated in a dire tone.

"A life of service to others," I said. "I plan on it, Dad." Just the words he needed to hear to drop the subject.

The All-Conference State Gymnastics Competition was held that weekend. Katie represented her team, and I attended with her parents. Several events took place simultaneously around the cavernous auditorium. The tone of the room was serious—intense concentration registered on every competitor's face. The crowd was respectful, whispering if talking at all. The sounds of leather slippers slapping the mats, wooden rings clamoring, grunts and groans had a distinct pitch of cutthroat competition. Katie was at her best, and it was a turn-on to me. She had competed with many of the girls for years, and this was the final test before college. Scholarships could be won or lost in this day's performance. Katie had no interest in competing in college. She made a point of telling me right before the meet she was not doing this for her parents. I had no idea why she had to tell me that. This would be Katie's last competition, and she was doing it for sheer pleasure.

Her top rival was a girl from Sacramento, Barbi, who looked like a Playboy bunny. Barbi grabbed everyone's attention when she slid up on the balance beam. Her routine was pure sexual energy screaming out through her splits and twists. Katie's routine seemed tame but more athletic. Katie and Barbi exchanged poisonous stares until the final results in the balance beam. It was painful to watch the anxiety build up.

At last, the judges announced that Katie had placed first. Dr. K and Katie's mother never exchanged a word. The agony and ecstasy of competition stood side by side in Katie and Barbi; there could only be one winner. Katie didn't look at her parents. She turned her back and celebrated with her teammates.

Mother and Dad spent Christmas vacation in Mexico. Don spent his time in Belmont with a new girlfriend. Katie and I went crazy alone in the house. I turned the bass up and blasted the stereo. We burned everything we tried to cook, drank beer and cheap wine, and snacked on nuts and chips until we couldn't stand it. Food didn't matter; we were living on love. We cleared the living room, making way for a dance floor. Every time our song, "So Happy Together," played on the stereo, we ended up each other's arms until we'd fall onto the sofa getting closer to making love.

She surprised me Christmas morning with her rosy red cheeks pressed against my bedroom window. She walked in, carrying a gift and my horoscope. I sat up on the bed an arm's length from my wallet, wondering if this would be the day I'd use the squished condom. She slipped into bed. The horoscope read: *Imagine you and me. I do. I think about you day and night. It's only right. So happy together. I love you!* Thank you, Mexico.

The wonderment of clumsy and inexperienced lovemaking opened a whole new form of physical expression. Vulnerability, trust, and desire raced through our bodies, climaxing out of control. We rushed into it again and again without a word exchanged. We were in a fantasy, naked, alone, and free. After a while, we jumped up and ran, still naked, into the kitchen for some food and drink. I turned on the stereo and blasted the house with holiday music. "Santa Claus Is Coming to Town" played. Then we both sang along on, "He knows when you've been bad or good. So be good for goodness sake." Katie spun around, spotting herself as though on a balance beam. It turned me on. She noticed. She teased. I fell on Mother's precious sofa. I knew she'd die at the thought of Katie and me making love in her prized living room. Katie gyrated seductively across the imaginary beam. Then with the lyrics, "He's going to find out who's been naughty or nice," she stretched her legs across the imaginary beam into the splits. I was sure glad I didn't go to Mexico with Mother and Dad.

I applauded her naughtiness and ran into Don's room. He had a Zodiac sex calendar behind his door with twelve sex positions. I knew Katie and I could do each and every one. I ran back so fast Katie was still in the splits. I placed the calendar on the sofa and sidled next to Katie. We maneuvered into the first of the twelve positions we would attempt that day.

Life had never been better for me. The clarity of life's physical pleasures emanated from my every pore. Buildings appeared friendly. People smiled. Traffic moved out of the way. I had a perpetual smile and a new pep in my step. Customers thanked me for doing a good job cleaning their windows; some even offered tips. Everything was beautiful in its own way. Even studying was better as everything began to make more sense. Katie and I were together on everything. The American Dream was coming my way.

My night watch gas station attendant job became the path to my independence. One night, Timothy Leary drove in for an oil change and service on his car. He watched while I inspected the car and changed the oil. Timothy Leary was an iconic counter-culture figure, a psychologist at the forefront of creating change. He called for the use of LSD and coined the slogan: tune in, turn on, drop out. By then everyone in Berkeley, as well as the nation, had learned about the futile war in Vietnam. American casualties were seen in magazines, combat newsreels, and newspapers daily, always with the term "senseless" or "unjustified deaths." We chatted about how important it was for youth to stand up for what was right. I was too intimidated to contribute my thoughts, but he took an interest in me when he noticed a book I was reading, Tom Wolfe's *The Electric Kool-Aid Acid Test*. "How do you like the book?" he asked. I had just read the section in the book where Ken Kesey and his group visited the Harvard psychologist standing in front of me. He had the answer to enlightenment in a tiny drop of LSD. I wanted the answer.

"Makes me want to buy a van and go see the world." I paused, alluding to the book. Then more directly, "Through the looking glass."

"You're only young once." He stood nearby as I vacuumed his passenger side seat. I pulled out a wedged-in set of glasses from under the seat and handed them to him. "Why, thank you. I haven't seen these in a while." They were prism glasses. He playfully put them on and smiled like a young kid. I giggled. He handed them to me. I put them on and saw bright lights bouncing around in different hues. I laughed. "Keep them," he said. "Enjoy them with this." He handed me two tabs of LSD. "Peace," he said with a wry smile.

I purchased two tickets for a Joan Baez concert, thinking that would be the perfect time for an LSD enlightenment experience. Katie agreed and planned an overnight stay wherever the night would take us. We took the LSD tabs on the walk to the concert and got there early. It was a love-in atmosphere with free-flowing food, drinks, and drugs. The Greek Theater was packed, and the show was sold out. It wasn't just a concert; it was the center of the anti-war movement.

Resistance pamphlets and lit joints were passed with a nod and a peace sign. In one area, a group of Black Panthers members stood wearing black leather jackets and berets. Huey Newton and Bobby Seal had started the organization and had been a presence in Berkeley from the very start. I had seen them at the park across the street from Berkeley High, passing out leaflets and collecting donations in ten-ounce coffee cans. Now they were selling Chairman Mao Zedong's *The Little Red Book* on communism and taking donations in two-pound coffee cans. They couldn't sell them fast enough. Throngs of white people stuffed bills and coins in the cans. The Black men called out, "Thank you, brother," or "Thank you, sister," and occasionally held up a clenched fist. I saw the unity that Black and white people had seemingly formed over the past two years.

I thought about the times Dad had talked about the plight of Black Americans and communism in Cuba. Now here, the two issues were unified by the Black Panther Party. I wondered what Wanda was doing just as the LSD entered my brain. In an instant, I was holding the *Little Red Book* while the black man dangled the coffee can in front of me. He greeted me with a big smile, called me "young brown brother," and patted my shoulder as though we'd been friends forever. Funny, I thought, he didn't pat anyone else's shoulder. I was okay by him. Especially since he'd thrust the book into my palm.

I felt a trust reminiscent of my friendship with Mr. Populus. Then his face took on a cartoon-like quality that startled me. I gripped the book tight and studied his face. His broad nostrils, now caves, Ali Baba's caves, held treasures of wisdom for me. His nostrils morphed into my childhood *Toro's* nostrils and instantly grew with horns. I edged closer to look in the cave where Willie Mays peeked out and waved. Then Martin Luther King Jr.'s face stared out, followed by Rosa Parks, Harriet Tubman, Frederick Douglass, Sydney Poitier, James Brown, and countless more Black faces of American history swirled around my black *Toro's* cavernous nostrils. Rosa Parks? A tug on the book snapped my attention back to the Black man with the coffee can. His features melded into amoeba-like patterns swirling around and around changing colors. The coffee can morphed into a box of chewing gum like the ones sold by hungry kids in Mexico.

People's faces started changing under the bright lights. Noses and eyes swirled into faces of good or evil. Eyes smiled over angry noses while lips wiggled, hiding good and bad teeth—white and yellow Chiclets, fangs, tobacco-brown choppers. Everything was in psychedelic freeform motion. Katie must have seen the same as we both licked our lips. I pulled away without handing the "brother" money. He winked, letting me know the book was mine to keep. Rosa Parks? Could she be half Mexican? Joan Baez was half Mexican. I questioned why my *Toro* had only Black Americans spewing out of his nose. *Que sera, sera.*

We took our seats and waited, speechless, watching cheek-to-cheek as the lights turned down for Joan Baez's introduction. We were in our own world heightened by the prism glasses that Katie and I shared. The monolith cement pillared stage lit up like heaven's gate. St. Peter stood center stage checking the microphone, then scurried away as God's booming voice introduced Joan Baez. She floated in, guitar strap over her shoulder, face glittering, and by the time she reached the microphone, a halo floated over her head. A divine angel had been sent by God himself to stop the Vietnam War and advance civil rights. Joan Baez's songs of peace and civil rights each made a social statement that rang through loud and clear to everyone present. I felt a part of this American movement, this LSD driven resistance, this call to action.

It may have been the LSD that bound our brains because Katie and I didn't say a word to one another, but she knew my thoughts, and I knew hers. We watched and listened motionless, stuck together like Siamese twins. In the end, Joan asked the men with draft cards to hold them up. I held up my card. "Gentlemen, you want to get laid tonight?" Joan Baez asked. In unison, we all yelled yes. "Ladies, tell your man to burn that card if he expects to get lucky tonight." The place roared with excitement as many cards went up in flames. Somehow Katie and I made our way to my car, made love all night, and woke up on Athenian Hill overlooking the bay.

Six weeks later, on an early Sunday morning, I knocked on Dad's bedroom door. "Come in," he answered. I opened the door and popped my head in without walking into the room. The look on Dad's face told me he expected bad news.

"Good morning, Dad and Mother," I said, placing a paper with Katie's phone number scribbled on it. "Dad, do you remember what you said about the car being a bed on wheels?" I waited for a response, but he simply looked down and shook his head. "Well, you were right. Katie is pregnant. Her parents want to talk. Sorry. I have to go to work." I stepped away and into the kitchen, where I found some pictures of Mother and Dad's dream home. They had started the building process on a hill with a view overlooking Guadalajara. One photo stood out with Mother and Dad standing on an open foundation. They were building their dream. And with that, I was set with a future of working and caring for a family. The fear of having Mother and Dad move to Mexico left me. I had my own responsibilities now.

I spent all morning at work thinking about my future with a baby. I knew I wasn't ready for that. I tried calculating the costs of raising a child. As unbelievable as it sounds now, back then it was possible to work at a minimum wage job and survive with some proper planning. I could make extra money fixing cars and go to night school. Whatever it would take, I was ready, willing, and able. After all, I had earned enough money to drive the best car in high school and was building a savings account for when Mother and Dad left.

Katie drove up as she had every Sunday with a bag lunch and horoscope, but this time it was different because our parents knew about our baby. She was mine. I was hers. We were happy together, and it would last forever. I vowed to care for this angel any way I could. If my parents were leaving, I had to establish roots, and they would be with Katie. I thought about her brother Victor's life with a baby and wife. If he could do it, so could I. A lot of couples had been forced to marry because of a pregnancy. It was the way of the world at the time with forthright Americans. "Our parents are talking," Katie said.

"Okay."

"They're talking right now on the phone."

"*Que sera, sera,*" I sang.

"That's not funny. I'm scared." She shook her head. I knew her fears. She had seen her brother drop out of school for an auto mechanic job. He had lingered too long in night school without a plan and opted out for a career in the auto industry.

"We can finish school and have a happy life. I'm not going to work in a gas station all my life," I assured her.

"I believe in you," she said and then sang, "*I do. I think about you day and night. It's only right.*"

"When are we meeting?"

She shrugged. "Wednesday is a good day. My dad 'ice skates' that day," she said, signaling quote symbols. That explained the ice-skating trophies and pictures in their living room.

Dad set up the meeting for the same day. We arrived at Katie's home at eight o'clock. Katie's parents and mine were cordial under the circumstances, and we all settled in the living room. Dad and Dr. K both wore suit and tie, which made the visit more formal. Dr. K sat in a sofa chair, gripped a tumbler full of scotch with milk, and pushed up his wire-rim glasses. His rosy cheeks signaled he was not on his first drink. Dad and Mother sat holding hands on the opposite side. Mrs. K and Katie sat together in a loveseat while I sat in a single chair close to Dr. K.

Between Dad and Dr. K, they had come up with a plan. Dr. K

owned a four-unit apartment building near the university that had a vacancy coming up in the summer. Our families would help with finances through college. Dr. K and Dad had our future all laid out, and they explained down to the small details of how many units I could take and how many hours I could work. My head started spinning as they laid out my entire future. All I had to do was decide on a career while Katie would go to Armstrong College and study business. I slipped into a daze. The voices blended into a soft but irritating drone. Dr. K's face distorted into liquid and fell in his tumbler. Katie shook my knee, bringing me back. I checked to see if her dad still had a head.

"Please explain your plans?" Dr. K asked. I didn't answer. "What do you intend to do? Study? What are you interested in? It doesn't matter if you want to be a doctor, lawyer, dentist, or engineer like your father. We are your support for as long as it takes. You need a vision. Do you have a vision?" I looked at Mother. She gave me a two-eyed wink of support. "You have to see the light at the end of the tunnel." He took a sip of his scotch. I imagined myself in a tunnel with a light at the end. It came toward me slowly. Then I heard a train rumbling down the track, picking up speed, closing off the light.

"I want an abortion!" I blurted out, causing alarm. Mother's face tightened. Katie reached for her mother's hand. Dad sighed. Dr. K's red, white, and blue eyes opened wide as saucers behind his steel rim glasses. He gripped his crystal tumbler, turning his knuckles white. Mrs. K lit a cigarette and took a deep inhale.

"We are Catholic," he grumbled. "My daughter is not going to have an abortion. You think we're going to allow some hack in Tijuana to perform a surgery with a coat hanger?"

"No, sir. I wouldn't suggest that. I will sell my car and have enough money to go to Japan, where abortions are safe and legal, sir." Dr. K took a sip, spun the ice round and round. The clinking of the ice rang through the room before he looked up. "I mean, Doctor."

"You will get married, raise your child, and never mention an abortion again. Your parents and I have an understanding." He looked at Dad for confirmation.

"Yes, you have our support in this, Charles," Dad said, holding Mother's hand. What? Marriage? Victor's framed picture of his young family loomed prominently over Dr. K's shoulder. I would be joining the ranks of the many couples whose dreams had been derailed by sex. There are no mulligans in sex.

"Okay, we are in agreement," Dr. K put his drink down. Mrs. K refilled his glass. "The next step is for Katie to come into the office for a checkup." The checkup was set for Saturday morning.

ILLEGAL ABORTION 1968

Unbeknown to me, this is what had happened the Saturday of the "checkup."

Dr. K went into his office early that morning. He prepared the examination room himself, checking and double-checking the stainless-steel instruments, tightening knobs, adjusting the table and stool height, and securing the padded stirrups. He reached for the stainless-steel speculum he'd performed so many gynecological exams with, took a deep breath, and in the name of the Father, the Son, and the Holy Spirit, crossed himself. He placed the instrument on a stainless-steel tray among an assortment of surgical tools.

At home, Katie had planned to drive herself to her father's medical offices, but her mother insisted on driving. She handed Katie a bible and rosary beads. Katie skipped breakfast and just drank the tea her mother had insisted on. They arrived in less than fifteen minutes, enough time for the drug that had been placed in Katie's tea to take effect. Katie felt woozy as she entered her father's medical building. Mrs. K locked the door behind them. Mother helped her daughter disrobe and put on a gown before walking into the examining room where Dr. K waited.

Katie slid on to the table, unable to maneuver her athletic legs in the stirrups without her mother's help. Dr. K warmed up the speculum and lubed it with a medical gel. He sat on a stool and slid it between his daughter's outstretched legs. Katie felt woozy, then helpless. She succumbed to her parents' directions, gripping her rosary beads.

That night, I telephoned Katie. Her mother answered, which was unusual because Katie had a private line in her bedroom. "Hello?" Mrs. K's voice seemed strained.

"Hi, Mrs. K, this is—"

"I know who it is. I'm sorry, but Katie is not available now. She's come down with the flu and is sleeping. She will stay in bed for the next few days."

"I'm so sorry. Okay, please let Katie know I phoned and—"

"Yes, I will. She needs rest. Good night." The phone went dead. I looked at the receiver and imaged Mrs. K standing at Katie's bedside.

It was the first Saturday night we hadn't been together since forever. I was at the gas station, getting ready to leave. I changed out of my uniform and into my street clothes. My new class ring sparkled under the night lights. That gave me an idea. I'd been consumed with upcoming responsibilities and the costs of raising a child while going to college. I'd have to be smart with money.

A craft store nearby had a kiln and design center for making jewelry. The following day I went in with my class ring, melted it and cast it into a wedding ring. It was magic. Two days later, I delivered the ring with a get-well card and red roses. I left everything on the porch and then talked on the phone. She sounded weak and stayed home for another two days.

By the third day, she showed up at my work with a drawn face. She kissed the ring on her finger, saying she loved it and handed me a few horoscopes and lunch. Katie's gym bag had three unopened letters from colleges she'd applied to—Berkeley, Stanford, and Nevada. "I'll bet you got accepted to all three," I said. She shrugged it off. I knew she had planned a sleepover with two childhood friends where they would all open the letters and decide together, one for all and all for one. What in the world is she going to tell her friends? How is she going to tell them? But it was the time before Planned Parenthood centers were established, and birth control pills weren't readily accessible. Everyone knew of marriages forced by unexpected pregnancies. Now Katie and I were about to join the ranks of the accidental parents.

"You want to elope?" I joked, looking for a smile. It didn't work. "How about a beach wedding?" Still nothing. "At sunrise . . . on a mountain top?"

"I just want to die," Katie mumbled and sat staring at her shoes.

"What can I do? Did you eat? It could be morning sickness. You want me to get you anything?"

"Fine, everything is fine," she said, still staring at her shoes.

"Your dad sure plays everything by the rules. Mr. Perfect kind of guy."

"He's not. He's a fake. So is my mom. All she cares about is appearances." Katie never sounded so forthright. She was reflecting on something without looking up. "Everything is a lie. Victor's life is a lie. He doesn't love his wife. He hates his life."

"I don't get it," I said. She looked up.

"Your mom and dad are real, and they're happy."

"They're moving to Mexico."

She stood up and kissed me. We held each other like monkeys. Thoughts of New York and Mexico and Orange County swirled around my head. Why were Mother and Dad moving to Mexico? Images of New York winters and Mexico City thunders came to me just as The Doors' hit song, "Break on Through," played on the radio. We held each other and listened to the lyrics. *Que sera, sera.*

Mother started knitting a baby blanket with a soft green and white pattern that captured a Mexican and American flavor. She brought it with her to the next meeting with Katie's parents and sat stoically knitting by my side. A fresh flower arrangement appeared to glow on the black piano.

"Have you decided on your plans?" Dr. K said, topping off his crystal tumbler with bourbon and a dash of milk. Dad didn't drink anything. Mrs. K. sat, staring at her husband's goblet.

"Katie and I would like a sunset wedding on the beach or a mountain." I figured it was a smart way to keep the costs down and get on with the marriage. Dr. K took a sip of his drink.

"I am not going to a mountaintop or a beach for a wedding," he stated. "What are your plans for what you're going to study and such?" He gripped his drink.

"You seem interested in how things work," Dad offered. "You're good at math. Engineering could be a good career for you." Mother's knitting needles made a rhythmic slapping sound as everyone waited for my response. Katie stared at her shoes.

"Teacher. I want to be a teacher," I said.

"That would be for Katie," Dr. K stated and sipped his drink.

"A man has to provide a lifestyle that a girl is accustomed to. Look around, Charles." Dad looked deep into my eyes.

Shit, I thought. There was a long silent pause with all eyes on me.

"It seems we have a new development." Katie's mom came to my rescue. Mother stopped knitting. "Katie has had some spotting." We all turned toward Katie.

Dr. K sipped his drink and reached for a coaster. He paused, still looking at his glass before speaking. "This discussion may be premature. Nevertheless, let's not make assumptions." He adjusted the coaster with one finger. "We cannot make a judgment now." He carefully positioned his drink on the coaster without letting go. He didn't look up. Mrs. K. sighed. Katie fidgeted with the engagement ring, saw me looking at her, and stopped. And with that, the baby and marriage conversation was laid to rest for the night.

That weekend, Katie and I went to the drive-in theater to see the movie *The Graduate*. She was on edge and talked through the whole film. Katie's view that life is a charade was reinforced. Mrs. Robinson's affair and all the adults working for the establishment were all plastic. It was the unveiling of the American Dream as phony. Dustin Hoffman's character, Benjamin, rejected it. Katherine Ross's character, Elaine, rejected it, and Katie was rejecting it. I wanted it.

She saw nothing good in the film from the moment it started. She questioned the whole system, rejecting the façade, the charade. She said Mrs. Robinson could only survive in her meaningless life with alcohol and drugs. Finally, she almost puked when Mrs. Robinson seduced Benjamin. At the end, when Dustin breaks up the wedding and drives off with Katherine Ross, Katie blurted, "Hypocrites."

"Huh?"

"Serves them right," she scolded.

Wednesday after school, Katie had an urgent tone and insisted I get in her car. We jumped in the car and drove to the ice-skating rink. "What are we doing here?" She didn't answer and walked to the front of her VW. She pulled out a set of skates. I followed. I rented skates while she laced up hers. Only three skaters circled the cavernous building ice.

"There is no baby," Katie said matter-of-factly and headed to the ice.

"No baby?" I shoved my feet into the skates and took off after her, barely keeping my balance. She skated ahead and around. I hadn't skated much since New York, but like riding a bike, it came back. I watched and waited for her to circle back. Baby life, family life, is planned and I'm good with it. Now, no baby, start a new life plan. I caught up with Katie.

"Are you all right?" I asked. She looked pained, nodded her head, and rushed ahead. I followed.

"Life is a lie. Today is Wednesday."

"So?"

"Look around, do you see Dad? No. He has a girlfriend. They go to her apartment, his apartment. One of the apartments that he owns."

"Okay. How do you know?" I was stunned.

"Victor followed Dad. He saw the whole thing, the fake ice skating story, the apartment, the private dinners at the restaurants. It's been going on for years."

"Does your mother know?"

"She doesn't care. She's only interested in keeping up a facade. And it doesn't matter. They're both liars!" She pushed on. "Everything is a lie. Dad's life is a lie. His wake-up pills, his sleeping pills, his pain pills, his friends — everything is a lie." She raced ahead too fast for me. She circled around furiously slicing across the ice. The punishing sound of her skates digging into the ice said it all. She was angry. I watched wondering what our baby might have looked like and what Katie was feeling. She circled four times before sliding up to me, breathing deep with red cheeks.

"You want the truth, the whole truth, and nothing but the truth? Mom and Dad gave me an abortion." She stopped, waiting for me to register the thought. My nostrils flared, my skin crawled, and eyes opened wide. Her steely stare pinned into me. "Mom drugged me in the morning, drove me to the 'checkup,' and Dad . . . They did it in his office. That's the truth. They made me lie about it. I did. That's the truth. I never had the flu. That was a lie. It's all a lie. This whole thing, everything is fake."

"He said no abortion. You're Catholic. He's Catholic."

"It's all a charade." She laughed in pain.

"Your dad and mom gave you —"

"Yes, they gave me an abortion. We're all going to hell. That Saturday they did it and kept me home. Now you know." She was spent, broken, barely holding on. I reached for her, but she skated away, slowly; she wanted me to skate with her. I took her hand and skated in silence for one, two, three laps.

She handed me an envelope. It was her acceptance letter from the University of Nevada. "I start this fall."

I heard Don spinning a knife in a mayonnaise jar at midnight. I walked into the kitchen and found him devouring a cheese sandwich. "What's wrong?" he asked. I didn't know I looked pained, but I was.

"I'm scared," I whispered, tears sliding down my face. Don handed me his napkin. "Katie is leaving. Mom and Dad are leaving. You're leaving."

"Mexico is a fantasy, an illusion," Don said, dropping his sandwich on the counter and taking me in his arms. "Mom and Dad are never going to be happy there. It's bullshit. That house is a waste of money. They won't last a year down there."

"Why do you say that?"

"Their only reason for leaving is because this country is corrupt in war and politics and racism and poverty. Good luck. Mexico is ten times more corrupt."

"But it's beautiful, and people are happy, and life is easy," I remembered Dad's reasoning.

"Beauty is in the eyes of the beholder." He took a knife from a drawer, cut off half the sandwich and handed it to me. "What happened with Katie?"

"We're not getting married. She's not pregnant." I couldn't say more.

"Good, congratulations. You dodged the bullet."

The next day at work, Paul drove up with a cigarette dangling from his lips. He had a cast on his left leg. It was the end of his football career. He had slipped off a boat, torn his knee, would wear a cast for the next two months, and had been forced to quit football. "I don't give a shit," he said, trying to convince himself. "I'm tired of bulking up and hitting people. That's not who I am." *So much for dreams,* I thought.

"I'm going to buy a boat and see the world." It sounded better than a commune. He took a deep drag of his filtered cigarette and nervously wiggled his free leg. "Open air, just throw the line out and catch your dinner," he continued. "What do you say? You want to do it? We work for a couple, three years, save money. We'll be free, white, and twenty-one." He took a long drag and blew the smoke up into the clear blue sky with a cock-sure smile. He had the world figured out. "What do you say?"

"You hate fish." I knew Paul was confused. His life without football was a life changer. "And I'm not white."

"So what? We're free. We're young. We can do anything we want."

"I'll believe this when I see you eat fish." I had heard him many times say he wouldn't eat fish if his life depended on it. "What about college?"

"Fuck it," he said, throwing his cigarette butt. "You're only young once." He looked frustrated as he hobbled into his car and roared off. He was as confused as I was.

Things were changing faster than ever. Paul didn't have football. I was not obligated to family life in an apartment. Katie was leaving for college. Don was studying drama at Berkeley and had his sights on law school. He had changed more than anyone ever thought possible. Once a lover and fighter, he now wanted to be a Mexican Perry Mason, the defense lawyer. I would have to tell Mother and Dad the no-baby news that night. I imagined them relieved and packing their bags for Mexico.

"Yes, that's the news. Katie is not pregnant—anymore," I repeated myself after the blank stare reaction from Mother and Dad. We sat in the living room. Dad and I ate ice cream while Mother knitted baby booties. Mother put down her knitting. "She lost the baby when she had the flu," I lied. Abortions were illegal, and doctors could lose their medical practices for doing them. Katie had sworn me to secrecy, and I couldn't imagine having to tell Mother and Dad the truth.

"*Pobrecita, de Katie,*" Mother used Spanish to emphasize the sadness she felt. She sighed and measured the unfinished booties. Dad said it would be easier for me to get an education without the burden of supporting a family.

"Discipline yourself. We have an overpopulated world, and the future is not certain for this planet. China is taking measures to ensure their population slows. They mandated the one baby per couple law. It takes self-discipline, it's hard, but it's necessary." He turned on the stereo.

"What happens if they accidentally have two babies?" I wanted to know.

"The government takes the second baby. Sometimes, mothers get an abortion." I stopped eating my ice cream. The image of Dr. K slicing through his daughter's insides flashed through my head. What kind of man and woman could do this? Why did Dr. K have a girlfriend? Maybe Katie was right about this whole thing being nothing more than a charade.

Mother studied her baby clothes and laughed before shooting me a two-eyed blink. She pulled me back to my safe world. "I'm so sorry for the scare. I won't do it again. And I'll get good grades."

"*Besame Mucho*" played on the stereo. Mom and Dad exchanged glances. "*Mi amor?*" Dad took Mom's hand, and they took the floor.

A few days later, Eugenia visited with her new boyfriend, Ron, a Ph.D. candidate in anthropology. He had been to Mexico on an excavation and brought some pictures. Mother and Dad were happy for Eugenia. She had found a man she admired intellectually and seemed more comfortable in her relationship than ever. In a short time, Eugenia announced a marriage plan. She and Ron would marry before traveling to India for two years. She would be with Ron on a field study for a doctoral dissertation. Dad was ecstatic with the news while Mother had reservations. She loved Herb, hadn't accepted the divorce, and kept a close relationship with him. Dad brought out the dream home plans in Guadalajara and invited Eugenia and Ron to go there anytime. Eugenia and Ron seemed like the ideal couple. Everyone was going to leave Berkeley.

Later that week, on April 4th, 1968, Dr. Martin Luther King Jr. was shot and killed in Memphis, Tennessee, by James Earl Ray. America changed overnight. It was no secret the then FBI director, J. Edgar Hoover, hated Dr. King. Hoover had called Dr. King the most dangerous man in America and a notorious liar. Hoover had placed Dr. King under FBI surveillance since the Montgomery Bus Boycott in 1956 and later wiretapped his phones. Everyone, it seemed, felt Dr. King's death was a conspiracy much the same as John F. Kennedy's death. Dad was beside himself. "J. Edgar Hoover has been calling Martin Luther King a communist for years," Dad commented as we watched the news that night. "He may be dead, but his dream will live on forever."

"Are you moving to Mexico?" I asked, making it clear I had no intention of living there.

"I don't know how things can get any worse," he answered, not acknowledging my question.

"*Mira*," Mom handed me a picture of their dream home under construction. I walked away.

Race identity became a mandate. Black pride, Black power, Black identity was infused everywhere. Newspapers started hyphenating athletes and anything that could be categorized by race—Black athletes, Black artists, Black students, Black leaders, Black teachers, and Black everything. Anything or anybody that wasn't hyphenated with Black had to be assumed white. White and Black races were at odds.

Dad felt the tensions one night when our neighborhood's only Black family, the Taylors, came for one of Mother's mole dinners. Hugh and Doris Taylor were about the same age as my parents and had a son my age. The Taylor family had visited many times over the years, and we had been to their home as many times. Hugh had the build of an NBA player, and Doris could have been a fashion model. They both dressed and looked like movie stars, wore sunglasses, and smoked. I could always tell if they had been there by the cigarette smell. They arrived that night with a flair. Hugh wore a white dashiki made famous by the Black Panthers. He had replaced his reddish sheen straight hair with a round afro that rubbed the top of the door frame as he walked in. Doris wore a colorful dashiki garment and white Kufi hat. She was a princess with her perfect teeth and shiny skin.

Mom and I stood politely, welcoming the couple with a bright smile while Dad reached for his camera. *"Payasos,"* Mother whispered with a smile. It was like having Huey Newton and Diana Ross in our living room.

Don walked in from his room, stuffed book bag in hand, set on making a quick exit when he noticed Taylor's new look. He had to stop. Huey Newton simply grinned and watched Diana Ross entice Don into having one glass of sangria. She had a way with men, and Don was no exception.

Hugh was exceptionally outspoken as he was usually a cool, laid-back kind of guy, leaving the limelight to his beautiful wife. Doris chain-smoked and poured herself several glasses of sangria before dinner. Then, with the new look, they set out to educate us on the Black experience. He ate and drank sangrias through dinner, making comments about systematic oppression in "all government entities." Mother and I stayed out of the conversation. After dinner, Hugh declared he was a victim of American imperialism that had conspired to suppress his upward mobility in his Port of Oakland administrative position. It wasn't so much the grievance that bothered Dad as much as the tone Hugh used, as though all white men had conspired against him, including Dad. Dad mentioned Ralph Ellison's book *Invisible Man* in support of Hugh's position. Hugh dismissed Dad with a sarcastic laugh, saying no white man could understand oppression without walking in a Black man's shoes. Dad added that he'd recently reread *Black Like Me* by John Howard Griffin but that only escalated the divide and raised Hugh's tone even further. That might have been the last time the Taylors came for dinner. Polarizing forces along racial lines were pulling people apart.

Dad grew concerned with my understanding of the racial identity/awareness situation. "You know, Charles, this whole race issue might be difficult for you," he said the following morning over breakfast. It stirred my blood. What could he possibly be thinking? After all, it was a Black and white issue, not a brown issue. "If anyone should question your background, you are simply an American."

"Dad, I'm brown, a Mexican," I said instinctively, prompting a puzzled reaction. "American Mexican, Mexican American." I hyphenated myself for the first time. "Don't worry," I paused, sensing a feeling of betrayal in my claiming an ethnic cultural identity.

"Well, yes, you are, but . . ." I could see Dad struggling with his feelings, maybe fears. "But the word American has no color."

"You know the old saying, 'You can take the boy out of the country, but you can't take the country out of the boy.'"

He sighed. I'd hurt his feelings. I didn't mean to question his efforts in making me an American. "Dad, all bones are white," I said with a deliberate smile trying to him. I was tactless. My faux pas was hurting the very man who'd done everything in his power to make me an American, and here I was saying I was a Mexican. "And who's going to question my background? There's no Gestapo yet."

"Just be careful, son."

It occurred to me that Black Americans had just lost Martin Luther King Jr. but still had a host of other heroes in American history. Also, they had many role models on television and school. Whites had John Wayne, every president since George Washington, and all of TV. What did I have? The only Mexican in the media was the Frito Bandito. Where and what was a Mexican American in American history and television? I'd been through a California public education without mention of a single Mexican role model.

"We have a house in Mexico if the government reopens the internment camps."

"What?" I asked, wondering if he meant I would be at risk with my hyphenated identity.

"President Franklin Roosevelt ordered them for the Japanese in World War II, just like the Germans put Jews in camps. Russia did it. Stalin put millions of people in camps, ethnic cleansing, some called it. Don't think it can't happen here." Had I opened a can of worms by claiming my identity?

I felt empty and confused. I feared I'd betrayed Dad in my pursuit of an identity. But my fear of moving back to Mexico was worse. I lost my appetite and couldn't sleep. I found an escape in school where teachers seemed to make sense of the world. They had purpose and clarity to their mission. My English teacher, Mrs. Winters, a gentle gray-haired soul, took an interest in me. She had me read out loud almost daily. I loved it.

One day the class read Shakespeare's *Romeo and Juliet*. I read Romeo. It was scary to feel so much emotion as I read. I fought back the tears, but Mrs. Winters belted out, "Don't fight it, Charles, go with it. Let it go." No way was I going to cry in front of the class. I felt Don's presence. What would he think of me crying in a class? Before I knew it, tears rolled down my cheeks, and the class applauded. I knew Romeo's emptiness. I felt embarrassed, but I liked the feeling of being in someone else's life. Her classroom became my sanctuary.

At work, I found a path to staying in Berkeley without my

parents. I became an unofficial clearinghouse for used cars. I had the tools and an auto rack. Joe supported my entrepreneurship by letting me fix and park vehicles at the station. Victor came by regularly to check on the Chevy and talk mechanics, which was now all in theory for him as he'd given up on his racecar dreams. One day Victor appeared with a friend, Badger. He was the outcast member of a highly respected Presbyterian pastor's family in the neighborhood. He rode with the Hell's Angels while his brother attended medical school. Badger was Paul Bunyan with a black leather jacket. He took to me right away, shaking my hand in a friendly manner and asking me about freedom. I thought about Mr. Brown, and a week later, I bought a 650 BSA motorcycle from a guy desperate to sell.

Paul Bunyan was right. I felt the freedom the instant I sat in the saddle above the engine on my very own motorcycle. It was my mechanical horse. Somehow it felt as though I'd tamed a bull. I rode across Grizzly Peak Road overlooking the bay with San Francisco and the Golden Gate Bridge. The past lay behind me while I rode into the future. I was ready to face the world alone. On the way down the hill, I stopped at Katie's house. It was awkward seeing her parents after learning what they'd done to Katie. It was, after all, an illegal abortion; a crime they had committed.

Dr. K's brother, Frank, was there. They had been together for some time drinking in the living room. Frank had a vicious look about him. He was the younger brother and a lawyer. Katie rushed downstairs and tried to usher us out, but Dr. K. stopped us. "Wait, Charles," he started. "Where do you think you're taking my daughter on that motorcycle?" I answered we were going for a little ride to catch the sunset. "I wish you wouldn't do that." That meant Katie wasn't coming.

"Have a seat, Charles," Frank commanded as he poured a drink. "Let's hear your plans now that we know Katie's." His condescending tone cut clear across the room. I sat. Katie didn't. "What are your plans?"

"College is next. That's my only plan so far."

"You still planning to marry and support Katie? She has your ring." I didn't know why he was asking since the marriage was Dr. K's idea. I didn't answer.

"Katie, why don't you go see your mother? I'm sure she would like that right about now," Dr. K said. Katie left.

"I understand your parents are moving to Mexico," Frank said.

"That's right, Guadalajara."

"Your father has had an exciting life living in two countries," Dr. K added.

"I think you'd be better off in Mexico," Frank said sloppily. "You were born there. That's where you belong."

"Not necessarily, but you do have the freedom to choose now," said Dr. K.

"You're young, Charles, or is it Carlos? No matter, you're young. Life is about adventure. You need to see the world. Maybe get on a boat and travel. How does that sound to you, Carlos, Charles?" Frank pointed at the small globe in the bookshelf.

"You listen to this man, Charles," Dr. K looked at his brother admiringly. "He knows adventure. He's a war hero. He fought Hitler. Saved Jews." A row of colorful German steins caught my eye and reminded me this was a German family. He fought the devil himself and won.

"I was there for both of us. You know that. You were on your way. Damn taxi. Go ahead, tell Charles the story." He looked at his brother, who shook it off. "Okay, I'll tell the story. My brother was fresh out of medical school and on his way to the front lines in France when tragedy struck one New Year's night. This man right here," he tapped his brother's leg and saluted, "being the smart man that he is, decided to take a taxi instead of driving home from the New Year's celebration in San Francisco."

"The stupidest thing I ever did," Dr. K said. "Taxi driver was drunker than anyone. We crashed. Driver died. I woke up in the hospital with a broken neck. I stayed there, bedridden for two months."

"Did your dad serve in the war?" Frank asked cynically.

"Navy Lieutenant intelligence officer in the Pacific is all I know. He doesn't talk about the war." I didn't like the question.

"It makes a man out of you. You should consider the Navy or Army before you decide what you want to study. The G.I. Bill will help with your bills."

"I'm not interested in going to Vi-et-nam," I said, dropping a Muhammad Ali-ish intonation on Vietnam as he had used in his recent and much-publicized U.S. Army induction refusal.

"You have a yellow streak? Is that it? Ah, the big man with the big dick has a yellow streak." Frank was sloppy drunk and threw in his attempt at Muhammad Ali intonation by emphasizing the hard K on *dick* and *streak*.

"Frank, no sense in offending the boy," Dr. K said. "Charles, we want you to leave Katie alone. She's going out of state. She'll meet new people and forget about you. It's inevitable. Now, if you leave, it'll make it easier on both of you."

My bullfighter blood boiled, and Dad's passive reasoning clashed inside me. I stayed still wondering how much these two grown men had been drinking; how many pills they had taken? Grace Slicks' song danced inside my head. *"One pill makes you larger, one pill makes you small . . ."* "White Rabbit" lyrics made more sense than this encounter.

"What's it going to take, Charles? How about ten thousand dollars? I'll give you my boat, and you can see the world. What do you say?" He looked at his brother. They were serious. If Paul only knew what had just been offered. "Seriously, ten thousand dollars can go a long way."

"I'm not a coward." I had to say that.

"Oh, no? Tough guy, huh. Well, let me tell you something, mister macho Carlos. I have friends in Chicago that deal with tough guys.

Do you know what they can do? Why, if you so much as got near my daughter with your Mexican dick, I'd have you up on a cross and cut your nuts off." If Dr. K could give his daughter an abortion and his brother killed Germans to save Jews, I imagined his brother could cut my balls off if he had a chance.

I wondered what Dad would do in this situation since he'd handled adversity so well. I searched for words he'd use but instead came up with my own. "But if I take the boat and the money?" I teased.

"You're safe. Seriously, get on my boat, go wherever you want, we'll wire you money wherever you choose." Frank spilled his drink. Dr. K looked spent, a little embarrassed, but focused on his glass. It occurred to me at that moment, these guys had no remorse for their crimes. Abortions were as illegal as stealing a car, yet they carried on in a holier than though existence. Criminals negotiating a boat is what we were at that moment. Three criminals and a fourth upstairs with Katie. Somehow, I felt vindicated for my crime, knowing I wasn't the only one in the room.

I'd gone through high school with a monkey on my back, feeling like the scourge of the community for a breaking one law, and these two grown men were feeling good about killing a baby and threatening me. Two voices rang in my head. Dad's calling me a criminal, and Mr. Populus saying all bones are white. Dr. K and his brother set me free of guilt. *Fuck these guys.* I left.

I hurried out the door and rode off on my motorcycle across the skyline road to clear my mind. I pulled up to Paul's house, revving the engine. Paul came outside. "What's wrong?" he asked. "Why are you crying?" I didn't know I had tears running down my cheeks until I tried to speak. "Come on in." He took my keys, and we walked inside. His mother, Betty, greeted me exhaling cigarette smoke.

I tried to talk, but tears and a flood of emotions held me speechless. Paul grabbed my shoulders and led me to his room, where I fell on his bed and cried like a baby. He closed the door, and

I fell asleep. Luckily it was my day off work.

I woke up and sat at the dining table where dinner was set. Cliff, Paul's dad, sat at the head of the table, cutting the biggest meatloaf I'd ever seen. "Hand me your plate, Charles," he said. He was a retired career army man and spoke with authority. "No need to talk at this table, Charles, if you don't feel like it. The only thing you have to do at this table is to finish your plate." He placed the thickest portion of meat I'd ever seen on my plate.

"You okay?" asked Paul. I nodded.

"Paul mentioned your parents are moving to Mexico," Betty said.

"Yes, that's the plan. Katie is leaving, my parents are leaving, my sister is going to India, Don will probably move soon," I said.

"We aren't going anywhere, Charles. You have a place to stay as long as you want," said Cliff.

"Or we can get on a boat and see the world," Paul said.

I burst out laughing and realized how ridiculous Frank and Dr. K had been. I immediately felt better and recounted the boat offer Frank had made.

"A boat and ten thousand dollars? Are you crazy?" Paul dropped his fork. "Dad, I need your car keys." He stood and looked for the keys in the hallway.

"Sit down, Paul. Finish your dinner," Betty said.

"I'm taking him back to get the money and the keys to the boat." He rushed through the door, looking for the car keys.

"They were drunk," I said.

"Good, better. Let's get up there before they sober up."

"Sit down and finish your dinner," Cliff said. Paul realized it may not have been a good idea to go back up there and took his seat.

"If you boys are looking for adventure, the Army is one way to go, but college would be better." By the end, we were all laughing.

I rode up to Grizzly Peak feeling the freedom the mechanical bull between my legs gave me. I stopped at the Athenian Hill and kept the engine running, wondering if I'd ever come up there again with

Katie. The sunset's red and orange hues looked like part of the Golden Gate Bridge. Mexico, New York, Belmont, and Fullerton were in the past. I didn't need an adventure. I needed a way to stay and be a part of the American Dream in a place I could call my home. I revved the engine, snorting like a mad bull and rode off. *Que sera, sera.*

Katie didn't bring my horoscope to work the next day and didn't answer my calls. I missed knowing what my day was supposed to bring me. A sharp pain ran through me every time our song came on the radio. I turned it off. Time passed slowly. A black Cadillac De Ville with tinted windows appeared just before closing time. The automatic window rolled down, and there sat Paul Bunyan. A leather-bound bible lay on the dashboard, and a clergy collar dangled from the rearview mirror. "Buddy, I got a tire to fix," he said.

I directed him to drive the car into the stall. He opened the trunk and took out two large suitcases from the trunk while I set up the lift. He said the car belonged to his father. "I borrowed it from the old man. Took a trip to Mexico." I asked which tire as they all looked fine. He said the rear tires had to be dismantled. I didn't question it. I pulled off the right tire and broke it down. To my surprise, it was packed with kilos of marijuana. I was caught off guard. Possession of marijuana could get a prison term. I must have looked scared. "Don't panic, Charles," he said. "This is a church car. Cops aren't looking for crime around here anyway."

"What are you doing?" I mumbled.

"Stay cool and do the left tire." He explained he was taking the weed to his delivery spot in Oakland. It would be the best weed ever introduced to the streets, and there would be a significant demand for it later. We packed the kilos into the suitcases fast as we could. "You're a good man, Charles," he said and placed two kilos down in front of me. "This is your cut." I didn't respond. "We'll do this again. If you want to make good money, take some orders. We'll deliver the best Acapulco Gold on the streets."

After closing, I sped to Paul's house and knocked on his window. He came to the window, startled. I held up two kilos of weed. He opened the window, grabbed the kilos, and threw them under his bed. I jumped inside. "What are you doing with this shit?" Paul asked.

"I don't know. I don't know." We stared at the bed in silence. "It's Acapulco Gold," I said.

"No shit? This must be worth a lot of money," Paul said.

"Enough to buy a boat," I said. "You want to sell it?"

"You want a dick up your ass, you go right ahead and do that." Paul lit a cigarette and paced back and forth.

"No, I don't want a dick up my ass," I said. "Why?"

"Because that's what happened to Mark. He got busted for half a lid. He got thrown in a cell with three big Black guys that were in for murder. They threw a blanket over the bottom bunk bed, put a knife to his throat, and fucked him in the ass." He laughed. I cringed.

The notion of getting butt rammed put the fear of God into us. Acapulco Gold was legendary, and everybody wanted it. It was too valuable to throw away and too risky to sell. I decided I'd give it back to Paul Bunyan and forget about it.

I was at work one night when the black Cadillac De Ville that Paul Bunyan had called the church car drove up. I rushed to a tire within the shop where I had stashed the kilos and walked to the Cadillac, ready to hand over the kilos. To my surprise, it wasn't Paul Bunyan. It was his father in clergy attire. Images of Paul Bunyan driving across the border in the clergy outfit crossed my mind. *Brilliant*, I thought. Then I wondered whether the pastor was in on it. "Nice car for traveling," I said. "To Mexico."

"We've never been to Mexico," he answered. I slid the weed behind my back, hoping God would forgive me. He needed an oil change. I guided him into the service stall and stashed the kilos away. I commented that I knew his son, trying to make small talk, but it saddened the pastor. He said Paul Bunyan had been arrested and wouldn't be out any time soon.

Arrested? It could have been me. He handed me a newspaper article. "Here, read all about it," he said, matter-of-factly. Paul Bunyan had confessed to disposing of a body. When he had completed the sale of a large quantity of weed to some black dealers, there was an ambush waiting. Paul Bunyan and four of his fellow Hell's Angels were held up at gunpoint. Before the night was over, one of the ambushers got killed. Paul Bunyan confessed to having cut the body up and strapping it to the trap door of the dealer's headquarters. "He took the rap for his friends," the pastor confessed. His expression was eerily similar to Dad's when he picked me up after my arrest.

The school year was coming to an end, and my relationship with Katie changed after Dr. K and Frank threatened to cut my balls off. We quit talking about any future plans. We were back to being regular seniors until the end of the year.

"Turn right," said Paul. I was driving to the last Athenians-Thebans party of the year. We were on a dark road in Walnut Creek, looking for the obscure location in the middle of what used to be walnut tree groves. I turned the corner.

"Holy shit!" Headlights zoomed up behind me just as I started up a long Tiki torch lined driveway. The car squeezed past with a honk and The Doors' top hit "Light My Fire" blasting. It was Katie with two friends in her mother's convertible Mercury. The car shot ahead and skidded to a stop beyond the horseshoe driveway. The party was in full swing with loud music, a bar and dance floor at the poolside, and a keg on wood deck in front. I parked next to Katie. She slid out, cigarette in hand, and took a deep inhale just like her mother. Susie Lawrence, daughter of Ernest Lawrence, the famed physicist and Nobel Prize winner, slid out of the car draped in a pool dress. The threesome came to party. Katie wore a new casual cotton dress and leather belt. Paul lit a cigarette with Katie's, and we all walked to the action through a torch lined pathway.

"Welcome to the house of ill repute," a friendly voice came. And just as quickly, we all had a beer in our fists—chug, chug, chug. The party was on. The home turned out to be one of Katie's brother's classmates. She introduced me to the host and a few older members from her brother Victor's class. "This is my friend, Charles . . ." Friend, not husband. We were not destined to join Victor's lifestyle. No baby, no apartment, no minimum wage job, no pressure to struggle through the dire rat race.

Kurt Sproul ran past chasing a now bikini-clad Susie Lawrence. They leaped in the pool splashing everywhere. "Childhood crush," Katie stated. She, Kurt, and Susie were childhood friends whose fathers were members of the famed Bohemian Club. Katie handed me a champagne glass, and we tipped and chugged. It was a moment of recognition that we'd dodged the bullet.

Kurt jumped out of the pool and gave me a thumbs up and rattled off a Greek fraternity name. Katie and Susie giggled and said I'd be joining a fraternity. Kurt turned back and handed me a fresh beer, challenging me to chug it. If I was going to be a frat boy, I had to learn to drink like one. We chugged the beers and tied. The music blasted, people danced, and everyone talked about college plans. Katie and Susie danced seductively, smoking, and holding drinks. It was time to let loose. I tried to keep up with Kurt and his frat friends, but after a few drinks, the world started spinning, and I was seeing double.

I was drunk, but not alone. People were falling over themselves and into the pool. It was safe, and we were in a secluded place built to party hardy. Tall trees swayed and danced to the music, calling me to climb up. I stepped toward one, but it morphed into two, then blurred into a tall skinny cave. I was in trouble. I needed a break and staggered out. Seeing double, following the Tiki torch lights through the pathway, everything bouncing to the music, I could only hope to find my car. Tall, friendly roses and carnations rocked left then right; I followed their pattern. I stayed on course watching the flowers blur and bounce up and down to the music. Everything jumped up and down, up and down, to the beat, melding together like soap bubbles. I was the Apprentice in *Fantasia*, the suds taking me away. Then one bubble sped up, bouncing, turning into two, a little offbeat, too fast. Faster, and faster, the two bubble-flowers bounced, pumped. "Oh, oh, oh!" a familiar primal scream rang out from the off-beat pair of bubbles. It was Katie's naked butt humping up and down in her convertible.

The following morning, I hopped on my motorcycle and rode to the top of the hills. Graduation was two days away, and Mother's precious castle in Guadalajara was completed. The skyline street to the best panoramic view of the west never looked better. San Francisco and its two bridges sparkled on that clear and bright morning. I was eighteen and had the freedom to do whatever I wanted. The Golden Gate Bridge called my name. It had the answer to my destiny. I had to ride across that bridge. But first, a little Acapulco Gold was in order. It enhanced the senses, and I wanted to feel every bit of this goodbye-high-school ride.

I took a few hits of the best weed in town and looked out at the city that I was proud to be a part of. Berkeley was a place to call my home. I kick-started the engine, revved it, felt the power between my legs, and hit the road. Riding without gloves or helmet, crisp air stinging my face, gave me the adrenaline rush I wanted. I was a warrior, a matador, superman, Dad, Don, Tonto, Willie Mays, and Mohamad Ali. I had the perfect balance of body and mind over the roaring motor beneath me. My destiny lay ahead, and it would start at the magnificent bridge on the horizon.

Throwing caution to the wind, I cranked the throttle, sending me across the hilltop and down Strawberry Creek Road. Racing down the hill, leaning into corners, feeling the anxiety right before powering through at the apex of the turn and easing back up was my "ole," my matador's Veronica pass. I was on my game, through the Berkeley campus, down Bancroft and Telegraph, over to Durant, where Dustin Hoffman picked up Katherine Ross in *The Graduate*. I eased down to Berkeley High. Mr. Populus's prophetic statement—all bones are white—rattled around my head along with the memories I'd take with me.

The Golden Gate called me down University Avenue to the Berkeley Pier and the Bay Bridge. Thoughts of Mr. Brown riding his motorcycle across the same route to hear poets, writers, and singers made the ride thrilling. Maybe I'd be inspired to journey to Mexico as he was. Anything was possible now.

The Bay Bridge came quickly. Traffic was light. I took the middle lane and revved up the engine, letting world know I was coming. A truck driver tooted his horn back at me. An Army truck with camouflage canopy battled along the right lane. A troop of soldiers rode in the back. I flashed a two-finger peace sign. Some returned the sign while others flipped me off. I raced ahead and settled into the gentle flow of traffic before reaching the Presidio exit. San Francisco never looked better. The magnificent green lawns, plants, and forested trees overlooking the Golden Gate felt like candy to my Acapulco-infused senses.

The walkway on the bridge was surprisingly empty. Maybe someone had jumped off that morning, or something terrible happened, but I had the whole catwalk to myself. I headed toward Marin slowly, in the quiet of the ocean. The stillness of giant cargo ships felt eerie like they were abandoned. I arrived at my destination. I was there to define myself as an American once and for all. Mother and Dad would be leaving for Mexico, and I resented it. It didn't make sense that they would leave. I stood alone on the apex of the Golden Gate Bridge, feeling the vastness of the ocean. I was calling up the courage, the machismo, to face the challenge—the *toro*—ahead. College would be a breeze compared to fighting a bull.

I had to get back for a commencement practice at the Greek Theater. Steve McQueen was filming the movie *Bullitt* in San Francisco, and traffic was blocked off on several streets. I thought of his film *The Great Escape* and rode right through a barrier on to Van Ness Boulevard. I flew up the street into the quagmire of downtown traffic without a cop in sight. I was safely heading back over the Bay Bridge, feeling immortal and ready to conquer the world. Riding the motorcycle in the open air was my release. Smoking Acapulco Gold did the same. Mixing the two would be costly.

Crash

Your son suffered extensive brain damage. There's no telling how or when he'll come out of this. I hope he's good with his hands. I'd look for college alternatives. Plenty of manual labor jobs with good unions available," I heard a strange voice say as I came to. It was a neurosurgeon talking with Dad. I had been in a coma, this conversation sounded like a bad dream, and I fell back out of consciousness.

When I woke up I heard, "You were in an accident," Don said, holding in his emotions. "You have a lot of broken bones." I moved my tongue around and felt a sharp pain. "You broke your jaw. You broke your pelvis." I wasn't able to see Don's face. My eyes were swollen shut, leaving a slit for me to see. "You've been in a coma. You cracked your skull." I breathed, unable to move my neck. "Cracked vertebrae and disks." I cringed as I moved my foot. "Broken toe, too," I grunted in pain. "Can you talk? Do you know who you are? Where are you? Do you know who I am?" I wanted to say yes, but my mouth wouldn't move.

I winced as my tongue moved across a cracked tooth. I'd lost five front teeth and had two still dangling. "This is temporary. Physical pain heals. Emotional pain doesn't." I slipped back out of consciousness.

The sound of engines—trains, motorcycles, cars, jets—roared past my open coffin. Faces of people I'd known in Mexico, New York, Belmont, Orange County, and Berkeley raced across my open casket. They laughed and cried and smiled and frowned, all trying to express something, but the sound of the roaring engines drowned out everything. The faces whirled by faster, spinning, flipping, melding together, and forming cartoon animal shapes. Finally, an angry bull appeared charging toward me. I screamed myself awake and felt my loose teeth churning, grinding together. Then my entire body throbbed in pain. I shouted until a nurse hurried in and stood over me. "Honey, you have a fractured skull and a lot of broken bones. You need to stay still," she said. I squirmed in pain.

"I just want to die," I muttered.

Don and Eugenia stood at either side of my bed, each holding a hand. I opened my eyes and saw their worried expressions. They looked like angels. I don't know what they were wearing, but I imagined them in white robes and wings. Eugenia had a halo. I didn't mind being dead if I was. No one said a word, each of us stuck in our own solitude, yet closer than ever. All that had been experienced since leaving Mexico for the United States was shared in that moment without talking. A blink, a nod, tears, and nervous smiles were enough. The blinding pain I'd been in vanished from my body as though my brother and sister had drawn it from me. I wanted to be closer to them, to know them better, to hear their journeys. I sensed Don's pain, the loneliness he must have sustained in reform school. Eugenia's intense and knowing stare studying my swollen head reminded me of the many times she'd checked my homework and helped me learn. They followed through with Dad's promise of being good Americans. I wanted to take the same road.

"Charles, hello Charles," Mrs. Winters' familiar voice rang through my foggy head. I peeked through my swollen eyelids. I wasn't dreaming. My English teacher stood at my bedside in a colorful Paisley pattern blouse and a worried expression. She was a male version of Dad. "You, dear boy, you've been through a lot." Her sweet, angel-like voice softened my pain. "This accident is a miracle in disguise. God spared you. He has a plan for you." I winced. "I think he's calling you to be a teacher." I frowned. "I brought you this." She handed me my high school diploma. "Leaving high school is symbolic of leaving our childhood." She placed the diploma on the nightstand. "You're going to make a fine teacher. I just know it," she said, then took my hand and prayed. I'd left a lot more than my childhood. I'd lost thirty pounds, five teeth, and probably my job. Whatever this miracle was about, it had to be better than my situation.

Paul walked in, wearing a leather headband and a denim shirt. "You look like shit," his eyes raced around. "A stick figure, I meant." He placed a card on the table. "Oh, shit!" He rushed into the bathroom and vomited.

"You alright?" I slurred.

"This whole city shit is getting to me. You, all these deaths, Vietnam, suicides everywhere, it's too much." One of our Athenian brothers had come home in a body bag.

"Huh?"

"Yeah, and James found his father in the basement dangling from a rope." Paul's football teammate, James, an Athenian brother, had been Paul's role model and inspiration. James had fulfilled a dream and received a full scholarship to Cal.

"Shit."

"And you really got fucked up at the party." He shook his head as though flushing out a thought. Soap bubbles floated out of his mouth as he spoke. I heard Katie's primal screams, "Oh, oh, oh!" and saw Paul's lips move, but I couldn't hear a sound. I was back at the party, watching Katie's bare butt. She stopped, turned, and saw me. Paul sat up and saw me.

"Huh?" Paul's lips were still moving.

"You fucked up. Katie jumped my bones. She fucks like a bunny in heat."

"Shit."

"All bones are white," Mr. Populus' voice echoed in my ear. "You're alive and have two good hands. Now, make the best of it." I opened my eyes. I was alone.

Dad and Mother stepped in, looking exhausted. Dad wore a gray suit with a black tie. Mother wore a black dress and sweater. I'm sure it wasn't that they were expecting a funeral, but it felt like it to me. They had spent days and nights at the hospital. The worry in their faces was painful to see, knowing I'd caused it. "Sorry," I whispered. Mother held my hand. Dad held her. Dad handed me a book, *Man's Search for Meaning* by Viktor Frankl, and said I was lucky to have survived. He said the book would help me find a light at the end of the dark tunnel I was in. I hoped the light wasn't a train coming down the track. I reached for the water cup, picked it up with two fingers, and sucked on the straw.

"Your dexterity appears intact," Dad observed. I wondered if I'd still be able to work on cars. My arms and hands felt all right, but I hadn't walked and knew my back was in trouble. I tried to slide out of bed, but Dad and Mother insisted I stay. Mother handed me a mirror. My head was the size of a watermelon. "Sorry," I said, unable to recognize myself. My deformed purple face with missing teeth belonged in a horror film. Mother and Dad did not deserve the pain of having to see me like this.

"There's no need to apologize. You concentrate on getting better," Dad said. I studied his face. Dad's hair was graying at the temples, somehow softening his blue eyes, and his crow's feet creases were deep and permanent. How much worry had I caused him over the years? William Allen had shown me the way to live. Now he stood over a disaster. If he only knew about the weed I'd handled, it would have done him in. I had to be the biggest disappointment of his life. I picked up the book he'd brought me. "The search for meaning, as in the only life worth living, is in the service of others?" I asked.

"One step at a time," he sighed. "Right now, we need you to get well." I had hit rock bottom. If I hadn't put Mother and Dad through enough already, this would surely drive them back to Mexico. I was in a mess, but I wasn't about to let myself go down the rabbit hole of guilt and shame. I'd been through high school with a scarlet letter A on my chest.

I fell asleep.

Two envelopes lay on my chest when I woke up. The first was from Katie with a note written on the outside saying she came by with her father and mother. I'd been asleep, but they prayed over me. The second was thick, bulging, barely holding. I opened it. Twelve Trojan rubbers fell out. In the card, a message scrawled in it said, "Charles, get well so you can use the enclosed. Wayne Wesley Garcia."

"No, Charlie!" Mother pleaded with me to lie down. I'd been at home in bed too long. I couldn't take the bedpan any longer. I tried standing, but my legs wobbled like a newborn colt's. Mother was beside herself, seeing me so weak. I crumbled back in bed.

A blue jay laughed hysterically at a squirrel in front of my window. "*Saquese!*" Mother scolded the bird as she opened the door. The bird cawed again, and Mother cried back. The birds, the squirrels, and our neighbor's cat kept Mother company in our quiet place. I'd been home two weeks, amused with my Mother's morning routine. Like clockwork, before breakfast, Mother placed peanuts or sunflower seeds in the garden intended for her pet squirrels. She'd rush back in the house, turn on her favorite music, and sit in her chair overlooking her domain with coffee and breakfast. The fat-tailed pets would arrive, peel their breakfast, savor the nuts, comb their mustaches, and wash their hands right in front of the window. All the while, a blue jay or two stood perched on a high branch while the neighbor's brown cat lay nearby. It was theater. True to their names, the furry animals would carefully squirrel away the unopened nuts in crevices around the garden. But before their job was done, the blue jays swooped down and stole the hidden morsels in plain view. The squirrels would rush back, alarmed they'd been robbed, dig for their food, and look around for the culprit. The blue jays' cawing laughter drove Mother outside, where she would make a futile attempt to stop the robbery and get on with her garden pruning.

I was grateful for the privacy we had. I'd deteriorated to skin and bone, too frail to walk. All I could do was recover at home with Mother's love and care. Watching Mother tend to her flowers in the garden helped me heal. "*Mamacita!*" Paul's voice came through the bedroom window. Mother opened the glass door and let him in.

He'd added a leather vest and guitar to his new identity. Mother's demeanor lifted as she greeted Paul and left. Without asking, Paul leaned over, lifted me, carried me to the kitchen table. "You look like shit. You need to eat."

"I missed you, too," I said. It was better to go along with Paul than try to figure out his reasoning. He knew Mother would have the customary black beans and quesadillas waiting for him. "Ah, just what the doctor ordered," he said. "*Mamacita, gracias.*"

After a while, Mother walked out to her flowers. Paul strummed his new guitar humming a medley of Bob Dylan songs. He seemed lost in his guitar. "I'm not going to college," he said. "Yet."

"Bad time to go in the Army," I counseled. He'd said many times: if he didn't get a scholarship, he'd join the Army. He stopped humming Bob Dylan's "Lay Lady Lay."

"I'm going to Sedona, Arizona to paint. It's a beautiful place far, far away from all the madness." I watched and heard him express himself from his heart. He was tapping into new energy.

"Crazy."

"Dad died." He played on. I waited, trying to make sense of it. "I didn't tell you, couldn't tell you. The whole world looks like shit."

It must have been more than I could take because I woke up a few hours later in bed wondering if I'd dreamt Paul's visit. It wasn't a dream. The world had turned upside down. I was stuck in bed for another month.

Mother and Dad didn't rush off to Mexico. They rented out their dream home and postponed their plans, at least until I got better. Don was in the drama department at Berkeley, and Eugenia was working on another one of her many degrees. Katie went off to college. She sent a letter every day with my horoscope and wished me good luck with my recovery. After a while, she packed the horoscopes in a weekly message and, finally, not at all. Paul decided to seek his inner peace in Arizona with a paintbrush.

I read *Man's Search for Meaning* and felt enlightened afterward. Many of the Holocaust survivors in Viktor Frankl's book had one thing in common: They found a reason to live for a higher purpose even through the nightmare they were in. I felt lucky to be alive. I had to find a purpose outside of myself. Dad had set a standard for Don, Eugenia, and me with his own life. He had given all of himself for us. He embodied compassion, sacrifice, giving; now it was our turn.

I had to get back on my feet and deal with a broken jaw and five missing teeth before going back to work. Slowly, I got well enough to start my life again. I grew close to my dentist through the process. He scheduled our appointments at the end of his day and spent extra time showing me the ins and outs of a dentistry career. He encouraged me to consider the profession, saying dentists had a good standing in society, and doing work like what he did for me was rewarding. He added medical doctors got a lot more respect. "Nurses bow to doctors in a hospital and get a lot of love. Nobody likes going to a dentist," he said. "You're the exception." I liked being there because it was a path to being in the service to others.

In four years, I could be in dental school. In time I settled into a routine of college courses and worked just as I had in high school. Joe liked having me back at the gas station and never learned about me smoking pot. He was glad to hear I was studying with plans of attending dental school. I was back on track with a purpose.

On May 15, 1969, a violent confrontation erupted over the use of an abandoned university-owned plot of land, popularly known as People's Park. Don was a senior by then, and I was a freshman. We walked together toward Sproul Hall when an angry crowd started marching toward the park. We heard chants of "Let's take the park!" and "We want the park!"

Months earlier, Ronald Reagan, the California governor, had promised to crack down on what he called "communist sympathizers, protesters, and sex deviants." The park had become a symbol of people's collective freedom. It was merely a community effort in cleaning up a filthy, neglected plot of land. Hundreds of people supported the park and wanted official approval for the use of the area. The chancellor's office had met with the People's Park committee and agreed to the use of one-quarter of the property for the park. But at 4:30 A.M. that morning, Ronald Reagan sent California Highway Patrol and Berkeley police officers into People's Park. Without warning, they cleared the park, destroyed all plants, grass, flowers, and shrub donated by local groups. They put up an eight-foot-tall perimeter chain-link fence. By noon a rally at Sproul Hall steps was in full swing when Don and I joined the excitement. The mass headed toward Telegraph Avenue but panic erupted when shots drowned out the chants. Don and I were by then on Telegraph Avenue when buckshot flew over our heads. People scattered back, screaming and crying as we turned and ran for our lives. The police had gas and buckshot. We learned later that James Rector was shot in the stomach, and he died. The day only got uglier and would forever be known as Bloody Thursday.

The next morning, National Guard soldiers moved in and stood in formation with rifles forward. It was a frightening moment. Student demonstrations had been a way of life on campus forever, it seemed. But gas-spraying helicopters and the killing of a demonstrator was shocking. Streets were barricaded with barbed wire all around the city while the nation watched on television.

My morning sociology class was canceled with a sign on the door that read: YOU ARE PART OF HISTORY NOW. WRITE A 2,000-WORD ESSAY ON YOUR EXPERIENCE. A brave female stepped up and urged students to walk together. She had a camera and lenses dangling on leather and lace shoulder straps, ready for business. We headed toward the armed guards past Sather Gate. She snapped picture after picture directing us toward the soldiers. They seemed torn, holding up their weapons while female students with flowers in their hair peacefully slid fresh daisies in the rifles. I later learned marijuana-laced brownie cookies and LSD punched lemonade had been passed around to students as well as soldiers. I had to forgo any more activities as I didn't have the conviction to tear up a city over a park.

I forged ahead in my studies and met a determined Black student in biology class, James Logan, who looked like Sammy Davis Jr. He had served in the U.S. Navy as a dental assistant and was now a pre-dental student. He wanted to open a practice near Lake Merritt, own a condo with a view, and drive a Rolls Royce. It sounded appealing with the advancement the Black movement was making in Oakland.

We hit it off instantly and studied together every morning. He showed up at my door every school day at five o'clock, ready to drill and review our chemistry and biology classes. I was getting a whole new perspective on chasing the American Dream. We talked about building a practice together, opening a chain of clinics, promoting the business through union trade papers, and driving matching Rolls Royces. The image of us cruising around the lake wearing matching fedora hats with a long feather and diamond-studded gold chains came to mind. We studied together until we were blue in the face and passed the courses.

I introduced him to authentic Mexican food one day in a new restaurant nearby. A beautiful young Mexican waitress took our order, smiled, and gave James a wink. His mouth dropped open; cupid had lanced an arrow through his heart. "What are you thinking?" I said.

"I want her to be my baby's mama," he said. Before we left, he had the number of the lady who would have his baby within a year. Somehow, he managed to show up at my door every morning until the baby arrived.

Awakening

One day I read an article in the *San Francisco Chronicle* about Spanish-speaking grammar school students not understanding the instruction they were receiving. The language barrier created a problem for teachers. They reported being frustrated with their inability to reach their students. Worse, Mexican American students in secondary grades had the highest dropout rates. It struck me that I was in a position to help. I rushed to the nearest elementary school to offer my help. I was welcomed into a school resource volunteer program by a retired teacher, Mrs. Hagg. She reminded me of Mrs. Winters in her delicate manner and soft voice. Her eyes lit up when I told her I had read about Spanish speaking students. She quickly led me to Mrs. Hurtt's classroom, where Black and white students sat on the rug listening to the teacher read while two brown students sat, removed in the back, staring at the walls. My heart sunk. "Would you like to work with these two boys?" She indicated the two Mexican boys. "They don't talk." A lump in my throat rendered me speechless. I wanted to help.

A few days later, after some paperwork and health clearance, I met the students who sat in the back of the class, Moises Garcia and Carlos Cabello. Mrs. Hurtt introduced us in English and placed paper and pencils on a table for us. We studied each other. "Hello, my name is Char—" I stopped. *"Hola, me llamo Carlos."* They had been reticent at first, not looking directly at me, withdrawn and speechless. But with four simple words in Spanish, I'd bridged the gap for them. Their faces lit up like lightbulbs. I'd tapped into something that felt good for them, and me. I volunteered for two hours a week.

One afternoon while tutoring Carlos and Moises, I wore one of Dad's pocket protectors that had a picture of a calculator he had designed. "What's that?" Carlos asked, intrigued by the picture on my chest. I handed them the pocket protector.

"It's a calculator. My dad designed it. It does math just like we're doing." I referred to the math book in front of them.

"Your Papi made this, "Moises said.

"How did your Papi learn to do this?" Carlos asked.

"My Papi learned math, just like you," I said, pointing to them. "Then he graduated from elementary school, then high school, and finally went to university. You know the college where the Campanile is, that big tower?" They both stared blankly. Oh no! I thought, how could these two boys not know the iconic structure that symbolized the whole city. I continued, "You know you too can build something like this someday. You just study hard and go to college, and you can be anything you want." They both sat back and looked at me as though I was crazy. "What's wrong?" I asked.

"Don't you know Mexicans can't go to college?" Ouch. I wasn't ready for that.

This was my call to duty moment.

I wanted to do something, anything, to change these boys' outlook. Mrs. Hurtt was open to everything I suggested that might help "my boys" as she called Carlos and Moises. I noticed the reading series books had all white characters. That was a revelation in itself; my boys couldn't identify with the stories. I volunteered to look for stories with Black and brown family characters. After an extensive search, I couldn't find any. Mrs. Hurtt was not surprised. "I've been looking for years, Charles."

"There's *Spot the Dog*," I joked, referring to the reading book. Mrs. Hurtt's face flushed with embarrassment.

"We'll have to do something about that," she said, handing me a brown crayon. In short order, I colored every boy and girl in the readers brown and black. By week's end, I had changed the names from Sally to Maria, Tom to Tomas. The next semester I signed up for a Mexican American history class.

Mexican American history evolved into Chicano Studies, along with African American history becoming Afro-American Studies. Ethnic Studies had been born, and I had a place to learn what I'd never been exposed to. Mexican Americans had a history in the United States that had simply been ignored in public education. I devoured books on Latin American history and Spanish literature. In a short time, I understood the positive influence Hispanic culture had on America and wondered why it had not been taught in public schools. California especially has a rich and colorful history of Native American, Spanish, and Mexican contributions to the Golden State. Yet very little beyond the Spanish Missions was ever mentioned in my history education.

Prominent historian Hubert Howe Bancroft was the authority on California history. His collection of books and materials were stored right there in the library that bore the Bancroft name. The fifth floor housed his works in a high-security room. Reading the prized material was by appointment only and required multiple forms of identification. I signed up for reading sessions and was issued soft cloth gloves to protect from transferring skin oils. With great anticipation, I checked out *California Pastoral*. It was a frightening experience. Chapter One: Comparative Civilizations and Savagism. My heart sank. I had a feeling this wasn't going to be a favorable description of Mexicans and Native Americans.

First paragraph: "Before penetrating into the mysteries of our modern lotus-land, or entering upon a description of the golden age of California, if indeed any age characterized by ignorance and laziness can be called golden, let us glance at life and society elsewhere on this planet, particularly as it existed in Spain and Mexico, and within the charmed circles of the highest earthly intelligences, the places and conditions being more intimately than any others connected with the spiritual conquest and occupation of Alta California in the eighteenth century." He argued that Aztec civilizations were inferior to European civilizations because God created both; thus, occupation and dominance was an inevitable part of His plan. He wrote further, stating that Mexicans were greasy, lazy, built close to the ground to serve in the fields.

Ouch. I wasn't ready for that. I thought about the kids in Orange County that had used racial slurs with me. I felt sorry for them. They, too, were victims of ignorance about the positive influence Mexicans had in America.

Here I was in the premier library on the U.C. campus reading absurd observations and conclusions about Aztecs. I had enough knowledge of Aztec civilization to know better. I went on to learn from other scholars about the influences that led to Mexico losing the northern states in the Treaty of Guadalupe. Manifest Destiny, expansionism, and the war with Mexico left Mexicans "foreigners" on their own land. Later, with the discovery of gold, Mexicans became second-class citizens. Carlos and Moises were in my thoughts with every new bit of knowledge I learned.

Cesar Chavez was making front-page news with his struggle to form a farmworker union. It was a hard-fought battle that needed attention on both sides of the picket lines. Transient labor was bused in and walled off by armed guards and local law enforcement. Luis Valdez had recently graduated from San Jose State and joined the struggle. He founded El Teatro Campesino and wrote satirical skits addressing the plight of the farm workers. One day in May, as part of a Cinco De Mayo festival, Luis Valdez's political activist troupe El Teatro Campesino performed rich, relevant, comedic plays that exposed the labor conditions farm workers faced. It was an empowering experience. He was telling the history of Mexicans in California, especially in agricultural business. I wanted Moises and Carlos to feel this eye-opening experience. I took every course offered in the new Chicano Studies department.

I had been awakened to a political arena that included Mexican Americans. The civil rights movement I'd studied and been a part of for five years suddenly expanded from Black and white issues to include me. I devoured books and courses on Afro-American, Chinese, or Asian Americans, as they were called, and Mexican American history. One course was taught by Dr. Harry Edwards, the foremost authority on Afro American studies and famous for his influencing the Black Power Salute, a protest on the 1968 Olympic stage. He provoked action for human rights by prompting sprinters Tommie Smith and John Carlos during the medal's ceremony. His courses were so popular they were held in lecture halls with fifteen hundred students. A popular activist of the time, Eldridge Cleaver, coined the phrase, "If you're not part of the solution, you're part of the problem." The Black Power movement started to make sense in a new way for me.

I could be a part of the solution for change in the Mexican American community. Throughout my courses, the faces of Moises and Carlos looking at me saying, "Mexicans can't go to college," haunted me. I had a revelation about the curriculum in schools. Text publishers needed to include Black and brown characters. My coloring-in the white faces with crayons was a lesson in "exclusion" that hit home. I'd never read a classroom basic reading book with any minority characters in New York or California.

A few days later, after a sociolinguistics class in Wheeler Hall, I walked through a corridor pondering a term paper. The hallowed walls and heavy brass doors reminded me that Dad, Don, and Eugenia had taken courses at one time or another in the same building. It was a blessing and a curse. It was comforting yet weighted with a responsibility to live up to a lofty standard. I pushed open the heavy door and walked out to a beautiful spring day.

I had to write a paper, but first, I had to buy my first pair of bellbottom pants as I was sorely behind the times in fashion. Telegraph Avenue sidewalks were jammed, filled with street vendors hawking their arts and crafts. I weaved through toward a popular clothing store, all the while trying to come up with a topic for my term paper. A skinny mime dressed in white overalls and multicolored tie-dye shirt eased up and tickled my ear with a red flower. She wore a Charlie Chaplin Derby hat and a deadpan white face. She peeled off a red petal, placed it in her open palm, and blew it up in the air. I followed the petal up, and she walked away, leaving a display window visible where a deadpan Charlie McCarthy ventriloquist puppet waited for me.

"Hey, hey, Carlos," said Enrique, my sombrero and poncho-wearing ventriloquist puppet. "Wake up!" I'd bought the Charlie McCarthy puppet and made a Mexican out of him.

"What? Who? *Que?*" I said, decked out in a *pachuco* outfit—a wide-shoulder suit and hat, a red feather proudly displayed. I was in front of my sociolinguistics class role-playing two Mexican stereotypes. I was a *pachuco*, criminal profile-type character. Enrique was a lazy sombrero-and-poncho wearing peon. If I could have, I would have brought a *burro* for Enrique and a switchblade for me. I looked up from my sleep, rubbing my eyes. Enrique and I looked out at the smiling students. "*Hijole, carnal*, where are we?" I asked.

"I don't know, but it looks like some Mexicans are here. Smart Mexicans," Enrique surmised. Chuckles and laughter.

I made eye contact with a friendly-looking fellow, smiling ear to ear. "Escuuuuse me, *carnal*. Can ju tell me where we are?" building laughter.

"University of California," the student said.

I nodded. Enrique's mouth dropped open. "I-i-impossible," he said.

"Why?" I asked.

"Look at all the Mexicans." We both turned toward the class.

Nervous giggles as the attention turned to the audience.

"Yes, I'd say there are some Mexicans."

"Then we can't be in a college," Enrique stated.

"Why do you say that?" More laughter.

"Mexicans can't go to college." He quoted Carlos and Moises. Mixed reactions from my classmates.

"Let's find out," I said and turned to an eager female. "Excuse me, my friend here, Enrique, believes Mexicans can't go to college. Have you ever heard this?"

"Yes," she said matter of factly.

"*Ves, te dije!*" said Enrique. Laughter and commotion.

"All the time. My counselor, my teachers, everyone," the eager female continued.

"Where?" I asked.

"Coachella," she said. Arms raised all over the room.

"Me, too," another student said, and another, and another. I'd opened Pandora's box.

"*Ves*, les go. We don't belong here," Enrique hurried.

"Please, Enrique, stay," a student said.

"*No te vas*," said another.

"You belong here!" someone shouted.

"Okay, okay. How did all you Mexicans get in here?" asked Enrique. More laughter.

"I have a question," I said, bringing a serious tone back in the room. I noticed for the first time the head of the new Ethnic Studies Department Chair, Dr. Lila Gonzalez, smiling and amused in the far corner. "My question is about schoolbooks. Did anyone see Mexican families in your grammar reading books?" Puzzled expressions and angst.

Tears and anger came as we discussed and heard the different paths that led these select few students to Berkeley. The heartfelt discussion brought up more emotion than I was prepared for. It turned out everyone had the desire to achieve and pursue their dreams, but they had little encouragement. The pent-up emotions had to come out, and we stayed well after class hours.

"Excuse me, Carlos," Dr. Lila Gonzalez, a tall, middle-aged woman stood in front of me. "I'm Dr. Gonzalez, I am impressed with your work. You're right. Chicanos need Mexican role models in curriculum."

1973

True to his word, Dad announced his and Mother's plan to move to Guadalajara. The turmoil of the sixties had settled after the U. S. Army pulled out of Vietnam, and Watergate had ended with Richard Nixon's resignation. I wanted to let them know I'd be all right and continue with my education but not necessarily in dental school. Dental school was a sure thing, as a recruiter had counseled me at the University of the Pacific. The recruiter was an Athenian alumnus whom I'd met at a party. Being an Athenian did have its advantages.

I was torn between going on to dentistry school with James or pursuing a teaching career. My heart said, go to the classroom. My mind said, follow the money.

I wanted Dad and Mother to leave for their dream home with the knowledge my interest in a dental career was waning. I thought they'd be disappointed and didn't want them to learn my decision through the mail.

"Dad, I might not go to dental school."

"Why is that?"

"Mexican Americans aren't in our schoolbooks. There's one story with Mexicans, and it's blatantly making fun of Mexicans. They wear sombreros and ride burros."

"That's sad."

"There are two Mexicans; one digs a hole while the other takes a siesta. Then they switch places, but the second guy fills the hole. They repeat the process. I'm not kidding."

"I'm sorry to hear it."

"Now I know why some kids called me names because I am a Mexican." The statement hurt Dad. "They didn't know any better. There are a million stories of Black Americans every day in schoolbooks, newspapers, television, and magazines."

"Well, I'm puzzled by all this. It's news to me."

"My assimilation is complete. I'm a Mexican American."

"And a fine one, you are. American has no single color or definition."

"I'm thinking about becoming a teacher."

"Good. Dentists have a high suicide rate," Dad answered. That was his seal of approval.

Eugenia had gone to India with her husband on a dissertation research project. She received a Ph.D. afterward and started a career in mental health. Don graduated from the University of San Francisco Law School and passed the California Bar exam. They had their purpose.

Don spoke of life as a meaningless venture where suffering and pleasure were of equal value. He started a novel about a dystopian society in which everyone was equally miserable. Government-issued food, clothing, shelter, books, and autos were part of the premise and stated in the beginning. The only freedom of choice was love. His main character fell in love with a married neighbor and had sex while the husband worked the night shift. I laughed hysterically watching him read since he'd violated the premise that suffering and pleasure were of equal value, and because I knew he had been having an affair with our neighbor's wife. It didn't make sense that he would be writing about misery after having passed the bar exam on his first try.

Nevertheless, he seemed tortured, depressed. Or maybe it was guilt, but he was not celebrating his accomplishments as he could have. I dared him to go skydiving with me. He agreed, and we headed out to Livermore early the next morning. After a two-hour training session, we boarded a Cessna airplane and flew into a clear blue sky. We donned army green overalls and a helmet for our new adventure. The splendor of flying over lush green fields at sunrise brought a childlike grin to Don's face. A train whistled and came into view along a foothill catching my attention, reminding me where our American assimilation had started. I gave Don a two-eyed blink. He blinked back. The jumpmaster called me to prepare for the exit. The pilot turned off the engine. I stepped out the door to the wing, counted to three, and let go of the plane.

The parachute opened, and I sailed like a bird dangling under the canopy. The serenity, the freedom I felt floating through the air gave me pause to wonder what would happen if the parachute didn't open. Why had I lived through a motorcycle accident? What was my purpose in life? I cleared my mind of any doubt I had about the right career for me. "*O-o-orale!*" Don screamed, grinning ear to ear to my right. His parachute flapped open and sailed next to me. He let out deep sigh of relief and exaltation. We hung in the air like angels enjoying heaven.

I hit the ground knowing I'd become a teacher. Don landed a few yards away, screaming at the top of his lungs. He had the biggest smile I'd ever seen on him. "Ho-o-o-lee shit! Death-defying!" he said, jumping and laughing. "Wow, better than sex."

"I'm going to be a teacher."

"Great." He was beyond himself. "The devil doesn't care."

"What the devil?" He wasn't making sense.

"God, devil, heaven, hell who gives a shit. This is better than sex." I witnessed a life-changing moment in Don. His demons or whatever kept him preoccupied with worry left that day.

He stopped writing his novel and visiting our horny neighbor. We grew closer than ever after that and started celebrating life together. I was proud of him, and he was proud of me. We joined the running craze that swept across America. We routinely ran along the hilltop and waterfront of Berkeley. Running with Don was about willing each other through rather than a competition. Run gently, run far was our motto. It was also our complementary therapy as we reflected on everything. It was also our time to grow together as adults.

We spent more time doing things together. We went to the Oakland Raiders games, San Francisco Forty-Niners games, we skied, attended a million plays, ran, and worked out. Our parents were in Mexico, and we had found our sense of belonging. Through it all, I slipped back into the younger brother role.

Don never had an interest in working for anyone. He was determined to make it on his own. He wanted to provide legal representation to a disenfranchised minority population. A vacant hole-in-the-wall retail space with plenty of foot traffic was perfect for his dream. With a five-hundred-dollar budget, he scraped together repurposed paneling and materials to fix up the place. His childhood friends from Belmont had all learned a trade and helped convert a rundown vacant store into an office. He put up a sign in English and Spanish and was quickly swamped with cases. Within a year, he had a full-time secretary and two interns working with him. He started making plans to buy his dream hillside home in Belmont.

Early in his career, Don took a case that seemed unwinnable. It involved a Vietnam veteran fireman charged with armed robbery. He had a drug addiction, had committed the crime, but had no recollection of it. The case was well before the "Twinkie defense" in the Harvey Milk murder trial. Don selected the chubbiest jurors possible. As he put it, "I'm looking for empathy, the experience to understand." I had to see for myself. He presented the idea that the fireman indeed had acted in an altered state. Watching him in court gave me goosebumps—my brother defending a white middle American firefighter in court. If Moises and Carlos could see this, they'd see a different America.

Don had the jury in his hands with his story that went something like this: "Look at me, and you see I fight my weight. I try to diet, but it's not always easy. Especially when you have a wife who eats whatever she wants and never gains a pound. Let me give you an example. One night my wife baked a chocolate cake and left it on the kitchen counter. The whole house smelled like chocolate cake. You could practically taste it. I took a shower and went to sleep. When I woke up at dawn with the light starting to come through the window, I pushed the sheets off and noticed a dark stain on the sheets and pillow. I thought I had a bloody nose. I jumped out of bed, looked at my hands; it was everywhere. I flipped on the lights, and lo and behold, it was the cake." Jurors had little trouble understanding. Don won the case.

Don took me to celebrate that night at one of Dad's favorite restaurants on the Berkeley pier. The view, white tablecloth, and the piano bar set a rich mood. Our neighbor Hugh Taylor was a regular there and greeted us as we entered. He wore a beige turtleneck and white coat under his three-inch afro. "Boys, the Allen boys, come on over." We hesitated as he was slurring his words. Hugh was by now riding out his days until retirement. "We miss your parents," he started, but a waitress's tight skirt caught his attention and caused him to spill his drink. We walked away quickly.

"That's what I call the walking dead," Don said.

"Why? He's just drunk."

"He's drunk because he hates his job. It's like Dad always says, live in the service to others."

"Like you in court. Dad would be proud to see you."

"It's fun. So what's going on with you?" he asked.

"Sad things I'm finding about kids and school. You know, there are kids in school that think they can't go to college because they're Mexicans. They have no role models. And there are no role models they can identify with in reading books. None."

"It's not just schoolbooks. It's everywhere, magazines, television, movies. That's kind of the basis of *Brown v. Board of Education*."

"I never heard about that."

"Thurgood Marshall did his research. He brought in phycological studies that showed segregation made Black children feel inferior to the point that it affected their learning. Maybe that's what's going on with Mexicans who feel they don't belong in college. What are you going to do about it?" Don said.

"I'm going to write stories with Black and brown doctors and lawyers. I want to write a story with a doctor titled Zapata M.D. And another story about a lawyer titled, Pancho Villa, Esquire."

"I'll toast to that!" We lifted out drinks and took in the view.

I applied to graduate school at St. Mary's College for a teaching credential and interned at the same school where I volunteered. Interning, for all practical matters, meant taking a class and leaving the door open for supervision by a mentor teacher. Carlos and Moises came to my room every day. Their happy faces made my day, as I could see they were immersed in the school by now. They spoke English and sat at the front of their classes.

My mentor teacher, Anne Bloomberg, came from a teaching family. Her mother and father, sister, aunts, and uncles were all teachers. She knew her purpose and displayed a calm I wanted for myself. She complimented me for having changed the names of the characters in our readers and suggested I write stories for children. I applied to a Ph.D. program at Berkeley with the single purpose of writing a curriculum that included Mexican characters and family values.

One day I was in the school office reaching for my mail when I heard a voice behind me. "The new boy who never sat down." I turned and found Wanda bright and beautiful as I'd remembered. My heart jumped. She wore a vanilla-colored sleeveless blouse. Chocolate-vanilla swirl ice cream came to mind.

"Wanda?" I undressed her with my eyes. She did the same to me. "Are you working here?"

"My first day," she said, oozing with lust. "How long has it been?"

"Long enough." She leaned in, making sure I smelled her.

"I always knew you would be a teacher. And here we are."

It was all we could do to contain ourselves through lunch without rubbing and kissing and grabbing and making love right there, in the lunchroom, on the cafeteria table in front of everyone. As soon as the end-of-school bell rang, we rushed to our cars. I followed a few blocks away to her single-story stucco home.

A bead and leather dream catcher swayed slowly on her porch. Two wooden flower boxes straddled the landing. We brushed together, purposely rubbing and bumping as she unlocked the door. Wanda's shiny brown skin matched a feather in the swaying dream catcher. "Catch any good dreams?" I said, reaching for the feathered halo.

"You're here, aren't you?" The door opened, and we rushed in embracing, kissing, intent on making up for the lost years. She pulled away, catching her breath, rushed to the windows, and pulled the curtains shut. "Mama lives next door." I stood up, buttoning my shirt, and noticed dozens of bead necklaces hanging all over the room and down the hall.

"Your mom?" I pulled her into my arms. "What would she do if she saw me doing this to you now?" I unbuttoned her vanilla blouse. She flung it across the room. Her breasts bulged over a vanilla bra.

"You like it?" she asked, displaying her bra. She had a sewn-in bright red bead between the cups. My chocolate and vanilla fantasy had the perfect cherry on top.

"Your mama is going to fire me if she catches us," I mumbled with my mouth between her breasts gnawing on the red bead. It was attached with elastic. I pulled it away with my teeth until the elastic snapped, sending the bead down my throat. "Shit, oops. Wanda!" I said, choking, trying to cough the bead back, but it was too late. It was gone.

"What did you do?" she said, panicking, patting my back.

"I swallowed your cherry." She went to the kitchen and brought back two soda cans.

"You are crazy, crazy, crazy!" We laughed, learned about each other's lives, exchanging highs and lows about our separate journeys. She had married and divorced a student-athlete in college and was raising their child alone. She bought the house next door to her mom, shared everything, and had a passion for beads and leather. She planned to sell her craftworks on Telegraph Avenue and swap meets. She was living her American Dream, so sure of herself, and had her mother next door. I envied and admired her sense of self. Being a Black American was sure and easy, it seemed, while I still wondered what kind of an American I was to become.

The phone rang. Wanda had a short conversation with her mother and arranged for her daughter to stay overnight. We were free of obligation. "I have a surprise. Close your eyes." I closed my eyes and heard her fingers rumble through her jewelry box. I heard a match strike, and the smell of incense wafted all around. "Almost done," she said, closer now. "Okay, open!"

She stood wearing the gold necklace I'd given her ten years earlier. My mouth dropped open. She placed a joint between my lips and lit it. "We're café con leche," she said proudly, displaying her Spanish.

"All bones are white," I said confidently. Wanda represented so much of what America had been through in the past ten years. The civil rights movement had opened the way for Black Americans to take ownership of their equal rights. Wanda was living proof of it. She was so comfortable in her skin living the American Dream, knowing who and what she was. I thought about Carlos and Moises starting school with the idea that they could not go to college. *Que sera, sera.*

Dad was involved in a head-on collision while traveling on a narrow highway between Guadalajara and Mexico City. He broke a clavicle bone and had a head injury that left a long scar across his forehead. For some reason, Mother and Dad never shared the extent of the accident. After that, Mexico wasn't as romantic as it once was for them.

They decided to return to their home in Berkeley. They rented their dream home in Guadalajara to American medical students. It was time for the family to come together and enjoy the fruits of our labor, but Dad's injury had taken something out of him. He seemed lethargic and just wasn't himself. He started watching television comedies, something he'd never done before. The canned laughter edited into the shows was his cue to laugh. He was depressed. The lines in his face deepened and appeared more from worry than age.

But his pride in all three of his children was undeniable. Eugenia returned from India with a newborn baby. Eugenia was intellectually well paired with her Ph.D. husband on a path of endless potential.

Don's law practice had taken off when he won a big case against a high-profile lawyer who had represented Patricia Hearst. Don's case made the front page of the *San Francisco Chronicle*. Overnight, Don was a legal eagle in high demand. His life changed dramatically. He bought a new Alpha Romeo sports car, a whole new tailored wardrobe, joined an exclusive club, and opened an office in the same building where Humphrey Bogart filmed *The Maltese Falcon*. He was set.

I was accepted to a Graduate School of Education Ph.D. program, having made a case for the need of a culturally diverse curriculum. One study I read brought me to tears in the library. The case study was in Watsonville, California, known as the artichoke capital of the world. It is a farming community with one hundred percent white ownership and one hundred percent Mexican field workers. There was a steady supply of residents to harvest the crops. A U.C. Santa Barbara graduate student discovered that Mexican students had a ninety-eight percent dropout rate. The school board members defended the numbers saying Mexicans must have a genetic predisposition for dyslexia. The school board members were themselves deeply entrenched in the agricultural business and were protecting their interests. The article spread quickly through academic circles and ultimately brought about a lawsuit that led to change. It was fuel for the fire inside me that drove me to study and learn more.

Don and I kept up our feel-good running sessions, lengthening our distance, and spending more time together. He wanted to buy a house with his Chinese American girlfriend, also an attorney, and eyes his eyes open for a hillside home with a skyline view of the bay area. We started running the hills looking for homes in Berkeley and Belmont. It was a flashback to when Mom and Dad would drive the hills with the single purpose of having the right view.

I met Gloria, a Mexican American graduate student, in a statistics course one day. We lingered in the hallway afterward, feeling the chemistry build, unable to part. She was studying criminology and wanted to work in the juvenile justice system. We had something in common. I asked her on a date and learned we were both runners. That set us off on a regimen of running together. We ran through the trails above the campus as I'd done with my brother a million times.

I told her about my experience as a juvenile delinquent. She loved that I had been successfully rehabilitated. The following week she visited the "experimental class" I was teaching at Martin Luther King Jr. Middle School. The class was inspired by the hit television series *Welcome Back, Kotter*, which starred John Travolta and Gabe Kaplan. I had volunteered to take at-risk students placed in the same classes. I thought I could get through to them. A lofty goal, but I was young and eager. Gloria showed up bright, cheery, and with a confident smile. She got a lot of attention in the office. Kids snickered as we walked through the hallway to my classroom. As we got to the door, Carlos Cabello appeared. "Hi, Mister Allen," he greeted me with a baritone voice. He was thirteen now and had a serious demeanor.

"Why good morning, Carlos," I answered and introduced Gloria.

"Carlos here is a long-time student friend of mine. What are your plans, Carlos?"

"I'm going to be a lawyer and go to Stanford Law School," he said without hesitation. I smiled with pride. He went on to say I'd influenced him a lot and mentioned his four-point-zero grade average. Carlos had gone from thinking he couldn't go to college to this.

"What about Moises?" I asked.

"He moved to Hayward, and we haven't kept in touch." The bell rang, and we were flooded with students clamoring to enter. Gloria selected a seat in the back and took out a notebook. The first session was perfect. Students are on their best behavior when a stranger is present holding a notebook. It couldn't have gone better for Gloria to see me in action. Everybody was in top form. She had observed enough to write a paper for one of her classes. We agreed to meet later for a run.

The second period turned out to be a nightmare. Larry, an eighth-grade boy with a troubled past and brother of two incarcerated criminals, stormed in late. His eyes were intense. He was high and looking for trouble. He swore up and down at the whole class and wouldn't take a seat. I asked him to settle down, but he turned to me, eyes distant, swept my desk with a forearm, and spit on the fallen student homework. "Fuck you, Mister Allen, make me," he challenged.

"Larry, I'm going to call security if you don't calm down." I reached for the wall phone. Larry came at me with a knife. I stood my ground. "Don't be stupid. Now put that away." He charged, blade at his hip. I instinctively slammed a Bruce Lee kick straight into his chest. He fell and dropped the knife. I kicked it away. A friend of his grabbed the knife, saying he had my back. Larry got up and ran away, screaming he'd come back with a gun.

I filled out a report while security and administrators interviewed students. They supported the story that Larry had cleared my desk and pointed a knife toward me before I kicked him. It was a Friday. Gloria and I stayed especially close the whole weekend.

Larry was kicked out of school and sent to continuation school, which turned out to be what he wanted. But that wasn't the end of Larry. One week later, I got a call from Allen & Robestoff Law Offices. Yes, Allen, as in my brother Don Allen. He had taken on a partner and was the first law office listed in the new Spanish yellow pages' directory. Larry's mother was convinced they had a lawsuit against the school and me. Larry told his mother I pulled out a knife and that I instigated the scuffle.

Don was out of the office, signing escrow papers on a hillside home overlooking the Belmont and the bay. Larry and his mother went to the only Spanish speaking law firm they could find. Nick Robestoff heard Larry's story of the bad teacher who attacked him, but the name Allen rang a bell. He put the name and location together and figured it could be me as he knew I was a teacher in Berkeley. "Did you read the sign outside? The Allen family is not capable of harming anyone." Larry confessed the knife was his and that he'd lied.

The following day Don and I ran the hills and laughed at the funny coincidence that led Larry to Don's office. It was a hot day, and we ran bare-chested, two Aztec warriors, across the hilltop trails, under a bright sun. We pushed ourselves to the limit that day, arms and legs pumping faster than ever and drenched in sweat. Don's skin glittered in the sunlight as he smiled and slapped a high-five with me at the finish. I noticed a lump on his chest. "What's that?"

"Probably a bug bite," he said, pushing a finger on it. "It doesn't hurt."

"How long's that been there?"

"I'll go have it checked out."

He did. "It's a cancer tumor underneath my pectoral muscle," he said, lacing up his shoes. We were getting ready for a morning run.

"Shit," I started, but he cut me off.

"They'll take it out and that's that." He didn't sound convincing. My superman was holding information. "Come on, let's go."

We started up the hill, Don in the lead. He set a pace too fast for any conversation. It took all I had to keep up with him the first two miles until we reached the bottom of Marin street, the steepest, straight up, legendary incline in Berkeley. It's known to runners as Heartbreak Hill. "Ready?" Don challenged. We headed up the grueling climb. It was slow and painful, but Don's determination carried us to the top. I just followed my leader, step for step.

"When are you having the operation?" I asked, catching my breath.

"In two days," he answered and took off running. It was different. There was an urgency about him; the lacing of his shoes, his gait, breathing, speech.

He had been referred to Stanford Medical Center for treatment. Stanford was one of the country's leading cancer treatment centers. Two days later I waited for Don to wake up from surgery. "So, what's the prognosis?" I asked, awkwardly.

"*Que sera, sera,*" he said in his hospital bed, soft eyes focused on me, still groggy from the anesthesia. "The future's not ours to see." My superman downplayed the operation, but his future became uncertain. He had leiomyosarcoma, a rare soft tissue cancer beneath his pectoral muscles. His right arm was suspended above him to keep away from his chest cavity. He moved his fingers as though pulling the toggle on parachute ripcord. "I want to jump again."

"You're superman. You can do anything you want."

"Three, two, jump!" Our jumpmaster shouted. Don let go of the Cessna airplane handle and floated away into the clear blue sky. He'd been looking to this day since his surgery some four weeks earlier. I jumped next. The rush of falling through the air made him feel invincible and I loved watching my superman fly. We hit the ground giggling like children.

Ole.

Don put cancer behind him and continued building his practice. He hired another attorney and raised his rates. He was in high demand and only took on high profile cases. I found solace and comfort in my classroom, working with disadvantaged students. It kept the world at bay, including Don's health. But outside of the classroom, his battle with cancer was a ticking time bomb for me. Cancer references appeared everywhere bigger than life, it seemed.

1980

It became apparent that Dad's accident had taken more of a toll on his brain than we knew. He appeared listless at times. He was having difficulty with his memory but was able to keep his job at a company that harnessed cyclotron uses for medical equipment. His demeanor took a turn. He seemed withdrawn. "Dad, what's wrong? Why are you always out of breath?" I asked a hundred times and got the same mollifying response: "Everything is fine." One night, I took him to a doctor. He was fine physically. His symptoms were emotional. Now I had two ticking time bombs in my life.

Doctors recommended psychological treatment, but Dad was not accustomed to admitting weaknesses. He had relied on his brain to make a living, and now he felt his mind was failing him. To make matters worse, the medical students that rented the dream home graduated and moved out. A corrupt administrative government official arranged for an illegal drug cartel to purchase the house. A Mexican army official had forged Mother's and Dad's signatures on a bill of sale and took over the property.

Mother and Dad traveled to the home and found two armed soldiers at the entrance claiming the house belonged to an army general. All they could do was seek legal measures. They returned and paid monthly fees to an attorney, but he was just as corrupt as the drug cartel's representatives. It never got resolved, and the Mexican general eventually got killed in a gun battle inside the home. Don called the Mexican attorney and was gearing up for a legal battle, but another tumor appeared in his chest. Don needed surgery. Dad dropped the fight for the home. Losing the house seemed insignificant compared to Don's health. "What's going to happen to the house?" I asked.

"*Que sera, sera,*" Dad's soft blue eyes sparkled. He'd let go.

After another surgery, Don and I continued running together, but his battle with cancer started taking the life out of him. Our favorite trails through the Berkeley Hills became increasingly difficult for him. We slowed our pace and distance to fit his condition. I stayed a half step behind, hiding my tears. Our pace eventually slowed to a walk, and our conversations turned to the past more than projecting the future. His once broad, muscular chest had dwindled to half its size, and he lost fifty pounds. It was a lot to deal with for everyone around him, and he knew it. He, like Dad, withdrew and kept to himself, choosing to fight his illness his way. He researched alternative cancer treatment in Mexico.

I grew anxious about the misfortunes in the family. I found myself growing short of breath thinking about Don and Dad. I couldn't make sense of it and wondered why I was even alive after the motorcycle accident. It felt like the world was breaking, collapsing rather than building up. Being in the classroom kept my mind occupied and away from the worry that loomed over the family. But outside of the classroom, I had to stay active. Running was a good escape during the day. I kept busy reading and writing. One night, while writing a story about a Mexican boy who wanted to be a medical doctor, I got carried away and wrote into the early morning hours. The story opened with the main character riding a motorcycle across the Golden Gate Bridge. By dawn, I had a story titled "Dr. Zapata." Writing the story was an escape and somehow ended up with a cinematic quality.

Don loved the story and said he'd finance and direct it someday. "It's a story that needs to be told." That encouraged me to submit the story to the American Film Institute writing program with an application to study film. Six months later, I was accepted into the AFI screenwriting program. I told my advisor in the education department, Dr. Kenneth Johnson, about my new development. "Charles, you're only young once. Go, tell your story, share your story on the big screen," he said. "If it's a hit, remember us. If not, come on back. We'll be here."

I headed for the American Film Institute. By fall, I was entrenched in film studies and writing my heart out. I took up with the Los Angeles Unified School District as a substitute teacher. I needed the peace and comfort of working with disadvantaged students. Children absorbing the world around them in my care became my sanctuary, my place to feel a part of something bigger than me.

The American Film Institute studies program featured weekly seminars with influential guests across the filmmaking process. Executives and movie celebrities were the highlight of our week, and we got valuable information and leads each time. A studio executive at Norman Lear's production studios was a guest that week. Two of Dad's favorite shows, *All in the Family* and *The Jeffersons* were there. I learned the situation comedy format, wrote and submitted a spec script as suggested by the executive. A week later I got a call from Glenn Padnick, an executive in development. Norman Lear's Embassy studios was a sitcom mecca with hit shows like *The Facts of Life, One Day at a Time,* and *Diff'rent Strokes.* Glenn invited me to his office and handed me a pile of scripts. "Take these, study them, and pick a show you want to pitch a story to." He went on to tell me the parameters; one arc, all characters must talk, two sets with one possible swing set, keep plot close to home, no guests. "Have fun with it. You're from Berkeley. Don't be afraid to make a social commentary through the characters. As long as it's funny everything is on the table." I had lucked out. I needed humor in my life. What could be better than jumping all in on comedy writing? I studied the scripts day and night, wrote forty pitches — ten for each show, mixed in some topical issues, and dropped them off at Glenn's office the following week. He called me back into this office.

"You put a lot of thought into this. A simple one sentence log line is all you need. I like what you're doing, and the producers will like it, but they develop the stories with a team. Right now, just get the idea across and let their imaginations fill in the blanks." He told me to read *TV Guide*'s show descriptions. *Brilliant*, I thought. I sped home, stopping along the way to pick up a *TV Guide*. Social commentary. My mind ran wild. How could I make the morose subject of cancer funny? I wrote pitch after pitch for every show dealing with cancer. *Facts of Life* episode: titled "Oncology;" logline: Drummond is diagnosed with cancer. By the end of the night, every character in every show had cancer. Big mistake. Cancer is not funny. Every story pitch was quickly dismissed.

One of the characters in *The Facts of Life*, Jo, was a tomboy. She wore a black leather jacket and drove a motorcycle. With my motorcycle accident experience in mind, I wrote a story warning about the dangers of not wearing a helmet. Helmet laws had not yet been established. It was a long shot to have a character crash and suffer a head injury, but I pitched it along with an idea of Jo embracing her femininity with a secret fantasy. She would take ballroom dance lessons. I pitched the stories right before Easter week.

The next morning, I received a phone call from Glenn. The producers of *The Facts of Life* wanted to meet me as soon as possible. I couldn't get there fast enough. I rambled over the busy Cahuenga pass and got pulled over by a growling motorcycle cop. "What's the hurry?" he said. I happily signed the ticket and continued on to the meeting.

"So, this is the way I see the story," I started after the introductions. "It opens with Jo getting pulled over by a motorcycle cop. He asks, 'what's the hurry?' She answers, she's late for her first ballroom dance class." Laughter and snickers came from the writers and producers. They bought the story and said they'd love to work with me but since they were bumping another story for this one, they'd develop it based on the notes I handed them. They said they'd love to work with me in the future if the show got picked up for another season. My mind was clear of worries when writing, creating, or imagining a story. My American Dream was changing.

I drove up to Berkeley for Easter week vacation. I arrived at our home Thursday night before Good Friday. Mother had dinner ready and waited for my arrival. Dad sat in the living room watching a rerun of *The Jeffersons*, canned laughter punching every line. He laughed along, mechanically, I thought. He reached for the television remote when he noticed me. Dad looked pale and sad. The creases in his face had a downward slope that screamed a private sadness. He had reached a low I'd never seen. I lost my breath. "You okay, Dad?" I asked.

"Yes, son. Yes, I am. I get such a kick out of this show." He turned off the TV.

"These are reruns."

"Yes, but by the time I watch a show again, I've forgotten it." He smiled wryly.

"We sat for dinner. I tried to overlook Dad's sadness. But his shortness of breath and deep sighs worried me. Had it been the accident? Maybe it was his sense of helplessness with Don. Perhaps I should hurry up and have a baby and name it after Dad.

"I have good news, Dad. I wrote a show to the same studios that produce *The Jeffersons*."

"Well that is good news, son. You're writing a show for *The Jeffersons* is great news."

"It's a different show. It's *The Facts of Life*," I said. I knew he didn't quite register the whole story, but he'd get it when the show came on next year.

"This television writing is suited for you and your fantasies," he said.

"It'll be on television, and I'll come up so we can watch it together." Something was missing for Dad. He didn't answer and barely ate.

I picked up my guitar and played a favorite childhood song, "*Cielito Lindo*," which had always brought a smile to his face, but tonight it was futile. Mother enjoyed the guitar with my off-key ad-lib singing and strumming. If I couldn't cheer up Dad, Mother needed it. She appreciated it by singing along as poorly as I. Try as she might, the sadness of Dad's failing interest in life became impossible to ignore. After some horrible singing on my part, Mother put on some classic Mexican music. She was reminiscing about her wonder years with Dad.

She brought out a treasured picture of her and Dad dancing, holding a bottle of tequila, wearing a wide sombrero, with a serape draped over the two. The pain and loneliness she lived in were clear.

"*Besame Mucho*" started on the stereo. Mom looked at Dad. He looked back, without expression. The room filled with sadness. Dad stood, excused himself for the night and walked away without kissing mom. I felt her sadness. "Tell me about your television show," Mom said.

"It's about a girl who wants to dance like you, Mamacita," I said and stood up, reaching for her hand. She took my hand. I bowed, took one step back, lifted her arm, and twirled. Two, three, step, back and forth. Twirl, step, back and forth; Mother's desperate eyes looked at me for comfort, tears rolling down her cheeks. She gave me a two-eyed blink. Tears rolled down my face. It was Thursday and tomorrow would be sanctioned start of Easter weekend.

I woke up and headed up for my running trails wishing my brother could be with me. Good Friday spring morning couldn't have been better for a great run. The fresh air under a clear sky was ideal for an Aztec warrior route across the hills. I ran fast, staving off thoughts of Mother's pain and worries. Two hours of hard running was just what I needed. Afterward, I went into a friend's natural foods store on Telegraph Avenue for a fresh carrot juice. It was a routine I'd made many times with Don. Steve, the owner, was in law school and wanted to work for Don. Steve handed me an extra-large juice. "It looks like you had a good run," he said, when the phone rang. He took the call and turned away. "Yes, yes I will," he hung up. "That was your brother. There's been an accident. You better get home." Accident?

I raced home. Don's green Alpha Romeo and Eugenia's blue Volvo were parked in front. Dad's carport spot was empty, but he would be home early. *A Good Friday early gathering and early dinner*, I thought. I stepped inside. Don held our inconsolable Mother, tears running down their faces. Eugenia sat detached across the room. "What happened?" I asked, slowly approaching mom.

"Dad's dead," Don whispered. His faint manner frightened me. Did Dad kill himself? I reached for Mother. Eugenia moved in. We gathered around Mother, hugged, held hands, and wept together.

"What happened?" I managed.

"He was struck by a train. It was an accident," Don said. Struck? Don had his lawyer cap on. How do you have an accident with a train? Horrible images spun around my head; he jumped in front of the train; he miscalculated and crossed the track too soon; a million images of Dad's body destroyed, pulverized, smashed against the speeding steel carriage; Dad in loin cloth carrying a wood cross across the tracks. It was too much. I fell into auto-mode. My brain and body weren't connected. I wanted to blurt out my suspicion that Dad committed suicide, but the look on Mother's and Don's faces was chilling. It would have killed them.

The phone rang. Don took the call. The accident had made the local news, and now the Unitarian minister was reaching out to the family. Don's grieving face registered more concern as he listened on the phone. "That was the fellowship minister. He'll be here soon," Don said and took a seat opposite the three of us. His eyes darted around the room, uneasy.

Eugenia, stroked mom's back gently. *"Tenemos que llamar a Tia Rosita,"* Eugenia said, we needed to phone aunt Rosita.

"Si,bueno," Mom managed. We had reverted to Spanish. It felt a lot like our first days in New York; we were in a strange new place. Eugenia walked to the phone. I scooted in and soothed mom's back as Eugenia had done.

"Quires te, Mami?" I asked Mom if she wanted tea. She rested her head on my shoulder, nodding no.

"Adonde esta Ron?" I asked where Eugenia's husband was. Mother flinched.

"Mejor sin el." Better without him, she said. I paused. *"No me gusta come te mira. Ese hombre esta voltiado."* She said she didn't like the way Ron looked at me. He'd switched. Mother had to let out somehow. We sat and waited in silence. A lean, bearded, mid-forties minister appeared at the entrance just as Eugenia hung up the phone. She opened the door and the man walked in.

After few consoling hugs and more tears, the minister spoke. "I'm sorry for your loss. I loved Bill. We all loved Bill. He was pillar of our fellowship." We were speechless. He held out a list of practical things that needed to be done for a service and a funeral. He sensed our need to be alone and left.

Bereaved, senses on high alert, the four of us moved about comatose, carefully keeping the silence. One by one, we all broke down and cried together until our lungs were drained. We were back in Mexico for the moment. "What do you say when a saint dies?" Don said.

"On Good Friday," I said.

We had to make funeral arrangements. Eugenia took Mother to the bedroom. "Why isn't Ron here with Eugenia? When's he coming?" I asked Don.

"He's not. He's had a life change. They'll be divorced now." Eugenia had a second baby and bought a house in San Francisco's Height-Ashbury area where the hippie movement had taken off a decade earlier. Everything in her life appeared ideal, and our family was excited, welcoming the next generation. Her husband, however, was unsettled with his sexuality and started exploring. He had recently come to terms with his sexuality and was living a separate life. He took up the new lifestyle in the Castro District, where Harvey Milk was standing up for gay rights. "Don't ask about him again. It'll just upset Eugenia." Apparently, Eugenia had confided in Don but kept the news from the rest of us. *Que sera, sera.*

Don rushed off to the newspaper offices threatening a lawsuit if the word suicide appeared in connection with dad's death. I set off to the Sunset Cemetery nearby. It was on the hillside where Dad often walked and had a view of the bay.

The mortician looked eerily like Dad, with pale skin, similar jawlines, receding hairline, and pleasant blue eyes. "Welcome to Sunset Cemetery," the man said, reaching it out with an open hand. I could not stop staring, hoping I'd wake up and this had all been a bad dream. I finally looked away and collected myself.

"We need to make arrangements for my Da-a-a-a-d!" I lost it. I cried from the depths of my soul for what seemed like an eternity. In time, after draining the tissue box, and downing a couple glasses of water, the man calmly led me through preliminary information he needed to start the arrangements. I asked for a plot with a view. He handed me a map, circled the highest available plots, and suggested I walk up and take a look. I walked up the perfect, deep-green lawns to the highest plot available. The view was perfect. It almost matched our living room view.

I collapsed on the grass, checked out the bay view, looked up at the sky, took a deep breath, laid down and closed my eyes. Peace, quiet, birds, a squirrel chirped, my heart pounded, and I let out a sigh. I knew it was suicide. I had a vision:

Dad emerged from work at lunchtime without his briefcase and headed for the train tracks a few blocks away. The noon train was on time heading his way. He had lived with whatever haunted him long enough. He would end it. Resolutely, he approached the tracks at just the right time to avoid being seen and slipped away from the railroad crossing. The train would thunder across the Gilmore Street crossing shortly after noon. Dad readied himself as he had before diving into the cold New York lakes. He took a deep breath. The train appeared, and the whistle blew its warning. It was about to cross Gilmore. Dad waited with great anticipation of leaving the unbearable pain behind. He kneeled just as the train blew its long whistle warning. He stretched his neck across the steel tracks. The panicked conductor hit the brakes, but it was too late. Dad's beautiful head rolled away.

What could he have been living with to take his own life? "Why, Dad?" I whispered to the sky. "Why? What went wrong? Why did your life end this way? Why am I here now? Why did we leave Mexico? Why did you make me your son? Would you still be alive if you'd simply gone back to New York without Mom? I'm going to have a son and name him William, Dad. Yes, William Allen but he'll never meet you." I slipped away, mind blank. Dark. Whatever Dad's thoughts were, I'd never know. I stirred back and opened my eyes. White clouds swept across the sky. I wanted to see my bull snorting, talking, smiling, making sense of this time. But my childhood fantasies had been left behind.

I returned the next day after consulting with Mother and Don about the burial plan. They agreed Dad would be in the right place. The mortician greeted me with a caring handshake. "There's one formality we have to tend to, Mister Allen," the mortician said.

"Okay."

"Normally, a family member has to identify the body, but in your father's case, you can identify his ring," he said.

"Can I see him?"

"I strongly suggest you spare yourself the experience, and we insist on a closed casket," he stated with conviction.

"Why?"

"Your father is unrecognizable."

"I know my dad."

"You are aware it was a train that ended his life. He was decapitated."

"Are you sure?"

"His head was recovered sixty yards away. Remember your father the way he was." He held up Dad's wedding ring.

"Yes, that's his." I chose an oak coffin honoring Dad's love of nature. I signed the papers and left.

Monday morning, I went into Dad's closet and took a suit and tie. The Unitarian Church was packed. Tearful speeches from his many friends and admirers were delivered while Mother, Don, Eugenia, and I stayed silent, unable to string two sentences together. At the gravesite, the minister gave a moving speech about Dad's gentle manner and quiet leadership, calling him a pillar of the community and steadfast supporter of humanitarian beliefs. A man about Dad's age expressed his sorrow with dance and freestyle movement, sparking Mother's patented shock reaction. A few ladies joined in the freestyle movement. I reached for a handkerchief in the suit pocket and found an open envelope.

It was from Dad's company addressed to him. I pulled away to a tree farther up the knoll, curious to see anything about Dad's life. The letter was a dismissal notice. Dad's memory had been failing him at work. How would I tell Mom?

Paul returned from Arizona. He had taken to a leather vest and matching headband. Without warning, he strummed his guitar and sang "Guantanamera." Weeping people from all walks of life, rich and poor, many nationalities, and every color were a good reflection of Dad's values. Paul's music rang over the green landscape and across the view of the Golden Gate Bridge. My head throbbed, ready to explode. I looked up and saw my *Toro* in the sky, tears rolling down his face.

I wanted to run. I needed to run. I looked for Don, imagining two Aztec warriors running across the hills. Then, Don's frail body near Dad's casket made me wince. Don was losing his battle with cancer. I strode across the green to Don's side. He stood pensive holding back emotions unable to look at me. I slid my arm around his fragile torso. "William Allen will be the name of my first son," Don whispered. Maybe he knew something I didn't.

"You better get your papers in order. There's nothing more we can do," the oncologist stated flatly. We were back in Stanford Medical Center where Don was recovering from a final surgery. This was the end of the line for traditional medicine treatment.

"What are you thinking about?" Don asked me.

"Dad, you, Eugenia, Mom, life," I omitted death.

"There's a treatment in Mexico . . ." He dosed off. Don, always the warrior, had been reading about the alternative cancer treatment centers made popular by Steve McQueen who'd died a few years earlier in a similar place. I'd read the information pamphlets hyping natural remedies: teas, enemas, organic produce, nuts and grains. The self-published books written by questionable medical doctors, performing modern witchcraft, and selling snake-oil remedies was Don's desperate last hope.

I called the center and explained Don's case. He was down to one hundred twenty-five pounds. His lung capacity was shrinking, and he needed a respirator around the clock and had been advised by Stanford's oncologists that there was nothing else to do.

Nevertheless, the voodoo practitioners gave Don hope.

Oxygen tank in tow, we flew to Ensenada, Mexico. We were Ratso and Joe Buck from *Midnight Cowboy* on an airplane, Don wearing three layers of clothes, scarf, and hat. "It's a short flight Don, just hang on," I managed. He fell asleep quickly. His head rested on my shoulder. Curious passengers watched with sympathetic nods as they passed the hovering brothers. We held hands under a blanket.

"You're so strong," Don said reaching up, touching my chest. "Your chest, beautiful and strong." Tears rolled down his face.

"I'm not half the man you are, Don. Just hang in here." His hand dropped. "Don, Don." I searched for a pulse. "Please don't die here, Don," I mouthed privately. He rolled his head up. My fears lifted.

We had arranged a private ambulance to pick up Don and take us to the renowned treatment center one fast ride away. Cash payment, four hundred dollars. We reached the gates where an ambulance waited with a covered body was being loaded. Maybe Don simply wanted to die in Mexico. We were placed in a cement floor and tile walled room with a simple bathroom that must have been a converted hotel. The smell of Pine Sol turned my stomach. It was the start of the one week, forty-thousand-dollar, coffee enemas and natural juices treatment fiasco that didn't help in any way. Every day an ambulance picked up a dead patient. Since the doctors didn't have legitimate licenses, they could not prescribe pharmaceutical drugs, so Don had to bear the pain, and his breathing grew shallower by the hour.

I went for a walk and found a licensed doctor to look at Don. I mentioned the clinic. He had done this before. We walked in and the doctor immediately pulled out a vial of morphine as Don was in sheer pain, unable to breathe. *"No hay nada mas que hacer."* The doctor said there was nothing left to do.

"Okay, that's it. I love you, goodbye. Go ahead, give me the shot." Don reared back wanting relief.

"Oh no, no, no, no. You're not dying here. You have to kiss

Mom," I said as the doctor injected Don with the morphine. We arranged a private airplane because Don had to fly with an intravenous drip and gurney. He settled in, took my hand, and said, "Don't cry."

A few hours later we were back at Stanford Medical. The morphine drip had settled Don's breathing. I stood over him holding his hand, feeling the peace he'd searched for as life left his body.

Que sera, sera.

I drove home, keeping nightmarish thoughts at bay, eager to return to my salve: my students. Teaching children was where my heart found a home. It was where I could live in world bound to Dad and Don and feel at peace with a purpose driven life.

"The matador was so upset that he started crying," I was in my sanctuary, where I had to be after burying Dad. I forged ahead reading to my kindergarten students and healing my soul. Their faces riveted on me as I blocked out the recurring image of Dad facing a train. "He would not be able to show the people how brave and strong he was," I continued reading. "And for all I know, he is still there, under the tree, sitting quietly, smelling the flowers." I finished reading and took in the innocent faces of these precious five-year-old children.

"Okay, boys and girls," I started. "Raise your hand if you liked the story." Hands shot up. "Raise your hand if you like Ferdinand." Cheers. "Now raise your hand if you like rainbows. Good. Now, turn around and look out the window." A glorious rainbow crossed our view. "Let's go look." I walked to the door and led my students outside. White clouds hovered above. A rainbow reached across the sky.

"Look!" yelled one child, then another and another, acknowledging the rainbow. "What is it?" shouted another. For some students, this was their first rainbow.

"*Que es eso?*" a brown girl whispered, pointing at the rainbow.

"It's a rainbow," a Black boy answered.

"Look, Ferdinand the bull!" screamed a white boy. He pointed to the clouds, and everyone searched for their *Toro*. I had found peace and purpose in my work with disadvantaged kids in the past and knew it was the only thing that could help me keep my sanity. Working with children in my little sanctuary where I faced the innocent faces in search of knowledge was a gift I'd cherish throughout my life as it brought meaning to my life.

Epilogue

Depression is a painful, invisible illness that interferes with daily life. Public awareness and treatment are available today more than ever after deaths of celebrities like Robin Williams, Anthony Bourdain, Kate Spade, and others. Unfortunately, Dad's symptoms were evident, but he was unable to seek help, and the family didn't have the awareness to deal with the problem effectively. Perhaps medication and therapy may have prevented Dad's desperate attempt at ending the pain he lived with, but we will never know.

Dad had set the bar for his adopted children by example. He raised three immigrant children to participate in the American dream and be productive members of society that would help make this a better world.

We have.

Made in the USA
Columbia, SC
25 September 2021